Television in Science and Industry

V. K. Zworykin, E.E., Ph.D., D.Sc. (hon.)

Honorary Vice-President
and Technical Consultant
Radio Corporation of America
Affiliate,
Rockefeller Institute for Medical Research

E. G. Ramberg, Ph.D.

Research Physicist
RCA Laboratories, Princeton, N.J.

L. E. Flory, B.S. (E.E.)

Research Engineer
RCA Laboratories, Princeton, N.J.

New York · John Wiley & Sons, Inc.
London · Chapman & Hall, Limited

Television in Science and Industry

Library of Congress Catalog Card Number: 58-6089

Printed in the United States of America

Preface

To the average man television is synonymous with home entertainment. The television receiver, in giving him and his family front-row seats for stage shows, sports events, motion pictures, lectures, and forums at the command of a switch, has granted him all that he is inclined to ask of it. And yet this "theater at a distance" or "teletheater," as we might call it, exhausts only a small fraction of the potentialities of television. The possibility of translating vision to distant and inaccessible points by electrical means can in its more general sense make a material contribution to all phases of human activity. In the present book we seek to explore the function of television as an extension of human sight, variously called closed-circuit or industrial television to distinguish it from the more specialized broadcast function, and to describe the tools which have been developed to realize it.

After a brief historical introduction in the first chapter, Chapter 2 proceeds to outline the principal fields of application of television in industry, research, medicine, education, commerce, military affairs, and home and farm. Chapter 3 describes in detail the equipment which has been developed for closed-circuit television. It concerns itself not only with the camera design and circuitry of the more conventional equipment, but discusses new developments in miniaturization made possible by the introduction of the half-inch Vidicon and the transistor, color- and stereo-television apparatus, and the television microscope.

Chapter 4 seeks to give a general view of the status of closed-circuit television in 1957. It does so by taking up once more the classification of Chapter 2 and citing examples from actual practice in sufficient detail to enable the reader to judge in what situations known to him closed-circuit television could be most effective, what equipment would be needed, and how it should be used. Although the presentation is essentially self-contained and does not require more of the reader than an elementary knowledge of electronic circuits, copious references are given both here and in Chapter 3. These permit further exploration in the technical literature of any point of special interest. A comparison of the performance limits of Vidicon and flying-spot television microscopes is given as an appendix, since this material, of interest primarily to the research biologist, is not otherwise available.

In Chapter 5, finally, an attempt is made to forecast the future development of closed-circuit television. It would be too much to expect that what is envisioned there will be fulfilled in every detail. Nevertheless, we are confident that the broad use of television as an extension of human sight, which was the central objective of the early pioneers in the field, will play an increasingly vital and beneficent role in human affairs. It is our hope that this book may make some contribution in this direction.

Princeton, N. J.
January 1958

V. K. Zworykin
E. G. Ramberg
L. E. Flory

Acknowledgments

The authors are deeply indebted to manufacturers and users of closed-circuit television equipment, both in the United States and abroad, for their generosity in making available illustrative material for this book. Their associates in the Industrial Electronic Products Division of the Radio Corporation of America in Camden, N. J., have been particularly helpful in providing photographs and diagrams. Original pen-and-ink drawings for Chapter 2 were contributed by Mr. Tom Cook of RCA Laboratories' photographic studio in Princeton, N. J.

Contents

Chapter

Chapter

Chapter

Chapter

chapter 1

Closed-Circuit Television in Myth and History

The desire to extend vision beyond the horizon, to see the unseen, is as old as man's ability to think, to ponder, and to hope. Yet, up to a century ago, the attainment of this objective in any general manner appeared so remote, so improbable, that it was regarded as the province of magic. Efforts to realize vision at a distance on a scientific basis began in the 1870's, even though one of the essential elements, the amplifier, was lacking until De Forest's invention of the audion in 1906.

The advent of the vacuum tube and the vacuum photocell eventually made television a practical possibility. It ushered in the mechanical era of television. In the 1920's numerous mechanical scanning devices of great ingenuity were constructed and demonstrated. Television stations were launched to provide visual entertainment, in emulation of the highly successful sound broadcasting stations. Yet the public appeal of the new medium remained limited; mechanical scanning proved unable to provide the picture quality demanded by the public.

Fortunately, before the mechanical era had ended in disappointment, the groundwork for the electronic era had already been laid. Television disappeared from the market place, but the work in the laboratories proceeded, with changed emphasis. When, at the end of World War II, the opportunity for a large-scale broadcast service presented itself once again, electronic television was ready. The subsequent phenomenal growth of the television industry is a familiar story.

This growth has been shared by closed-circuit television, although it was initially completely eclipsed by broadcast or entertainment television. More and more effective ways were found in which the new medium could serve industry, education, and research. These wider uses form the subject matter of the present book.

At the same time the uses and methods of television were extended in both areas by the introduction of color. Here the special requirements of broadcast television had led to solutions which will prove of great value in the closed-circuit field.

THE PRESCIENTIFIC ERA

In earliest times the gift of vision unlimited by space or time was believed to be conferred on favored individuals by the supernatural powers. Men came from far and wide to consult and give tribute to the priests of Delphi and to other oracles. Specific devices, also, were believed to give the possessor the ability to see beyond the natural range of his eyes.

The mirror, in particular, is frequently invested with magic powers in the traditions of different cultures.[1] Some of these traditions, such as the mounting of mirrors on the lighthouse of Alexandria and on the Colossus of Rhodes to aid in detecting approaching vessels at great distances, seem so reasonable that they may have been founded on fact. Others, telling of concave or convex mirrors which revealed the whole universe, are clearly fanciful extrapolations derived from the strange and uncomprehended behavior of actual mirrors. The frequency with which this notion recurs in the tales of different peoples reflects the universal yearning to exceed the limits of natural vision and to see what goes on beyond the horizon.

Even long after the belief in magic had ceased among the educated we find references in fiction to remote vision by magic powers. An interesting example is Sir Walter Scott's *My Aunt Margaret's Mirror*, published as one of the Waverley novels around 1825. Scott lets his heroines, who are attempting to locate an unfaithful husband, consult a physician with the reputation of a conjurer. The conjurer leads them into a chamber containing a very tall and broad mirror, where, in Scott's words:

> Suddenly the surface assumed a new and singular appearance. It no longer simply reflected the objects placed before it, but as if it had self-contained scenery of its own, objects began to appear within it, at first in a disorderly, indistinct, and miscellaneous manner, like form arranging itself out of chaos; at length, in distinct and defined shape and symmetry. It was thus that, after some shifting of light and darkness over the face of the wonderful glass, a long perspective of arches and columns began to arrange itself on its side, and a vaulted roof on the upper part of it; till, after many oscillations, the whole vision gained a fixed and stationary appearance, representing the interior of a foreign church . . . .

[1] See Thomas (reference 1).

Scott's description is here strikingly reminiscent of what a television viewer might observe during the warming-up time of a receiver.

While reference to the employment of magic for the extension of human sight is not uncommon in literature, relatively few writers have given television a share in their view of the future. An exception is George Bernard Shaw. In the third act of *Back to Methuselah*, which is supposed to take place in A.D. 2170, Shaw lets the President of the British Islands communicate with his associates in various parts of the world by two-way videophone. For this purpose, in the presidential office "the end wall is a silvery screen nearly as large as a pair of folding doors." To establish visual connection the President and his counterpart are provided with a switchboard and dial on which they set the desired number.

Back to Methusaleh was published in 1921. By this time television had become a distinct technical possibility, although several years were to pass before the first crude demonstrations. Nevertheless, what may well have been the first cartoon joke at the expense of television had appeared in *Punch* some forty years earlier, so that the idea of seeing at a distance by electrical means must have been familiar to a considerable fraction of the population. Clearly, the history of the ideas on which modern television is based goes back far beyond the publication date of Shaw's play.

THE ERA OF SPECULATION

As we turn to the development of television on a scientific basis we encounter a period lasting approximately forty years which we may properly call the era of speculation.[2] In this time numerous useful and ingenious proposals were advanced, even though essential factors for their practical realization were absent.

The first system for the electrical transmission of pictures known to the authors was described by Alexander Bain in 1843.[3] It was designed specifically for the transmission of type face. In Bain's system signals were transmitted along parallel wire lines connected to the insulated teeth of a wire comb. The comb was translated across a plate containing short, parallel wire sections in an insulating matrix while the type

[2]Hogan (reference 2) applies the term speculative period" to the interval ending in 1890. We extend it here up to approximately 1920, when workers had the essential elements for the practical realization of television at their disposal.

[3]See Korn and Glatzel (reference 3). The historical references to the early history of television, where not otherwise indicated, are derived from this source, Hogan (reference 2), Goebel (reference 7), and Jensen (reference 18).

face connected to a battery was pressed against the opposite side of the plate. At the receiver a similar comb was translated across chemically treated paper, which, like the other pole of the battery, was connected to ground. Thus, whenever a tooth of the comb at the transmitter passed over a section of type face, current passed through the corresponding tooth of the comb at the receiver and effected discoloration of the paper.

Bain's system was never built. However, Frederick Collier Bakewell, about four years later, transmitted written matter over a single telegraph line; the original was written with insulating ink on metal foil placed on the mantel surface of a drum rotated by clockwork. The foil was explored by a probe translated slowly parallel to the axis of the drum, so that the written matter was scanned along a series of closely spaced, parallel lines.

Bakewell's apparatus resembles in many respects modern facsimile—the electrical transmission of printed material, photographs, or drawings. It also exhibits certain features, such as scanning, which have been of primary importance to television. However, neither Bain nor Bakewell appears to have had the remotest idea of applying their techniques to the instantaneous transmission of pictures of action. This was natural, since they lacked not only the means of transmitting pictures at sufficient speed to permit the subjective merging of successive frames into a continuous representation, but also the essential photoelectric means for converting variations in light intensity into variations of current or voltage. Edmond Becquerel's discovery of the photovoltaic effect a few years earlier (1839) appears to have excited little notice among inventors.

The effect of the observation of the photoconductivity of selenium by May and Willoughby Smith in 1873, on the other hand, was pronounced. It is true that the first description of a television system, by G. R. Carey of Boston in 1875, did not contemplate use of this material. Carey proposed that a picture of the object to be transmitted be projected on a photosensitive insulating surface, such as a layer of silver halide. Terminal pairs, in the form of closely spaced platinum wires, of a multiplicity of electrical circuits were buried in the photosensitive layer, so that they would be short-circuited with the partial reduction of the silver halide to silver by the incident light. Each circuit controlled, eventually through a relay, an electric light source in a panel of sources arranged in the same geometrical order as the terminal pairs in the photosensitive layer. Thus a projection of a light pattern on the photosensitive plate would result in the formation of a similar light pattern on the "receiver" panel.

Clearly, Carey's system as described above was not operative. However, it corresponds in essence to a method employed even at the present time to animate advertising signs. Furthermore, it was the only early system that could have functioned with photosensitive materials having a response as slow as the early selenium cells. In Carey's system, with a separate channel for each "picture element," the cell response had to be only fast enough to permit the observation of continuity of motion. In the nonstorage scanning systems, subsequently introduced, the rise time and decay of the response had to be faster by a factor equal to the number of picture elements in order to prevent the washing out of the picture by overlap of the picture signals from one picture element to the next.

A selenium cell panel serving the same purpose as Carey's photosensitive plate was built by Ayrton and Perry in England in 1877. In 1906 Rignoux and Fournier built an array of 64 selenium cells, each coupled to a shutter in front of an extended light source, and used this system to transmit simple patterns. However, the main line of development of television lay in another direction—at least with respect to the method of signal transmission. Even as early as 1880 it was realized that at least 10,000 picture elements would be needed to reproduce pictures with adequate detail.[4] The employment of parallel transmission lines and shutter or relay devices in such numbers appeared clearly impractical.

The remedy lay in the application of the scanning principle, applied at a much earlier time by Bakewell to facsimile transmission. The first suggestion of its application to television appears to have been made in 1878 by the Portuguese physicist de Paiva, who suggested that the picture to be transmitted be projected on a selenium-coated metal plate scanned by a metal point. The metal point and plate were connected in series with a battery and relay. The relay controlled the current through an electric light bulb which was translated in the same manner as the metal point. Since the bulb would light up whenever it occupied positions corresponding to the bright portions of the picture, it would trace out a replica of the latter.[5]

This and innumerable later proposals existed, of course, only on paper. Thus a contemporary of de Paiva, M. Senlecq, first suggested the scanning of a picture formed on a ground-glass screen with a small selenium cell and, at a slightly later date, the scanning of an array of small, stationary selenium cells with a metal brush. In either case the picture was to be reproduced on paper, either by a soft pencil pressed against it by a magnetic armature or by electrochemical action. Thus Senlecq was actually dealing with facsimile rather than with television. Few of the early authors were aware of the essential distinction between television and facsimile.

However, a number of devices and principles, which proved important

[4]See Sawyer (reference 4).

[5]See Mihaly (reference 5).

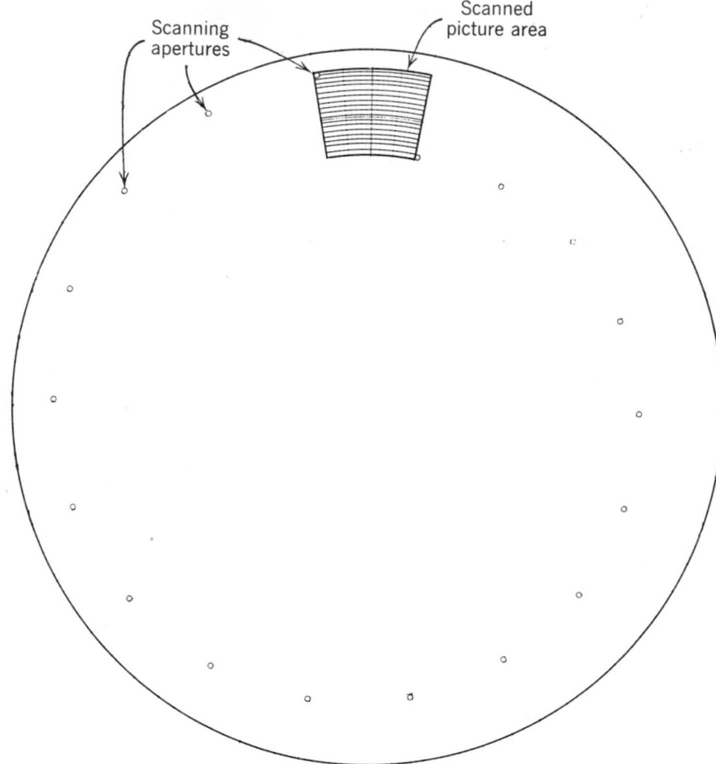

Fig. 1.1. The Nipkow disk.

to the later development of television, were developed in this period. Paul Nipkow's invention of the scanning disk in 1884 not only gave television its first practical means for transmitting pictures at sufficient speed for continuous observation over a single channel, but also presented it with the instrument which had the greatest survival value of all mechanical scanning devices.

The Nipkow disk (Fig. 1.1) is a round disk with a series of apertures placed along a spiral. If a picture corresponding in width to the angular separation of successive apertures and in height to the maximum radial separation of the apertures is projected on the rotating disk, the apertures scan the picture in a succession of parallel lines. Thus, if the light transmitted by the apertures falls on a photocell, the photocurrent generated in the cell will correspond to the brightness variation of the picture along the scanning lines. If a second Nipkow disk, whose rotation is synchronized with the first, is placed at the receiver in front of a light source modulated by the current from the photocell, the original picture will appear reproduced in the plane of the disk; the rotating disk apertures will light up with a brightness proportional to that of any particular element of the picture at the moment when they occupy a position corresponding to that particular element (Fig. 1.2).

Nipkow and his contemporaries suggested many other techniques which were investigated experimentally at a later period. Nipkow himself proposed the employment of lenses in the scanning-disk apertures to increase the amplitude of the picture signal and the use of the Faraday effect for inertia-free light modulation in the receiver. Le Blanc, in 1880, suggested the employment of two mirrors oscillating about mutually perpendicular axes for scanning the picture. Weiller, in 1889, developed the mirror drum, with as many mirrors as there were scanning lines, each tilted by a slightly greater angle than the preceding mirror with respect to the axis of rotation. Thus the rotation produced the horizontal deflection of the picture element, and the increasing tilt, the vertical deflection. Many other mechanical methods of scanning, as well as practical means for synchronizing scanning in the transmitter and receiver (e.g., by the use of phonic wheels, as suggested by Nipkow), belong to the contributions of this period.

However, the inventions of the speculative period were not limited to mechanical devices. The cathode-ray oscilloscope, developed by F. Braun in 1897 for the study of the time variation of electric currents, was utilized for picture reproduction by M. Dieckmann and G. Glage in 1906. The objects in their apparatus were metal patterns which were explored by twenty contact brushes replacing the scanning apertures on

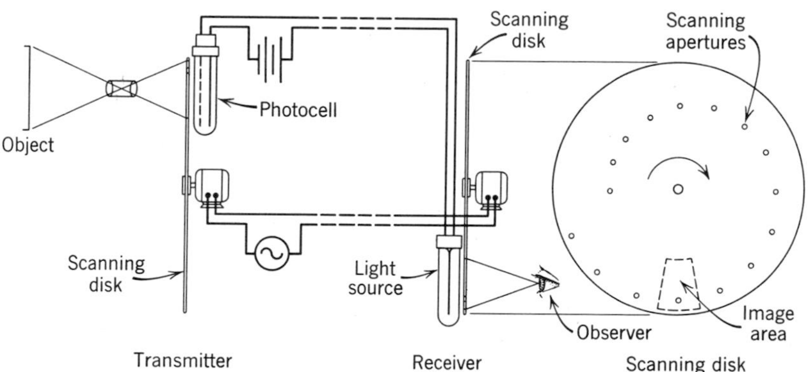

Fig. 1.2. Mechanical television system employing Nipkow disk in pickup and receiver. (From V. K. Zworykin and E. G. Ramberg, *Photoelectricity*, Wiley, New York, 1949.)

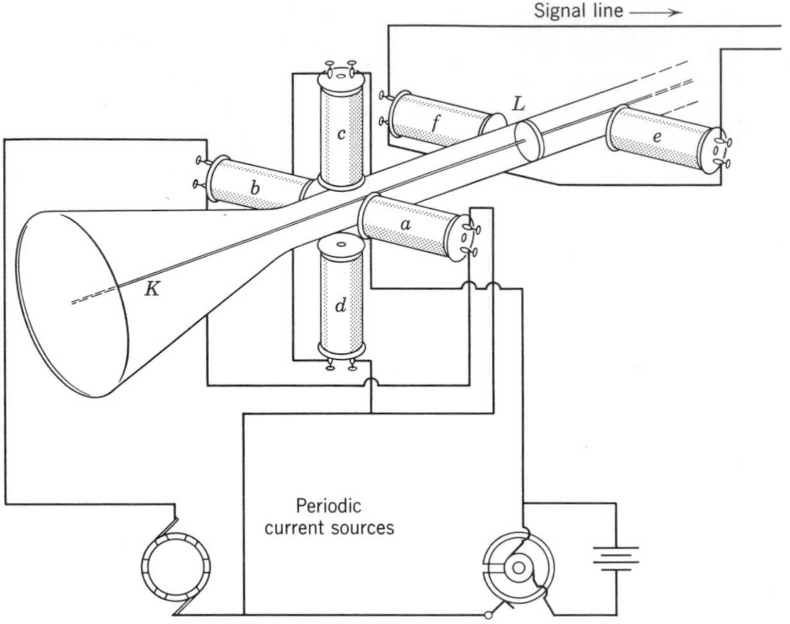

Fig. 1.3. Cathode-ray tube receiver of M. Dieckmann and G. Glage. *K*, electron beam; *a*, *b*, vertical deflection coils; *c*, *d*, horizontal deflection coils; *e*, *f*, intensity modulating deflection coils; *L*, diaphragm limiting transmitted beam current. (M. Dieckmann and G. Glage, German Patent 190102, Sept. 12, 1906.)

a Nipkow disk. The Nipkow disk was coupled mechanically to a generator delivering horizontal sawtooth current to the horizontal deflection coils on the cathode-ray tube and to the contact brush on a slide-wire potentiometer delivering the vertical deflection currents to the vertical deflection coils. Whenever the brushes on the Nipkow disk made contact with a point on the metal pattern, they caused current to flow through an electromagnet which deflected the electron beam in the oscilloscope so as to miss an aperture in its path. Thus conducting portions of the pattern were reproduced dark on a luminous background on the oscilloscope screen. Since a complete scan (a rotation of the Nipkow disk) was completed in 0.1 second, displacements and rotations of the pattern could be followed readily on the screen.

The transmitter of Dieckmann's apparatus was such that, viewed as a whole, it was a facsimile system rather than a television system. Since there were no means for amplifying photocurrents at the time, the facsimile-type transmitter employing contact brushes alone enabled Dieckmann to realize his system physically; the apparatus employed in

1906 to transmit written matter and simple drawings is at present in the German Technical Museum in Munich. Although the system as a whole was a facsimile system, the receiver (Fig. 1.3) was an operative electronic picture reproducer.

Shortly after the publication of the patent granted to Dieckmann and Glage, a patent was issued, in 1907, to B. Rosing of St. Petersburg for a television system employing a cathode-ray tube receiver. It employed at the transmitter two mirror prisms rotating about mutually perpendicular axes, which effected the scanning displacement of the picture to be transmitted across an aperture. This feature was not novel, of course. However, Rosing's system possessed the important innovation of replacing the very slow selenium photoconductive cells employed as light-sensitive elements (placed behind the aperture) by inertia-free alkali phototubes. Thus one of the basic obstacles to television over a single signal channel was overcome. The other difficulty, namely the fact that the photocurrents were much too weak to actuate any receiving apparatus without amplifying means, prevented the practical operation of Rosing's apparatus, just as in all the single-channel television systems of his predecessors. Nevertheless, the apparatus actually was constructed and exhibited in St. Petersburg in 1910. In Rosing's system both the horizontal and the vertical deflection of the beam were effected by the current induced in pickup coils, series-connected to the deflection coils of the cathode-ray tube, by permanent magnets associated with the individual mirrors of the mirror drums. Otherwise the picture-reproducing system was essentially the same as that of Dieckmann and Glage.

The first suggestion of eliminating mechanical devices altogether from a television system was made by A. A. Campbell-Swinton in 1908. Campbell-Swinton saw in the deflection of electron beams in the transmitter and the receiver (by electromagnets actuated by alternating currents of two greatly differing frequencies) the only method of achieving adequately high picture definition. He gave his ideas more precise form in a lecture to the Roentgen Society in London in 1911[6] (Fig. 1.4). The novel part of his system, as compared to those of Dieckmann and Rosing, is, of course the transmitter, or, in modern parlance, the camera tube. It employed a mosaic of mutually insulated photosensitive elements (e.g., cubes of rubidium), which was scanned on one side by an electron beam. The other side of the mosaic formed a wall of a receptacle "filled with a gas or vapour, such as sodium vapour, which conducts negative electricity more readily under the influence of light than in the dark." The same receptacle contained a collector screen for this negative

[6] See Campbell-Swinton (reference 6).

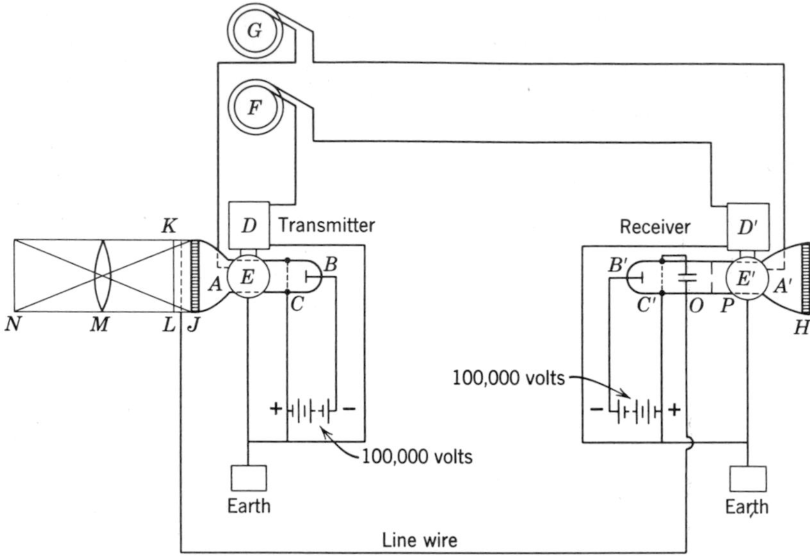

Fig. 1.4. Electronic television system proposed by Campbell-Swinton. (From V. K. Zworykin and G. A. Morton, *Television*, 2nd Ed., Wiley, New York, 1954, Fig. 7.13.)

charge. A line wire connected this collector screen to the control element in the receiver, so that the magnitude of the current received by the collector screen determined the brightness of the scanning spot on the receiver screen.

In greater detail, the manner in which Campbell-Swinton pictured the operation of his camera tube is indicated by the following sentence:

> In the case of cubes (of rubidium) on which no light is projected, nothing further will happen, the charge dissipating itself in the tube; but in the case of such of those cubes as are brightly illuminated by the projected image, the negative charge imparted to them by the cathode rays will pass away through the ionized gas along the line of the illuminating beam of light until it reaches the screen *L*, whence the charge will travel by means of the line wire to the plate *O* of the receiver . . . .

He regarded as one of the chief advantages of his system the fact that he employed a multiplicity of photoelectric cells in parallel, each of which was called upon to deliver an electric pulse once in a picture period (e.g. $^{1}/_{10}$ second). This was unlike

> . . . other arrangements that have been suggested, in which a single photoelectric cell is called upon to produce the many thousands of separate impulses that are required to be transmitted through the line wire per second, a condition which no known form of photoelectric cell will admit of.

The parallel arrangement of photosensitive elements, or the photosensitive mosaic, proved indeed an essential feature of high-sensitivity television camera tubes, though for other reasons than those given above. With the introduction by Rosing of the high-vacuum phototube into the television art, the slow speed of response of photoelectric devices ceased to be a barrier. This had taken place even before the writing of Campbell-Swinton's article.

Needless to say, Campbell-Swinton's television system was never constructed. Furthermore, familiarity with his proposal would scarcely have altered the verdict reached by Arthur Korn, a pioneer in the field of facsimile, after an exhaustive review of earlier television efforts in 1911: "With means now known to us, practical television, employing a single line or a small number of lines, cannot be realized."

At the time this was unquestionably a reasonable position. Nevertheless, the mental effort and experimentation applied to the television problem in the period of speculation contributed materially to the speed with which it was solved when the means essential to the realization of television became available.

It is also of some interest to note that the only kind of television with which the speculative period concerned itself was closed-circuit television; the whole idea of broadcasting is of more recent origin. We cannot do better than to terminate this account of the speculative period with the vision of one of its outstanding exponents, B. Rosing, as expressed in an article in the French journal *Excelsior* published around 1910.[7]

> The range of application of the telephone does not extend beyond human conversation. Electrical telescopy will permit man not only to commune with other human beings, but also with nature itself. With the "electric eye" we will be able to penetrate where no human being has penetrated before. We shall see what no human being has seen. The "electric eye," fitted with a powerful lamp and submerged in the depths of the sea, will permit us to read the secrets of the submarine domain. If we recall that water covers three quarters of the earth's surface, we readily realize the infinite extent of man's future conquests in this portion of his domain, till now inaccessible to him. From now on and in all future times we can imagine thousands of electric eyes traveling over the floor of the sea, seeking out scientific and material treasures; others will carry out their explorations below the earth's surface, in the depths of craters, in mountain crevasses, and in mine shafts. The electric eye will be man's friend, his watchful companion, which will suffer from neither heat nor cold, which will have its place on lighthouses and at guard posts, which will beam high above the rigging of ships, close to the sky. The electric eye, a help to man in peace, will accompany the soldier and facilitate communication between all members of human society. Yet we need not fear that it might pry into the

[7]Quoted in Korn and Glatzel (reference 3).

private life of families, as some might think; it is incapable of seeing through walls.

THE MECHANICAL ERA

The speculative era came to an end when all the means essential to translating television into practice became available to workers in the field. These were, in particular, the almost inertia-free photoemissive effect, utilized in the vacuum phototubes of Elster and Geitel and others; the electronic amplification of voltages and currents, based on the three-element vacuum tube introduced by De Forest in 1906; and light sources permitting rapid modulation, such as the negative-glow neon lamp of D. MacFarlan Moore, introduced in 1917. By 1920 these factors had been combined to make television workable.

It may occasion surprise that the cathode-ray tube, whose ability to reproduce images was demonstrated by Dieckmann as early as 1906, was not generally considered an important factor in television in 1920. This may be attributed to the fact that the early cathode-ray tubes had to rely on gas focusing of the scanning beam; hence they were short-lived and limited in spot sharpness and permissible speed of deflection. Long-lived tubes delivering sharp, bright images at high scanning speeds became possible only with the application of electron-optical principles to the focusing of electron beams in vacuum.

Accordingly, mechanical methods of scanning, both in the transmitter and in the receiver, were generally preferred in the period beginning about 1920. They dominated the field up into the early thirties, when they were replaced by electronic scanning techniques, first in the receiver and then in the transmitter. Thus it appears appropriate to designate the relatively brief period from 1920 up into the 1930's as the mechanical period of television.

The year 1920 also marks the beginning of commercial sound broadcasting in the United States. The enormous success of radio broadcasting for entertainment purposes redefined the objectives of television. The prospect of television broadcasting eclipsed all other uses. Only one other objective was pursued to any extent during the mechanical era: two-way video communication. The early studies by H. E. Ives and his associates at the Bell Telephone Laboratories, carried out in particular in the years 1927–1930, were largely concerned with television as an extension of telephone communication. In Germany G. Krawinkel demonstrated a two-way television system at the radio exposition in Berlin in 1929, and from 1936 to 1940 the German Post Office provided public, two-way, videophone service between Berlin, Leipzig, Nürnberg, and, eventually, Munich.[8] With this minor exception attention was concentrated on broadcast television for entertainment purposes.

Thus, from the point of view of the application of television to science and industry or of closed-circuit television in general, the mechanical era may well appear as an unproductive diversion from the main path of development. The mechanical scanning techniques, utilizing scanning disks, rotating mirrors and prisms, mirror screws, rotary commutators, etc., though developed to a high level of perfection, had limited permanent significance in television. On the other hand, the same period was extremely productive in formulating the requirements of television communication and developing the necessary circuitry.

To begin with, the number of lines in the picture, which determined the discrimination of detail in a vertical direction, was limited by the sensitivity of the transmitting equipment and by problems of mechanical construction. Thus in 1926 J. L. Baird, in England, showed 30-line pictures scanned at a frequency of five pictures per second. In the following year H. E. Ives and his co-workers at the Bell Telephone Laboratories transmitted 50-line pictures between Washington and New York at a rate of 17.7 pictures per second. The first television standards established by the German Post Office, in 1929, prescribed 30 horizontal lines, an aspect ratio (width : height) of 4 : 3, and a picture frequency of 12.5 per second. However, technical improvements forced an early upward revision in the line number and frame frequency. By 1932 the Radio Corporation of America transmitted pictures from New York with 120 scanning lines and a frame repetition frequency of 24 per second.

It became increasingly clear that technical factors alone would not indefinitely prescribe reasonable upper limits to the frame frequency and line number of television pictures. Hence tests were carried out with pictures artificially broken up into picture elements of uniform intensity and varying size and with others projected intermittently at varying frequency and with varying duty cycle.[9] The structured pictures were viewed by a number of observers, who determined the closest distance from the picture for which the detail appeared satisfactory. It was found that this corresponded approximately to the distance for which a line spacing subtended the minimum angle of resolution of the average eye, or about two minutes of arc. This finding, together with the observation that the closest viewing distance for which the entire picture could be seen clearly and simultaneously was four times the picture height, led to the standards of 400 to 600 lines prescribed in most coun-

[8]See Goebel (reference 7).

[9]See Engstrom (reference 8).

tries of the world today. The aspect ratio of 4 : 3 was taken over from motion-picture practice.

The tests with intermittently projected pictures sought to determine the lowest field frequency for which the viewer perceives no disturbing flicker effects. This increases with picture brightness and is considerably higher than the frequency required to give an appearance of continuity of motion. Thus in motion-picture practice it is customary to project each picture twice, making the field frequency (48 per second) twice as large as the frame frequency (24 per second). Since, in television, the individual fields are not presented to the eye as a unit, but are built up by a process of line scanning, the flicker tests on projected pictures were eventually supplemented by tests with television pictures of varying brightness and field frequency formed by cathode-ray tubes. These tests showed that the field frequency of 48 per second adopted in motion-picture practice gave an entirely flicker-free presentation for picture brightnesses up to 20 foot-lamberts. To minimize the disturbing effects of hum (crosstalk from the power lines into the deflection circuits), the field frequencies were generally set equal to the power-line frequencies in the service area, or 50 per second in Europe and 60 per second in America. The relatively high field frequency adopted in America has proved particularly fortunate, since it provided flicker-free viewing even at the very high picture brightnesses realized in more recent years.

As in motion picture practice, the frame frequency was chosen to be half as large as the field frequency. This was made possible by interlaced scanning. In alternate fields all the odd lines and then all the even lines of a complete frame are scanned. Interlaced scanning has the advantage that the fineness of picture detail in a vertical direction and the freedom from flicker are determined by the total line number in the scanning pattern and the field frequency, respectively, whereas the scanning speed and consequently the frequency band required to transmit the picture information are determined by the product of the line number and the smaller frame frequency.

The above-mentioned studies, which formed a sound basis for the standardization of the number of the scanning lines and the field frequency of the television picture, were supplemented by careful theoretical studies of picture reconstruction in television.[10] These established, among other things, the relationship between horizontal resolution and the frequency bandwidth of the transmission channel between picture pickup and reproducer and the influence of the size of the scanning spot in either on the reproduced picture.

[10]See Mertz and Gray (reference 9); for a more comprehensive review of the subject, see Zworykin and Morton, Chapter 5 (reference 10).

Finally, satisfactory methods for generating and utilizing synchronizing signals were worked out. These assured the proper framing of the received pictures. Since the synchronization methods were intimately linked with the mechanical scanning methods employed, they have not carried over into current practice. However, they indicate a clear understanding of television synchronization requirements.

Although the mechanical era did not succeed in creating satisfactory television systems, it did provide a clear formulation of the problems of television. Furthermore, to a very considerable extent, it saw the development of the auxiliary means required for any successful television system, mechanical or electronic.

THE ELECTRONIC ERA

The mechanical era of television merged into the electronic era as the limitations of mechanical scanning systems came to be recognized and electronic systems were made available to replace them. This occurred first for the receiver (about 1930) and somewhat later, in the middle thirties, for the transmitter. Several individual workers had, of course, committed themselves to an entirely electronic solution of the television problem at a much earlier date.

We have already seen that a form of cathode-ray tube had been employed for picture reproduction by Dieckmann and by Rosing in the speculative era of television. In these early tubes the scanning spot intensity was modulated by deflecting the electron beam across an aperture. No method of beam focusing other than gas focusing was known or employed. The modern practice of beam intensity modulation by an axially symmetric grid was adopted in experiments in electronic television demonstrated by the senior author in 1924 and described in a slightly earlier patent application.[11] Five years later he described an essentially modern television viewing tube which incorporated grid modulation, a hard vacuum, and (electrostatic) electron-optical focusing.[12] He named this tube a "kinescope" (Fig. 1.5). A fuller description of the operation of improved tubes of this type, in terms of the language of electron optics, was given a few years later;[13] a general theoretical basis for this new science had been created in the meantime by Hans Busch.[14]

The cathode-ray viewing tube speedily replaced mechanical picture

[11] V. K. Zworykin, U. S. Patent 2,141,059, Dec. 20, 1938 (filed Dec. 29, 1923).

[12] See Zworykin (reference 11).

[13] See Zworykin (reference 12).

[14] See Busch (reference 13).

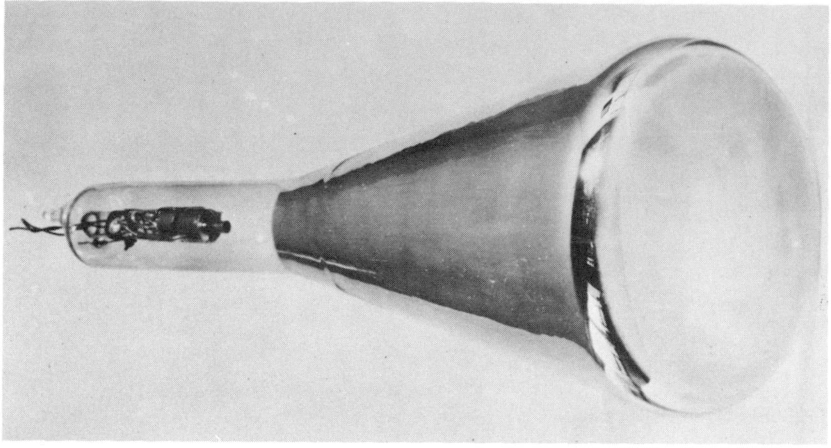

Fig. 1.5. An early kinescope. (Zworykin, 1929.)

reproducers in the early 1930's. The Farnsworth "oscillite"[15] and the picture tubes built by M. von Ardenne[16] in Germany incorporated improvements similar to those realized in the Zworykin kinescope. Magnetic deflection, effected by electronically generated sawtooth currents, was employed quite generally. Correct timing was achieved by the application of synchronizing pulses to the control oscillator of the deflection generator, as at present.

The problem of developing a satisfactory electronic pickup device proved more difficult. Although Campbell-Swinton had pointed out that the realization of a workable television system demanded the adoption of electronic scanning in both the transmitter and the receiver, there is no evidence that he ever constructed such a system. However, late in 1923 the senior author, then associated with the Westinghouse Electric Corporation, succeeded in transmitting a crossmark with a television system which utilized the tube shown in Fig. 1.6 as transmitter and a cathode-ray tube as receiver.[17]

The tube in Fig. 1.6 employed a thin aluminum signal plate which was oxidized on one side. The insulating (oxidized) side was photosensitized and faced a metal grill which served as collector. The picture to be transmitted was projected through the grill on the photo-

[15] See Dinsdale (reference 14).

[16] See von Ardenne (reference 15).

[17] V. K. Zworykin, U. S. Patent 2,141,059, Dec. 20, 1938, application filed Dec. 29, 1923.

sensitive layer and built up on it, by photoemission, a charge image. An electron beam issuing from the gun at the narrow end of the tube scanned the signal plate and penetrated the oxide layer so as to establish a conducting path between the signal plate and the photosensitive elements on the opposite side of the layer.

The tube just described was capable of transmitting only very crude patterns. On the other hand, it demonstrated not merely the possibility of transmitting pictures by electronic means, but illustrated also the important principle of storage: the charge which gave rise to the picture signal was not just that liberated by photoemission from the picture element in question at the instant of scanning, but was built up on the insulated photosensitive "mosaic" during the entire period which had elapsed since the preceding scan. Ideally, the storage principle permits an increase in sensitivity over a nonstorage device by a factor equal to the number of picture elements in the transmitted scene, or, roughly, the square of the number of scanning lines. For modern television pictures this factor lies between 100,000 and 1,000,000. The transmission of television pictures under a wide range of illumination, indoors and outdoors, has become possible only through use of the storage principle.

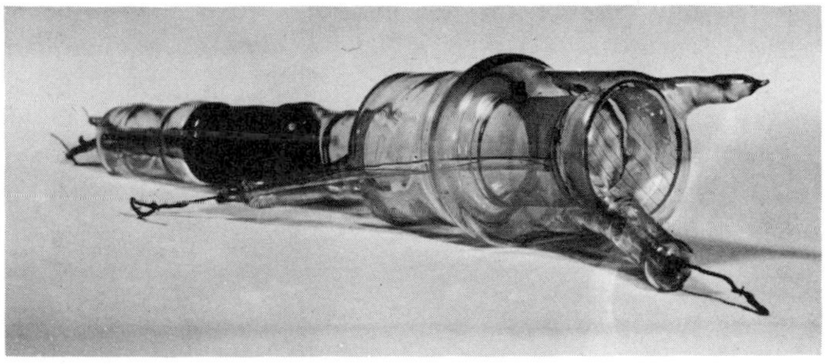

Fig. 1.6. Early storage-type television camera tube. (Zworykin, 1923.)

The *iconoscope*,[18] the first storage-type television tube to find practical use, is shown schematically in Fig. 1.7. In it, the picture to be transmitted is projected on a mosaic consisting of silver globules photosensitized with cesium and deposited on a mica sheet. The back of the mica is metalized to form the signal plate. In contrast to the tube in Fig. 1.6 the beam now scans the insulated side of the photosensitive target and returns its surface to an equilibrium potential by secondary emission, both photoelectrons and secondary electrons being collected by

[18] See Zworykin (reference 16).

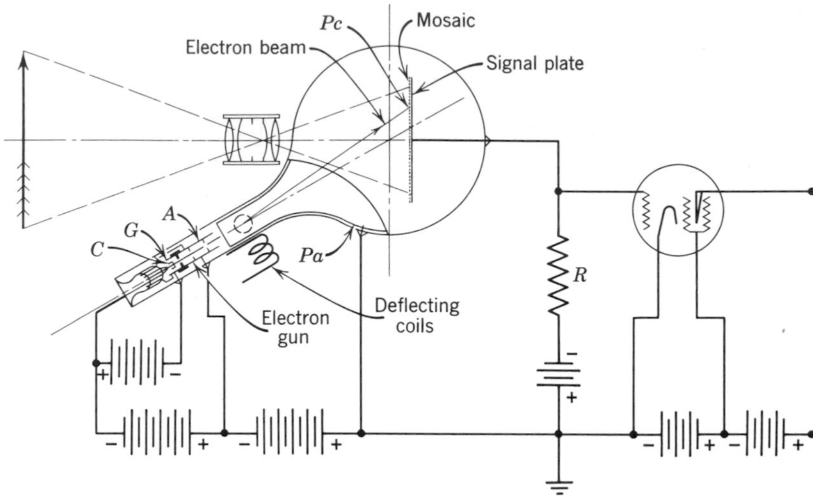

Fig. 1.7. Diagram of single-sided iconoscope (Zworykin, reference 16). *C*, cathode; *G*, grid; *A*, anode; *Pa*, photocell anode; *Pc*, photocell cathode; *R*, signal resistance.

a metal coating on the tube envelope. Since the charge deposited by the beam at any point of the mosaic depends on the charge built up at that point by photoemission during the preceding frame period, the current capacitatively induced in the signal plate lead corresponds to the intensity of illumination of the scanned element of the mosaic.

Iconoscopes of the above type were constructed by the Radio Corporation of America in 1931 and after 1934 rapidly displaced mechanical picture-pickup devices. Later developments, culminating in the image orthicon, aimed at a more complete utilization of the gain in sensitivity permitted by the storage principle and at the elimination of residual drawbacks of the iconoscope. Several of these newer tubes, which are of special interest in closed-circuit applications, are discussed in Chapter 3.

Besides the iconoscope two nonstorage electronic pickup devices were developed at an early date. One of these is the cathode-ray tube flying-spot scanner. Suggested in a Zworykin patent application filed in 1923,[19] flying-spot scanners of this type were built by M. von Ardenne, both for live transmissions and for film pickup.[20] In the flying-spot technique a scanning pattern of uniform intensity, described on the face of a cathode-ray tube, is imaged onto the subject to be transmitted, and

[19] U. S. Patent 2,141,059.

[20] See von Ardenne (reference 15).

the light passing through (for film) or reflected by the subject (for a live subject) is collected by a phototube. The photocurrent, which at any instant is proportional to the transmission or reflectance of the point being scanned, generates the picture signal. If the light emission of the phosphor persists longer than the transit time of a single picture element, the scanning spot is stretched into a line, and the horizontal resolution is reduced correspondingly. Early cathode-ray tube flying-spot scanners suffered from this defect as well as from the low sensitivity of the available phototubes. For these reasons they did not come into practical use until very much later, when efficient short-persistence phosphors and highly sensitive multiplier phototubes could be utilized.

The other nonstorage electronic pickup device which has been applied quite widely both in broadcasting and in industrial television is the image dissector. Here the image of the scene to be transmitted is projected on a photocathode, and the stream of photoelectrons issuing from the cathode is deflected by crossed magnetic fields over an aperture in such fashion that the aperture selects, in succession, electrons from different picture elements along a scanning line. The electrons passing through the aperture are collected and generate the picture signal. This technique, first described and demonstrated by Dieckmann and Hell,[21] was perfected by Philo T. Farnsworth.[22] Farnsworth's important addition was a longitudinal magnetic focusing field which formed a sharp electronic image of the scene in the plane of the aperture. Without this refinement only crude images could be transmitted. Farnsworth's image dissector was introduced in 1934. Later types were greatly improved by the replacement of the collector by an electron multiplier. In this manner they achieved the maximum sensitivity of which a nonstorage television pickup device, operated with available photocathodes, is capable.

The entire technical development which has been described took place with the realization and perfection of a broadcast television service in view. Temporarily, in World War II, this motive was supplemented by the potential uses of television techniques in warfare. In the accomplishment of its main objective television proved remarkably successful. Thus in the United States a majority of households enjoyed television programs originating at the cultural centers of the country within seven years after the establishment of television broadcasting services at the end of World War II. A comparable spread of the new medium of en-

[21] M. Dieckmann and R. Hell, "Lichtelektrische Bildzerlegerröhre fur Fernseher," German Patent 450,187, issued April 5, 1925.

[22] See Farnsworth (reference 17) and U. S. Patent 1,773,980 of Jan. 7, 1927, and 1,986,330 of April 17, 1928.

tertainment and instruction, eventually delayed by unfavorable economic circumstances, may be anticipated for most of the rest of the world. Everywhere television is becoming a part of the prevailing cultural pattern.

It is not surprising that the broader aims of television as an extension of human sight, which animated many of the pioneers of the art, were temporarily forgotten. They were eventually brought back to public attention by some of those early workers who had not lost their original vision and by the insistent demands of men in industry, education, and research who realized the importance of the services that television could perform for them. The following chapters are devoted to a survey of these services, a description of available apparatus, and a review of the achievements of closed-circuit television in science and industry thus far.

REFERENCES

1. N. W. Thomas, *Crystal Gazing*, Dodge, New York, 1905.
2. J. V. L. Hogan, "The Early Days of Television," *J. Soc. Motion Picture Television Engrs.*, Vol. 63, pp. 169–173, 1954.
3. A. Korn and B. Glatzel, *Handbuch der Phototelegraphie und Telautographie*, Nemnich, Leipzig, 1911.
4. W. E. Sawyer, "Seeing by Electricity," *Sci. American*, Vol. 42, p. 373, 1880.
5. D. Mihaly, *Das elektrische Fernsehen und das Telehor*, Krayn, Berlin, 1926.
6. A. A. Campbell-Swinton, "The Possibilities of Television," *Wireless World and Radio Review*, pp. 51–56, April 9, 1924.
7. G. Goebel, "Das Fernsehen in Deutschland bis zum Jahre 1945," *Archiv für das Post- und Fernmeldewesen*, Vol. 5, pp. 259–393, 1953.
8. E. W. Engstrom, "A Study of Television Image Characteristics," Sect. I, *Proc. I.R.E.*, Vol. 21, pp. 1631–1651, 1933, and Sect. II, *Proc. I.R.E.*, Vol. 23, pp. 295–310, 1935.
9. P. Mertz and F. Gray, "Theory of Scanning," *Bell System Tech. J.*, Vol. 13, pp. 464–515, 1934.
10. V. K. Zworykin and G. A. Morton, *Television*, 2nd Edition, Wiley, New York, 1954.
11. V. K. Zworykin, "Television with Cathode-Ray Tube for Receiver," *Radio Eng.*, Vol. 9, pp. 38–41, December 1929.
12. V. K. Zworykin, "Description of an Experimental Television System and the Kinescope," *Proc. I.R.E.*, Vol. 21, pp. 1655–1673, 1933.
13. H. Busch, "On the Operation of the Concentrating Coil in the Braun Tube," *Arch. Elektrotech.*, Vol. 18, pp. 583–594, 1927.
14. A. Dinsdale, "Television by Cathode Ray. The New Farnsworth System," *Wireless World*, Vol. 28, pp. 286–288, 1931.
15. M. von Ardenne, "The Braun Tube as Television Receiver," *Fernsehen*, Vol. 1, pp. 193–202, 1930; Vol. 2, pp. 65–68 and 173–178, 1931.

16. V. K. Zworykin, "The Iconoscope—a Modern Version of the Electric Eye," *Proc. I.R.E.*, Vol. 22, pp. 16–22, 1934.
17. P. T. Farnsworth, "Television by Electron Image Scanning," *J. Franklin Inst.*, Vol. 218, pp. 411–444, 1934.
18. A. G. Jensen, "The Evolution of Modern Television," *J. Soc. Motion Picture Television Engrs.*, Vol. 63, pp. 174–188, 1954.
19. G. R. M. Garratt and A. H. Mumford, "The History of Television," *Proc. Inst. Elec. Engrs.*, Vol. 99, Part III-A, pp. 25–42, 1952.

chapter 2

Fields of Application of Closed-Circuit Television

The sphere of application of closed-circuit television has been defined as follows:

> Whenever it is too dangerous; too difficult; too expensive; too inconvenient; too inaccessible; too tiring; too far; too hot; too cold; too high; too low; too dark; too small to observe directly, use television.

Indeed, the television camera has a place wherever observation is needed and where, at the same time, direct viewing is impossible, undesirable, or inconvenient. It not only provides great freedom in the choice of the vantage point for observation, but may even endow the human eye with increased sensitivity, contrast discrimination, and spectral range.

In the following pages we examine more specifically the ways in which closed-circuit television can be of assistance in various fields of human endeavor.

INDUSTRY

In industry television can aid in reducing hazards to life and limb, eliminate particularly undesirable occupations, increase the efficiency with which personnel is utilized, help to coordinate operations, and facilitate inspection. In certain special industries its utility may go well beyond this.

Safety. There are countless ways in which television can protect personnel from physical damage. Thus it permits close visual control of the remote handling of high explosives and radioactive materials without the complex and bulky ductwork required by mirror systems and periscopes for direct viewing. In atomic energy installations, ordnance depots, and plants employing hazardous chemical processes it makes it possible to increase the distance between the operations and the control personnel, since the brightness and sharpness of the picture on the monitor can readily be made independent of the length of cable coupling it to the camera. Furthermore, corrective measures can be taken more quickly in reaction to happenings observed on a large, bright screen image than in response to observations made through a viewing port or periscope eyepiece.

Similar advantages favor the use of closed-circuit television in wrecking and blasting operations. The easily installed, low-cost, and lightweight cameras can be trained on critical structural suppports or walls which are not directly visible to the operator, indicating to him signs of weakening and impending collapse. In mines, cameras in explosion-proof housings can protect the lives of mine crews by monitoring instruments indicating atmospheric conditions in the shafts. Similarly, pulleys and cables of mine lifts can be checked continuously to permit immediate correction of developing defects.

In the testing of new machinery—in particular, the flight-testing of aircraft—television permits the operator to watch the functioning of critical components which are not in direct view. Examples in aircraft are the jet exhaust, the control surfaces of the plane, and the landing gear. Catastrophe may frequently be avoided by prompt corrective measures in response to the first sign of malfunctioning.

Also in routine transportation television can be a material aid to safety. On large aircraft a camera mounted under the fuselage facing the wheels would provide the pilot with a final check of his altitude just before touchdown, giving him better control of the last few feet of his approach. Likewise, cameras in the wing tips would greatly facilitate maneuvering the plane in parking areas in which aircraft are often lined up with wing tips almost touching.

Furthermore, on large trailer trucks it is difficult for the driver to see to the rear, particularly when he is coupling the tractor to the trailer. A camera strategically placed would give him a closeup view of the coupling. As a simple rear-view device, television would find utility in bringing trucks into docks for unloading or for maneuvering trucks and buses in close quarters.

Finally, on the large barge trains which operate, for example, on the Mississippi the tugboat pilot has great difficulty in seeing any obstacles which may be in the way of the forward barge. A television camera mounted in the forward position could aid the pilot materially in the prevention of collisions and other entanglements.

A different safety problem may be solved by television in highway traffic control. Television cameras placed at critical intersections, tunnels, and bridges and connected with monitors in traffic-control offices would permit traffic police to take quick action in dispatching emergency equipment and in rerouting traffic when warranted because of accidents or other causes of congestion.

Elimination of Undesirable Occupations. In many industries there are numerous occupations which for various reasons, such as excessive heat, high noise level, excessive cold, or unhealthy atmosphere, must be regarded as undesirable. In many of these jobs the function of the worker is simply to watch a process and to report his observations by hand signal, voice, or telephone to the operator controlling the process. In such instances the worker can almost invariably be replaced to advantage by a television camera, which is immune to factors annoying and painful to the human observer. The employment of the camera has the additional advantage of reducing the chance of human error.

Obvious examples of such undesirable occupations can be drawn from the metals industry. The pouring of castings, the proper loading of annealing furnaces, and the progress of steel strip from the furnaces to the processing machines all expose watchers to relatively high levels of heat radiation. In the paper industry it is difficult to dissociate the direct watching of sulfite pulp digesters from the inhalation of sulfur-dioxide fumes. Few industries, indeed, are entirely free from occupations which can be classed, in the above sense, as undesirable and which could be eliminated advantageously by the use of television equipment.

Economy in Personnel. In the examples cited the saving in personnel resulting from the use of television equipment may be regarded as incidental. In many others it would be a primary, and very important, advantage. In nearly all mechanical loading operations efficiency demands the observation of the loading process. Frequently this is impossible or inconvenient from the control point.

Observation is particularly needed in the loading of freight cars with larger objects, such as scrap iron or baled waste, since a shifting of the load during transit can result in a serious accident or damage. Similarly, television cameras strategically placed at yard exits would afford the dispatching office a final check on freight-car closures, weather protection, proper mounting on flatcars, and the fulfilment of other transport requirements. Other cameras could transmit freight-car numbers on trains entering or leaving the yards. Direct observation of the numbers on monitors in the dispatching office simplifies the keeping of records and minimizes chances of error. Here the employment of television would not only reduce the number of yard workers required, but would also effect a saving in auxiliary structures, such as sheds and observation towers.

Similar advantages can be derived from the use of television to aid crane operators in the loading and unloading of ships' holds. Furthermore, the operation of conveyor-belt systems in refineries, smelters, and all types of processing plants can be monitored at the control point most conveniently by television cameras located wherever pile-ups or jamming are most likely to occur. In power plants the checking of boiler gages and of flame conditions in furnaces no longer demands a crew of watchmen; television permits the operators to observe them continuously on monitors in the control room, which may be a long distance from the gages and furnace ports.

Coordination of Operations. Closed-circuit television not only permits observation at a remote point, but simultaneous observation at a number of separated remote points. Thus it lends itself well to the coordination of a number of different operations from a single, central control point. In factories it permits the surveillance of complete production lines at one place where monitors are mounted side-by-side on a console and the several cameras are aimed at the critical points of the production line. If only occasional inspection is required, a single monitor may be provided with a selector switch for the several cameras. In a similar manner the instrument panels of unattended substations and pumping stations can be monitored continuously from the control center of a power system or pipe line.

In large power stations monitors giving a view of the boiler gages and the flame conditions within the furnaces can be supplemented by additional monitors showing the smoke emission from the stacks. This aids the furnace engineer to adjust fuel and air supply for complete combustion and facilitates compliance with local smoke-abatement ordinances.

In railway marshaling yards tower-mounted television cameras can give the dispatch office a full view of the yard trackage, even though the view from the control tower may command only a small part of it. Similarly, television may aid in the assignment of parking space to air transports at large airports and in the supervision of reloading at truck terminals.

Inspection. Product inspection by television is obviously an advantage when high temperatures make direct inspection impracticable. It is also very useful whenever X rays are utilized for inspection; examples are the detection of flaws in metal machine parts and the proper filling of opaque containers. Two factors render the use of closed-circuit television advisable in this instance. On the one hand, it greatly simplifies the protection of the inspecting personnel from stray X rays; the monitor may be located in a shielded room at some distance from the X-ray source and the television camera. On the other hand, the monitor image can be made much brighter than that which would appear on an X-ray screen, thereby permitting improved detail recognition without dark adaptation. Closed-circuit television can properly be regarded as an essential accessory for X-ray inspection.

Quite a different inspection problem is imposed by plant security. Wherever it is advisable to restrict admission to certain persons or vehicles, a camera installation outside the plant entrance makes it possible to transfer the decision regarding admission from an exposed gatehouse to the plant offices, from which the gates can be operated by remote control. This not only renders the employment of guards stationed at the gatehouse superfluous, but facilitates referral to higher authorities in doubtful cases.

Inspection of equipment can also be aided frequently by television. Whenever such inspection demands the use of a microscope or telescope, the employment of a television link, showing the image on a large-screen monitor, reduces fatigue and, consequently, improves care and accuracy.

Specialized Applications. In certain industries television does not merely make it possible to do things better and more cheaply, but opens up entirely new possibilities. An example is marine salvage, in which effective work has been limited in the past by the maximum depth at which a human diver can operate, or less than 350 feet. By contrast, television cameras have been built for operation at depths of 3000 feet. Thus the use of remotely operated tools guided by television observation from shipboard could enormously increase the range of salvage and deep-sea operations in general.

Again, the motion-picture industry can benefit from the use of television in a number of ways. The possibility of combining television cameras with film cameras, so as to show the director the scene precisely as viewed from the several camera positions, is only one way, if an important one. Television can also be very useful in the editing of the film, since it can produce a positive image from negative film. Thus, with television, the master can be prepared without the printing of the separate sequences. This applies to both black-and-white and color productions employing separation negatives.

The same technique which in motion-picture production can help the director to obtain the effect he wants may be employed in photographic portrait studios to produce a likeness which will satisfy the subject. To assure this, the photographer commonly takes many shots of different poses and under different lighting conditions and later submits proof of them to the customer, giving him a choice of effects achieved. By means of a television camera placed beside the regular camera and a receiver on wheels which can be set in a position within the subject's field of vision, a picture can be composed and the lighting adjusted to suit the subject. The mobility of the receiver permits the subject to see the picture as it will appear in profile or full-face shots. In fact, with more than one camera, two or more views can be presented for comparison. The same information can be made available to the photographer at the camera, giving him a right-side-up view of the picture in black and white, just as it will appear in the finished print.

PHYSICAL AND ENGINEERING RESEARCH

In research, the seeking out of the unknown, television finds its special province. It relieves the human observer of danger and discomfort; it sharpens his vision and extends it beyond the spectral range of the unaided eye; and it enables him to gather information from remote points.

Safety. Personnel safety frequently presents even greater problems in research than in industry. For here, in the research laboratory, industries are born and safety procedures are yet to be established. The forces which may be released and their physiological effects can only be guessed by the research worker. Thus a large factor of safety is essential in research operations. Such a factor is afforded by television.

In work with radioactive substances or explosive reagents remote handling with observation by television permits the placement of impenetrable, shockproof barriers between the work and the operator. At the same time the process may be observed in the finest detail, and color and depth may be added to the image when necessary.

The study of fuel combustion in jet engines demands a close observation of the flame exhaust. Here high temperatures and an unbearable noise level are added to the danger of physical injury by explosion. Remote viewing by television does away with both hazard and discomfort.

In the examination of the functioning of machine parts the camera may be attached to a moving element to show displacements relative to it on the monitor. Studies of the operation of car suspensions in road tests, observed by a camera attached to the chassis, provide an example. The camera here translates the observer's vantage point to a location from which direct observation is excluded by space considerations. The underwater study of the operation of a ship's propeller by means of television is another striking example of the flexibility of this new medium for extending human sight.

Extending the Spectral Range and Acuity of Vision. Camera tubes have been developed which are sensitive to the infrared, the ultraviolet, and even to X rays. They permit the visual examination of spectra in any of these ranges. An important application in astronomy is the study of the solar disk, as revealed by the emission of specific spectral lines, as well as the study of stellar spectra. Furthermore, the value of closed-circuit television in fluoroscopic research, such as X-ray studies of engine operation, is as pronounced as its usefulness in routine inspection.

Camera tubes can be made more sensitive than photographic materials and the human eye without extended dark adaptation. The bright image formed on the monitor frequently reveals details in a dimly lighted scene which are quite imperceptible when viewed directly. This property, also, can serve to extend the range and usefulness of astronomical cameras and telescopes. In particular, the shortened exposures made possible by a television link make it possible to utilize shorter periods of "good seeing," unmarred by atmospheric perturbations.

Data Transmission. Television can help astronomy to overcome the obstacles of atmospheric turbulence in still another manner. If a telescope equipped with a television camera and microwave transmitter is sent aloft in a high-altitude balloon, the picture may be examined and recorded at a monitor on the ground. This technique not only eliminates atmospheric disturbances, but also permits spectral studies in a range of ultraviolet radiation which is normally absorbed by the upper atmosphere.

A more general function of television in research is the transmission of data from one or several remote points to a central point for correlation with direct visual observations or with each other. In such telemetering applications television has important advantages. It can transmit more information over a single channel than nonvisual telemetering techniques, and the direct observation of the meter face or other indicator on the monitor screen minimizes the chance of error.

MEDICINE AND BIOLOGY

The life sciences and medicine offer a vast range of important applications for television. Setting aside temporarily its use in medical and surgical instruction, we can cite examples in the fields of biological research, routine diagnostic techniques, and medical and dental practice.

Biological Research. In many branches of biological research the television microscope, or the combination of a television chain and a conventional microscope, is a tool of extraordinary power. Part of its advantage is derived simply from the great reduction in viewing fatigue experienced in observing the large, bright image on the monitor as compared with looking at the microscope field directly through the eyepiece.

Another important gain rests in the possibility of electronic contrast enhancement, which may be superposed on other techniques for emphasizing important detail, such as phase microscopy. The study of changes and motions within organic cells is greatly facilitated by both factors.

The employment of the television microscope with ultraviolet illumination may possibly be even more significant in the study of cell structure and of the composition of cell constituents, since organic materials generally exhibit the most marked differences in absorption in the ultraviolet spectrum, particularly in the range from 2600 to 2800 A. Thus observation in the ultraviolet is as effective as the employment of specific organic stains, without introducing comparable disturbances in the material studied. The use of infrared illumination, on the other hand, is often helpful in the study of structures hidden by material which is opaque in the visible but transparent in the infrared.

An attractive feature of television microscopy is the ease with which the qualitative visual observation can be supplemented by quantitative measurements. Thus with uniform substage illumination the variation in amplitude of the video signal corresponds directly to the variation in transmission of the specimen along a scanning line. If the video output of the television camera is applied to a line-selector oscilloscope, the latter will give a quantitative plot of the specimen transmission along the chosen scanning line.

There are many uses for the television camera in biological research quite apart from microscopy. In ultraviolet chromatography, which depends on ultraviolet absorption for the identification of molecular fractions, the ultraviolet-sensitive television camera permits immediate observation and measurement of the relative concentrations in the sample. Studies of animal behavior, undisturbed by the presence of human beings, are greatly facilitated by television. Television cameras with infrared sensitivity, in particular, should prove helpful in the investigation of nocturnal habits.

Rudimentary television systems, or "area displays," finally, find application in the study of the distribution and variation of skin potentials and their correlation with external stimuli and physiological processes. Such area displays give a more complete picture of the electrical phenomena studied than the conventional one-dimensional records of electroencephalography and electrocardiography.

Routine Diagnostic Techniques. The use of the video signal delivered by the television microscope is not limited to a quantitative representation of specimen transmission. Applied to appropriate electronic selection and counting circuits, it can provide valuable statistical information.

In particular, if the image field contains a dispersion of essentially similar particles, such as blood cells or cell nuclei, the signal can be analyzed to give the total particle count, the mean particle size, or a count of particles above an established level of size or density. The development of automatic counting methods employing television techniques is assuming increasing importance in view of the role of the blood count as the ultimate test for radiation exposure and the use of abnormal cell counts for early cancer diagnosis. Such methods should ultimately increase the speed and accuracy of the tests and relieve technicians of an irksome and tiring task.

Medical and Dental Practice. An obvious use of television in medical practice is in consultation. During surgery it can provide the consultants with an intimate view of the incision and the surgeon's work. Then, for a biopsy, a slide may be prepared and demonstrated by means of a television microscope to aid in the formulation of a diagnosis. In both instances color television equipment is advantageous, for improved discrimination of tissues and for the identification of stains on the slide.

The consultants may be in the same room, in different rooms of the same hospital, or even in different cities, provided a television link has been established between the sites of transmission and reception. Thus the skilled pathologist can greatly extend the efficiency with which his time is utilized and the geographical area he can serve. Television, accordingly, can increase both the quality and quantity of service provided by the medical profession.

Another field of medicine in which television can make a material contribution is fluoroscopy, the direct examination of the patient by means of X rays. The conventional, direct viewing of the X-ray screen demands long periods of dark adaptation by the radiologist. Even with such preparation, the visual process he must employ—scotopic or rod vision—is incapable of distinguishing fine detail.

Both the necessity of dark adaptation and poor detail discrimination are obviated if (1) a high-sensitivity television camera is trained on the conventional screen; or (2) the screen is replaced by an image-intensifier tube coupled with a television camera or by a special X-ray pickup tube, and the picture is viewed at a high light-level on a monitor. As in industrial fluoroscopy, this procedure has the incidental advantage of reducing the hazard of excessive radiation exposure for the radiologist.

Television affords hospital personnel similar protection against radiation exposure in X-ray and radioactive therapy. Here it may guide technicians in the alignment, by remote control, of the sources of irradiation.

Also in general hospital care television can improve the service pro-

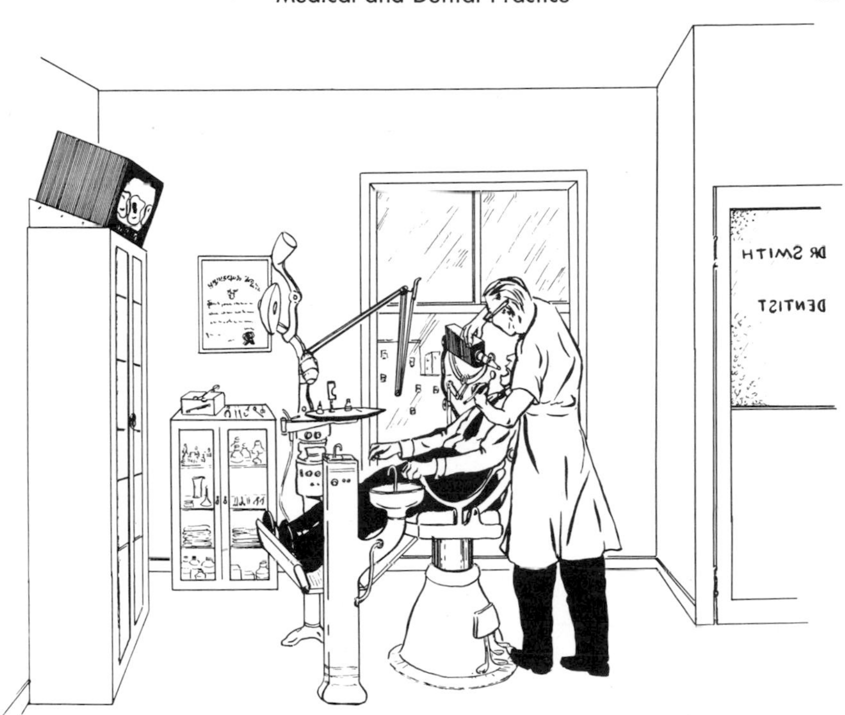

Fig. 2.1. Television in the dentist's office.

vided by the staff. Particularly in critical wards, television cameras mounted over the hospital beds make it possible for the floor nurse to keep a continuous check on the patients' condition by watching a monitor at her desk. A similar technique, employing disguised cameras, is helpful in studying the behavior of mentally disturbed patients. Conversely, mental patients can receive treatment from a skilled psychotherapist by establishing contact with him on closed-circuit television.

In dental practice television can aid the dentist in pointing out to the patient defects which must be corrected, in explaining the work which he is about to undertake, and in showing the finished work. This tends to relax the patient and increase his confidence in the dentist. As compared with the dental mirror, commonly employed for such purposes in the past, a television system, adjusted as in Fig. 2.1, has the advantage of providing a larger, more detailed picture, unobscured by the holder of the mirror. When not employed for demonstration purposes, the television receiver can serve to entertain the patient, a common practice even now—particularly with children—to set him at ease.

EDUCATION

The contribution of closed-circuit television to education promises to be vital, both because of the severe and continuing teacher shortage and because of television's effectiveness as visual aid. This applies both to formal education and to specialized training.

Television as Teaching Medium. In a report to the Fund for the Advancement of Education Alexander J. Stoddard, former Superintendent of Schools of Los Angeles, Bronxville, N.Y., Providence, Denver, and Philadelphia, recommends that no new school should be built without facilities for classroom television.[1] He estimates that by the use of television the number of teaching positions to be filled could be reduced by 100,000, with a saving in salaries of a half billion dollars annually. All this could be accomplished with a simultaneous improvement in the quality of instruction.

Stoddard recommends in particular that a variety of subjects, such as art and music, be taught by skilled specialists through the medium of classroom television. On the one hand, this would improve the quality of teaching in these subjects and permit the use of superior equipment; on the other, it would reduce the number of subjects to be taught by the classroom teacher and permit him to give more attention to individual needs.

We can think of three different stages in the use of television for classroom instruction. First of all, we may have a closed-circuit television system confined to a single school building. Here there may be a limited number of originating centers, such as studios, demonstration rooms, and workshops. In addition, the school antenna system would give access to programs provided by television broadcasting stations. Television receivers placed in every classroom would, in principle, be able to tune in on any of these programs.

This is, in fact, one possibility. The locally originated programs would modulate unused television channels and the resulting radio-frequency signals would simply be added to the antenna output. The selection of the programs would be entirely at the discretion of the classroom teacher or his representative.

As an alternative, a central switching unit can be provided from which both locally originated and off-the-air programs can be monitored and distributed to classrooms. This gives the supervisor's office complete control of the programs presented and facilitates the keeping of

[1] A. J. Stoddard, "Schools for Tomorrow: An Educator's Blueprint." Fund for the Advancement of Education, New York 1957.

full records of the television instruction provided. It is a relatively simple further step to install a camera and microphone in each classroom in order to permit remote supervision and to eliminate the need for the presence of a teacher during television instruction.

In the next stage the units in a school system or the buildings of a college campus may be linked by a community television network. Within the network, programs may be originated at a single central point or injected into the system from any of the component units. In the single-school, closed-circuit television system the specialty teacher can reach simultaneously a large number of classes of the proper size for discussion and recitation, and time losses incidental to the trooping back and forth of pupils between classrooms, demonstration rooms, and assemblies can be avoided. In the community system the outreach of the specialist is further increased, and school construction can be simplified by the centralization of specialized teaching equipment at the originating studio. Savings in transportation costs of teaching materials, such as films and exhibits, are an incidental advantage.

Finally, the primary source for specialized instruction may be the broadcasting studio of an educational television station or a commercial station under contract to the school authorities. The use of topflight instructors and the greatest care in program preparation are warranted by the large number of students who benefit by the presentations. At the same time, the extensive use of this method of instruction will demand a high degree of standardization in the schools of the area covered. While this should have the welcome effect of establishing relatively high minimum levels of preparation for all the schools, care should be taken that it should not act as a brake on the efforts of the most competent and progressive of the supervisory staffs.

It must not be imagined, of course, that the three stages described above are to be regarded as progressive. It is clear that a school fully equipped for the first stage is in a position to take advantage of any further developments in community networks and educational broadcasting. The final balance between locally originated programs, community programs, and broadcast programs may vary at different schools, depending on the relative emphasis placed on the use of outstanding talents, the development of local initiative, and on purely economic considerations. It may also be noted that some subjects lend themselves better to closed-circuit presentation than to broadcasting. It is true that in the field of public-school instruction this is likely to be a minor consideration. Here the broadest possible dissemination of the programs—to parents and adults generally as well as to school children—is to be welcomed.

Television as Visual Aid. In the preceding section we have considered television simply as a means of giving a larger number of students access to the teaching of a limited number of particularly well-qualified individuals. However, it can do more than this. It enables the teacher to show things to a class which cannot be demonstrated in any other way.

This is particularly true in the physical and biological sciences. Suppose, for instance, that the instructor wishes to explain the behavior of protozoa in pond water to his class. With the television microscope the whole class can view together the motions of the protozoa on the large, bright monitor screen, and the instructor can point out their various peculiarities. Moreover, he can show the effect of external stimuli and continue the demonstration as long as interest persists. The demonstration may have added meaning for the class, since the pond water may have been collected on a field trip.

Such a demonstration is certainly much more meaningful than one using individual microscopes, in which every student sees a different field, or than a prepared film on protozoa which bears little relation to previous experiences of the class and answers only those questions which the film maker has anticipated.

Television possesses similar advantages in the demonstration of physical experiments. These are frequently on so small a scale that they can be viewed satisfactorily by at best a handful of students at a time. The television camera, in translating an optimal view of the phenomena to the monitor screen or screens, gives the whole class "ring-side seats" for the demonstration.

Television in Specialized Training. Whereas most phases of formal education can be carried out equally well by closed-circuit and broadcast techniques, specialized training generally demands the use of closed-circuit methods, in view of its limited audience and, frequently, its confidential nature. Here the great effectiveness of television as a visual aid plays a special role.

This is well illustrated by the use of television for teaching surgery (Fig. 2.2). The camera can be placed directly above the surgeon's work—a vantage point inaccessible not only to a group of students, but even to a single student. Furthermore, the viewing area is not limited to the operating theatre but can include any other areas of the hospital or medical school which are linked to it by television cable. The operation may even be transmitted by leased cable or microwave facilities to hospitals, medical schools, and conclaves of physicians in other cities to keep them abreast of advances in the art.

One of the advantages of television teaching in surgery is the avoid-

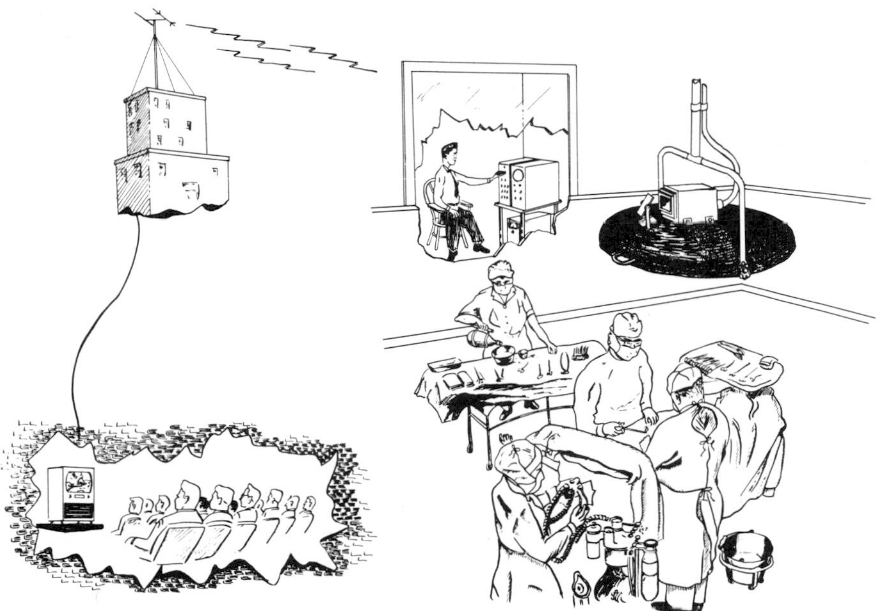

Fig. 2.2. Television in instruction in surgery.

ance of the physical interference of the observers with the work of the surgeon. Similarly, in advanced training in psychotherapy the use of television cameras hidden in the consultation rooms to demonstrate treatment techniques to students prevents their psychological intrusion upon the relationship between psychiatrist and patient.

Television is particularly serviceable in instruction in dentistry. Both in dental surgery and in dental prosthetics we are dealing with delicate, small-scale operations which are presented much more effectively by television, with its arbitrarily adjustable scale of magnification, than directly. Furthermore, a single well-presented demonstration on television, clearly observed by an entire class, is of greater benefit to the students and pleasanter for the instructor than an indefinite succession of identical demonstrations to small student groups.

Similar techniques are effective in teaching skills, such as the assembly of instruments and the testing and servicing of machinery to production workers, technicians, and service men within an industry or an organization. As compared with the training film, television has the advantage of permitting the adaptation of the presentation to the immediate requirements and enabling the instructor to respond to questions presented over an intercommunication system.

COMMERCE

In commerce the primary function of closed-circuit television is to expedite the transmission of information. The information may be in written or printed form or be communicated by "live" pickup. Other functions are sales promotion through advertising and the protection of property.

Transmission of Documents. In some instances the visual transmission of a document is the only alternative to its physical transport and the attendant time delay; in other instances, it is also to be preferred to other methods, such as reading it over a telephone line, from the point of view of accuracy.

An example of the first circumstance is the verification of signatures on checks or contracts. Thus television permits a teller or bank officer to compare, without delay, the signature on a document submitted by a client with the signature card in the records department, even though this department may be in a centralized location serving different branches or divisions of the bank.

Examples of the second kind can be drawn from all kinds of commercial activities. We may cite the transmission of market reports and balance sheets from the files to the offices in banking and brokerage houses; the transmission of orders from the central offices of wholesale or retail houses to stockroom or warehouse; and the communication of book requisitions to the stacks in libraries. Others are involved in the checking of applications for reservations at ticket agencies against the seating plans of theatres and against vacancies on ships, trains, and airplanes. In all these cases the advantage of television communication over voice communication is derived from the fact that the eye can take in information at an enormously more rapid rate than the ear can accept it or the voice can communicate it. In addition, the television method avoids the possibility of error in the translation of written matter into the spoken word and in the interpretation of the latter by the listener.

The same advantages attend the use of television for communicating arrival and departure bulletins in the public rooms of airline and railroad terminals.

In a sense, the transmission of documents is the province of facsimile rather than of television; correspondingly, it may be advantageous to employ special, slow-scan systems for this purpose when long-distance transmission is required, since this permits the use of ordinary telephone lines in place of television cable or microwave facilities. For transmission over shorter distances the instantaneous response and low cost of the standardized closed-circuit television system give it preference.

Intercommunication. Closed-circuit television can be an exceedingly effective means for coordinating the activities of commercial organizations. Audio-visual conferences between executives are not only more effective than telephone conferences in injecting the personalities of the participants, but permit, in addition, the use of charts, tables, documents, and samples to illustrate the discussion. The same applies to the launching of new products by presentations from the central office to gatherings of agents and distributors in various geographical areas. The television method has the further advantage over a series of presentations made by a traveling representative of the company that all districts receive the information simultaneously.

Television can also be very helpful to management in making progress reports at stockholders' or directors' meetings. Unlike a motion-picture record, a television tour of company facilities can be modified and interpreted at will in response to questions. It is never stale or out-of-date.

It should be noted that television conferences, like telephone conferences, need not be limited to two parties. Cameras at each location can feed video signals modulating separate carriers into a common transmission line tapped by the several receivers. In this manner every party can tune in on any other party connected to the line.

Advertising. Advertising by broadcast television has proved itself an exceedingly effective means for stimulating consumer interest in goods and services. After it has brought the customer to the store, with the intent of making a purchase, closed-circuit television can be used to direct his attention to articles which may prove particularly attractive or which the store management is most eager to move. As part of a window display, a monitor on which demonstrations are made and exhibits shown adds the attention-compelling element of motion and activity and makes it possible to present the feature of the moment without delay. In lounges and rest rooms footsore customers may be given the opportunity of watching fashion shows and other events taking place in other parts of the store.

In hotels and motor courts, where television receivers are becoming standard room equipment, unused television channels can be employed to inform clients of the opportunities offered by the establishment and to present local news, menus, and floor shows. If a distribution system has already been provided for broadcast reception, only very simple and inexpensive auxiliary equipment is required.

Protection of Property. In a large store a few television cameras, strategically placed for the transmission of views to monitors in a conveniently located security room, can be more effective in the apprehension of pickpockets and shoplifters than a large number of store detectives circulating among the customers. Furthermore, the presence of the cameras, alone, may have a salutary effect in discouraging theft. Whenever it seems wiser to hide the cameras from view, it is, of course, an easy matter.

The same technique is particularly applicable to post offices, banks, jewelry stores, and other places in which maximum security is required. The surveillance by television of loading platforms of warehouses and factories can also do much to minimize losses from pilferage.

In the small family business closed-circuit television, which may take the form of inexpensive camera units linked to the family television receiver, can play a broader role. In slack periods it may permit the owner to leave the store unattended while he busies himself elsewhere. When a door-operated buzzer or bell announces the entrance of a customer into the store, the store owner can follow his movements on the monitor and guide him, by an intercommunication system, to the proper shelves. If the customer finds the desired article, the owner can then direct him to leave payment, debit his account, or leave his work to attend to him. If the article is not available, the owner need not interrupt his work. Thus the television camera can save him much time and exertion.

MILITARY USES

It is clear that nearly all the potentialities of closed-circuit television which have been listed can be diverted to military use. Below are indicated briefly some of the field uses of television and its application to military training.

Field Uses of Television. In the field television may be used in particular for weapon-guidance and in reconnaissance. A television camera and associated transmitter mounted on a remotely controlled missile can inform the control station continuously of its aim with respect to the target. In this manner the control station can adjust steering signals to assure impact at the intended point.

In reconnaissance the very high sensitivity of specially designed television cameras and their response to invisible infrared radiations render them useful in night operations. Television cameras and transmitters carried by scouts on mobile units or in planes can transmit views of battle operations from the front lines to the command in the rear, thereby facilitating coordination of operations.

Other obvious uses are the transmission of weather maps and other flight information to military planes and the maintenance from the bridge of a visual check on the various operating centers of a naval vessel.

Television as a Training Medium. The armed forces face the problem of training large number of men of varying backgrounds in a great variety of manual and other skills and of doing so in the shortest time possible. Furthermore, much of this training has to be modified continuously to meet changes in equipment and operating techniques.

Television meets both of these requirements. The visual methods which it employs are most effective in the transfer and retention of information and minimize reliance on an understanding of the spoken word. It is exceedingly economical in its use of skilled teachers and is not subject to obsolescence in the same manner as training films.

Television is also an exceedingly flexible medium. Thus, in a single sitting, a class can be given a lecture illustrated by charts and diagrams, interspersed, when desirable, with views of field maneuvers transmitted by a mobile unit, shop demonstrations, and films. All of these offerings may be presented on the same screen by a television projector or appear on an arbitrarily large number of conveniently distributed receivers.

HOME AND FARM

The various uses of closed-circuit television which have been considered in the preceding sections are of great social and economic importance at present and can be counted on to gain still greater significance in the years ahead. Yet the amount of equipment they will require may well be dwarfed by that needed in the home and on the farm.

There are over 40 million television sets in use in the homes of the United States. By the addition of a television camera, which is not only much smaller, but may also be much simpler than the receiver, the set could serve the family in any number of unexpected and worthwhile ways. The very existence of this mass market makes possible, and justifies, mass production which, in turn, could reduce the price of the equipment to a universally attractive level.

Consider some of the ways in which television cameras, operating on unused channels of the receiver, could be utilized in the home. We can imagine them installed in the baby's room, supervising the play area outdoors, checking on tradesmen and visitors at the front door, and monitoring the range in the kitchen (Fig. 2.3). A flick of a switch would inform the housewife, relaxing after her daily chores and watching her favorite program or listening to a concert, whether she were needed in

Fig. 2.3. Closed-circuit television in the home.

any of these areas. Life would become less hectic and home management more efficient.

These cameras would also have their place in family fun. As attachments to the home movie projector they would permit daylight viewing of family movies; and, with the eventual introduction of home-video tape recorders, the same cameras could be used for taking the movies. Amateur radio enthusiasts could make their hobby even more interesting by adding sight to sound for face-to-face, long-distance visits with their fellow amateurs. Photographers could enjoy, and show the rest of the family, their vacation pictures from the negative film. In sports, too, the television camera would find application; for instance, in target-shooting a view of the target could be brought up close by a camera and monitor to show the shooter his exact performance.

Closed-circuit television should prove particularly useful on the farm. For instance, the installation of one or several cameras in the stables would save the farmer many a trip out in the cold to check on the condition of his livestock. In surveying, a miniature camera attached to the eyepiece of a transit or level and a portable receiver would enable the farmer to run fence lines and contours unassisted, since the receiver would show him when he had placed the marker in the proper position. The same combination of camera and portable receiver could help him in diagnosing equipment troubles. In brief—in the country as in the suburbs and in the city—the addition of the camera to the receiver would greatly extend the use and enjoyment which the owner could derive from television.

chapter 3

Closed-Circuit Television Apparatus

THE CAMERA

The essential components of any television system are the camera, the receiver, and some communication system coupling them. It is the function of the camera to convert a picture—a two-dimensional pattern of light and dark—into a time sequence of electrical pulses. In the receiver this sequence of pulses is utilized to reproduce the original picture on a viewing screen.

To give the impression of continuity of motion in the transmitted scene, pictures of the scene must be transmitted and reproduced in rapid succession. Thus, in broadcast television, the requirements of continuity of motion and freedom from objectionable flicker in the reproduced picture have led to the acceptance of a "frame frequency" of 30 complete pictures per second. There is no obligation to adhere to this standard in closed-circuit television. However, since continuity of motion and freedom from flicker are, in most applications, of as much interest to the observer of the closed-circuit receiver as to the viewer of the home set, comparable frame rates have been quite generally adopted. Also, in a practical sense, it is advantageous to adhere to the standards used in broadcasting in order to be able to use standard receivers, monitors, etc., as auxiliary equipment.

Similarly, the number of scanning lines which make up the picture raster is generally the same, or of the same order, in closed-circuit television as in broadcast television. The number of scanning lines determines the finest picture detail which can be resolved by the viewer in a vertical direction. The finest detail which can be resolved in a horizontal direction is determined by the maximum number of electrical pulses which can be transmitted in the time allotted to a single scanning line, or the frequency bandwidth of the system. Normally, frequency bandwidth and number of scanning lines are so related as to make the resolution of detail the same in the vertical and horizontal directions. In broadcast television they have been selected so that, for a normal observer placed at the preferred viewing distance from the receiver (viewing distance = 4 × picture height), the finest detail reproduced lies at the threshold of vision. This is realized with approximately 500 scanning lines in the picture and a transmission bandwidth of about 4 megacycles per second. In certain applications of closed-circuit television it may be advantageous to increase the resolution in the horizontal direction by utilizing a wider bandwidth, although maintaining the standard number of scanning lines. This can be especially true in such uses as reading fine printed matter.

The basic requirements to be fulfilled by the closed-circuit television camera and the broadcast television camera are thus similar. It may be concluded that their basic components, also, are similar. This is true. However, the closed-circuit, or "industrial," television camera must satisfy a number of secondary conditions which materially affect its construction. These conditions are (1) low cost; (2) small bulk; (3) high stability; and (4) ease of operation by unskilled personnel. To fulfil them, along with the common requirements of high sensitivity, high resolution, and pleasing picture quality, some compromise may be demanded, and certainly a new approach to the overall design of the camera is needed. In any case, the camera must contain a camera tube or an equivalent converter of a light picture into an electrical signal, a lens or optical system, and an electronic preamplifier to bring the electrical signal to a sufficiently high level for transmission by cable to a remote-control unit or receiver.

The Camera Tube. In any discussion of camera tubes and television pickup systems it is convenient to distinguish between nonstorage systems and storage systems. In a nonstorage system the only light utilized is that falling on a picture element during the generation of the corresponding electrical pulse. In a storage system the light falling on the target in the time interval between successive pulses corresponding to the same element is utilized as well.

Perhaps the simplest *nonstorage pickup system* is the flying-spot system represented in Fig. 3.1. At the present time it finds application primarily in the transmission of slides and film, and we shall encounter it again only in connection with the flying-spot microscope. Its essential components are a flying-spot tube equipped with a pair of deflection coils, an objective and a condenser lens, and a multiplier phototube. The flying-spot tube is simply a flat-faced kinescope with a short-

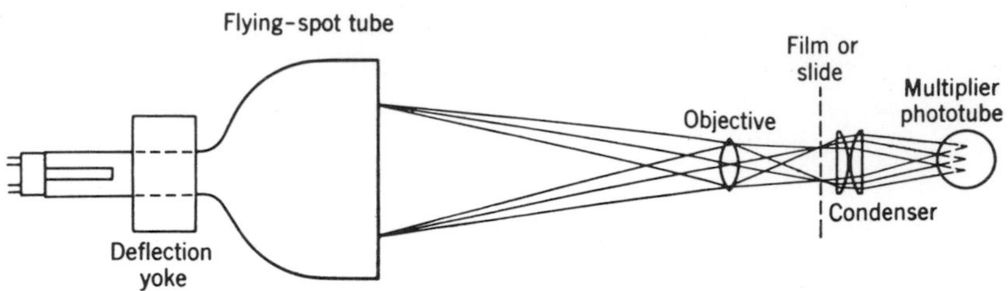

Fig. 3.1. Flying-spot system for the transmission of transparencies. (From Zworykin and Morton, *Television*, Wiley, New York, 1954.)

persistence screen and an unmodulated electron beam. The scanning pattern described by the beam on the screen is imaged on the transparent object by an objective, and the light transmitted by the object is directed by the condenser lens onto the photocathode of the multiplier phototube. By imaging the objective aperture onto the photocathode, the distribution of light on the latter becomes independent of the position of the flying spot, and shading arising from nonuniformity in photocathode sensitivity is avoided. The photocurrent in the multiplier phototube represents the picture signal.

When the persistence of the flying-spot tube screen is of the order of the traversal time of a single picture element (a fraction of a millionth of a second), only one such element on the object-transparency is illuminated at a time, and the picture signal measures directly the variation in transmission over the object area. When the time of persistence is materially larger than the traversal time of a picture element—and this is commonly the case—the spot is smeared out in a horizontal direction. Even then, however, a crisp picture can be obtained by adjusting the frequency response of the amplifier for the persistence of the spot on the tube screen.

The signal amplitude of the flying-spot system is limited by the light output of the flying-spot tube and the optical efficiency of the objective. On the other hand, the efficiency of utilization of the light which traverses the object is very high; object points are in darkness except at the instant of signal generation. However, because of the nonstorage nature of the operation the instantaneous intensity of the light must be correspondingly higher. The flying-spot pickup system is advantageous primarily in specialized applications in which the light tolerance of the object is limited.

A nonstorage pickup system of wider utility is the Farnsworth image dissector (Fig. 3.2). Here the scanning and signal generation functions are combined in a single envelope which constitutes the camera tube. An objective projects a picture of the scene to be transmitted on a transparent photocathode. The photoelectrons emitted by the photocathode are accelerated toward the opposite end of the tube, and, at the same time, they are focused by the magnetic field of a solenoid enveloping the tube into a sharp image of the photocathode at the opposite end of the tube. A metal diaphragm with a small aperture transmits only the electrons coming from a single picture element of the photocathode. As vertical and horizontal sawtooth voltages are applied to the pairs of deflection coils mounted on the tube envelope, the photoemission of the cathode is swept across the aperture in such fashion that the point of origin of the transmitted electrons describes a conventional scanning pattern on the photocathode. The electrons passing through the aperture enter an electron multiplier structure which acts essentially as a noise-free amplifier for the picture signal.

Unlike the flying-spot system, the image dissector is not limited in the nature of the picture or object which may be transmitted, provided that adequate illumination can be supplied. The illumination must be sufficient so that the light from a single picture element can eject, during the time in which it is imaged on the aperture of the dissector, a relatively large number of photoelectrons from the cathode. These electrons constitute the picture signal for the element in question. Since the ejection of photoelectrons is a random process, their number will not be exactly proportional to the light intensity; it will deviate from the expected value by an amount with a root-mean-square value equal to the square root of the expected value. The ratio of the expected value of the signal to the root-mean-square deviation, or the "noise," is a measure of the number of brightness steps distinguishable in the fine

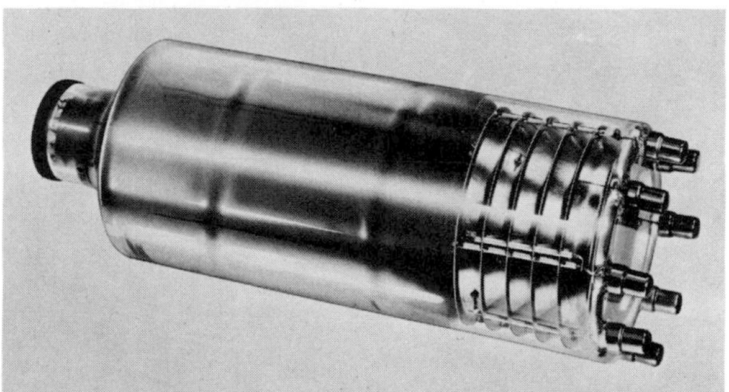

Fig. 3.2. Farnsworth image dissector. The transparent photocathode is at the right, the electron multiplier at the left. (Courtesy of Diamond Power Specialty Corporation.)

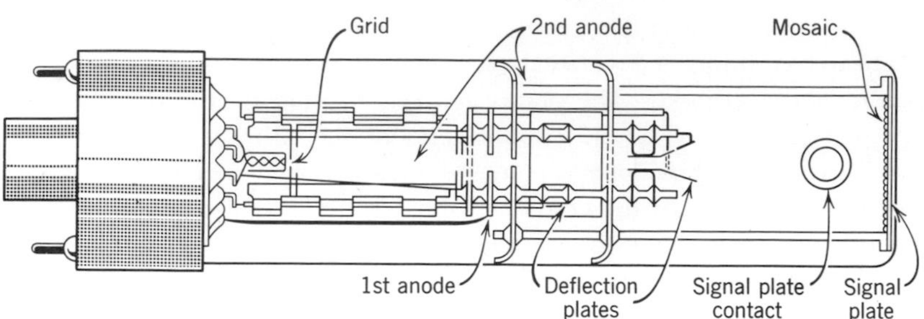

Fig. 3.3. Small iconoscope with electrostatic deflection (Type 5527). (From Pender-McIlwain, *Electrical Engineers Handbook, Communication and Electronics*, Wiley, New York, 1950.)

detail of the picture. It is thus commonly employed to describe the optimal picture quality that can be obtained with a given system. For a television picture, a signal-to-noise ratio of 100 is generally regarded as excellent, a ratio of 30 as acceptable.

To attain a signal-to-noise ratio of 30 with an image dissector having a 15-square-inch cathode area and a photosensitivity of 20 microamperes per lumen operating on broadcast television standards requires, with an $f/1.4$ objective, a scene illumination of at least 2000 foot-candles. These excessive light requirements can be reduced by lowering the required resolution. Since both the size of the current-selecting aperture and the time during which it collects photoelectrons from a single picture element increase inversely as the square of the resolution, a reduction in resolution by a factor of 2 cuts the light requirements by a factor of 16.

The dissector is thus restricted to applications in which a high light-level is assured and in which moderate resolution is acceptable. Here, however, the absence of a thermionic cathode gives it the advantage of very long life. Furthermore, it enjoys, along with other pickup tubes with photoemissive cathodes, a wide range of temperature tolerance. The built-in electron multiplier, with a gain of 1 million, provides an output level of about ½ volt and minimizes additional amplification requirements. The last advantage is to some extent balanced by the need of a 2000-volt supply for the multiplier.

The drawback of insufficient sensitivity, inherent in the earlier television pickup systems, was finally overcome by signal storage. The first storage pickup tube—and, indeed, the first effective electronic camera tube—was the *iconoscope*. Figure 3.3 shows a diagram of a small iconoscope which has been used for closed-circuit applications.[1] The princi-

[1] See Barrett and Goodman (reference 16).

pal novel component of the iconoscope is the mosaic. It consists of an array of mutually insulated, photosensitized surface elements deposited on a sheet of mica which has a continuous conducting coating, the signal plate, on the other side. Every photosensitive element constitutes, in effect, one plate of a condenser which is continuously charged by photoemission at a rate determined by the brightness of the portion of the picture projected on the photosensitive element. As the scanning beam sweeps over the element, the elementary condenser is discharged. The resulting current pulse in the signal-plate lead constitutes the picture signal for the picture element in question.

It is seen here that the photocurrent emitted by the element throughout the period between successive scans contributes to the picture signal, the charge being stored in the condenser element up to the next scan. Thus storage is in principle capable of reducing the light requirements by a factor equal to the number of picture elements, or several hundred thousand times for a standard television picture. In the iconoscope the gain was much less than this, namely of the order of a thousand. This deviation from ideal performance may be attributed to two causes: first, the electric field in front of the mosaic is such as to prevent the complete collection of both photoelectrons and secondary electrons emitted by the mosaic; and, second, the level of the output signal of the iconoscope is so low that the noise, or random fluctuations in voltage, contributed by the first stage of the thermionic preamplifier greatly outweighs the root-mean-square deviation in the stored charge.

The mosaic is an insulating surface with a secondary emission ratio greater than unity for the beam electrons with an accelerating voltage of the order of a thousand volts. Consequently, under the scanning beam it attains an equilibrium potential slightly positive with respect to the tube walls, which act as secondary-electron collectors. Normally, this equilibrium potential, at which the secondary electron current leaving the bombarded area equals the primary beam current, is of the order of +3 volts. Most of the electrons which do not return to the bombarded element fail to contribute to the picture signal. Instead, they rain back or are redistributed over the remainder of the mosaic, driving it down to zero or a slightly negative potential. Similarly, the photoelectrons emitted by the mosaic are largely returned or redistributed, thereby reducing the charge stored by illumination in other parts of the mosaic. As a result, under typical operating conditions, the picture signal generated by the iconoscope is only about one-twentieth as large as it would be for a tube with perfect secondary emission and photoemission collection. At the same time, the electron redistribution gives rise to spurious "shading," which is superimposed on the transmitted picture. How-

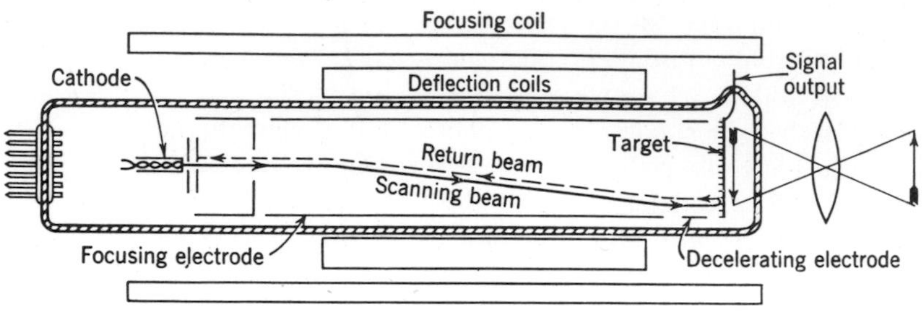

Fig. 3.4. Orthicon-type camera tube. (From Zworykin and Morton, *Television*, Wiley, New York, 1954.)

ever, techniques have been developed in broadcast practice to nullify shading. If these are applied, extraordinarily pleasing, high-quality pictures may be transmitted with the iconoscope. The circuit refinements for shading compensation are not warranted for most closed-circuit applications, however.

Signal loss from redistribution and shading are avoided in the *orthicon*[2] (Fig. 3.4). It differs from the iconoscope in that its mosaic is maintained at approximately gun-cathode potential. Thus when the mosaic is in darkness none of the beam electrons can land; instead, they are turned back to their point of origin. When the mosaic is illuminated photoemission drives the surface positive, and the scanning beam, at its next passage, deposits just enough electrons to return it to its equilibrium potential, at which landing is just prevented. The picture signal so generated is equal to the stored charge. Furthermore, since photoelectron collection by the tube walls, which are several hundred volts positive with respect to the mosaic, is complete, the stored charge is proportional to the incident light.

To obtain sharp focus over the entire target area a longitudinal magnetic field is provided on which the transverse horizontal and vertical magnetic deflecting fields are superposed. Under these circumstances the electrons tend to travel along the resultant magnetic field lines, eventually oscillating about them with an amplitude determined by initial transverse velocity components. The longitudinal magnetic field is chosen so as to make the "wavelength" of the oscillation equal to the distance between the gun aperture and the mosaic, or an integer submultiple thereof.

The orthicon has been found to exhibit the expected gain in sensitivity

[2] The British CPS Emitron (Cathode-Potential-Stabilized Emitron) and Remington Rand's Vericon resemble the orthicon in construction and operation.

and freedom from shading arising from redistributed electrons. At the same time, it exhibits instability at very high light-levels. When the scanning beam is no longer capable of fully canceling the charge stored by photoemission the mosaic potential may rise beyond the point at which the secondary-emission ratio equals unity. From this point on the beam charges the mosaic positively, generating a blacker-than-black signal, until the mosaic surface assumes anode potential. Normal operation can be restored only by temporarily interrupting the high-voltage connection of the electron collector surfaces.

To overcome this difficulty, the E. M. I. Research Laboratories in England have manufactured a small-sized, orthicon-type tube (target diameter 1.4 inch), the CPS Emitron Type 5907, which has a fine-mesh grid maintained 17 volts positive with respect to the cathode and placed 1 millimeter in front of the target.[3] The grid prevents the target surface from rising to a potential at which the secondary emission ratio exceeds unity. Hence this tube, developed specifically for closed-circuit applications, is stable at all light-levels.

Apart from instability, the output signal level of the orthicon is sufficiently low that the noise contribution of the preamplifier materially depresses the signal-to-noise ratio for the transmitted picture signal.

In the *image orthicon* (Fig. 3.5) both the instability and low output signal level of the orthicon are overcome, while the advantages inherent in low-velocity scanning are retained. Here an optical image of the scene to be transmitted is projected on a continuous, transparent photocathode. The photoelectrons emitted by the photocathode are accelerated and focused by a longitudinal magnetic field onto a thin glass target. The secondary electrons ejected from the target are collected by a closely spaced, fine-mesh target screen. Since at the bombarding voltage of the primary photoelectrons (approximately 500 volts) the secondary emission ratio of the glass target exceeds unity, a positive charge image corresponding to the original picture on the photocathode is stored on the target.

The opposite side of the target is scanned by a low-velocity beam. Since the target potential rises wherever positive charge is stored, beam electrons land here sufficient in number to neutralize the stored charge; the conductivity through the target is adequate to prevent the build-up of appreciable potential differences between the two sides.

The landing of a certain fraction of the beam electrons on positive portions of the target reduces the beam current, which is turned back and strikes the disk electrode with the minute limiting aperture of the electron gun. The potentials applied to the surrounding electrodes are

[3] See Boddy and Gardner (reference 19).

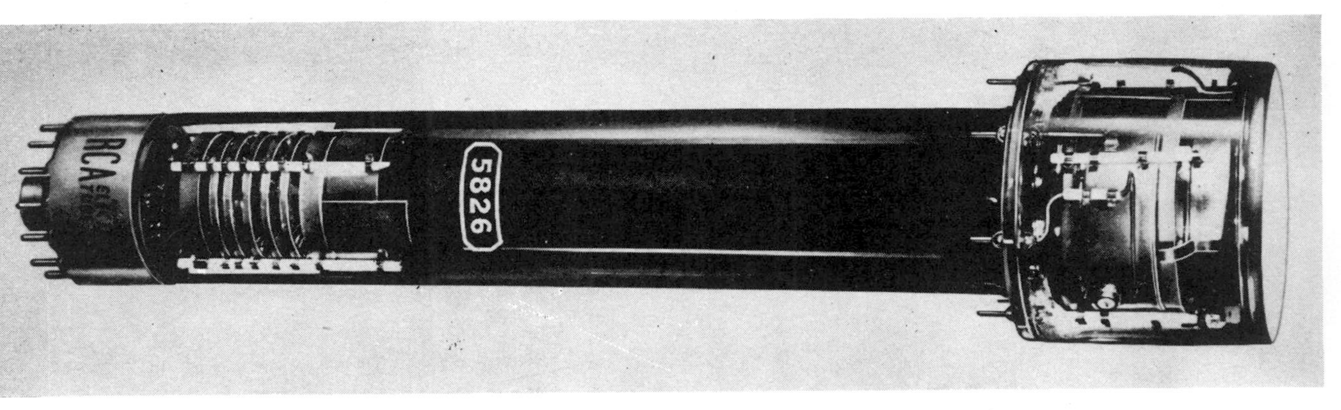

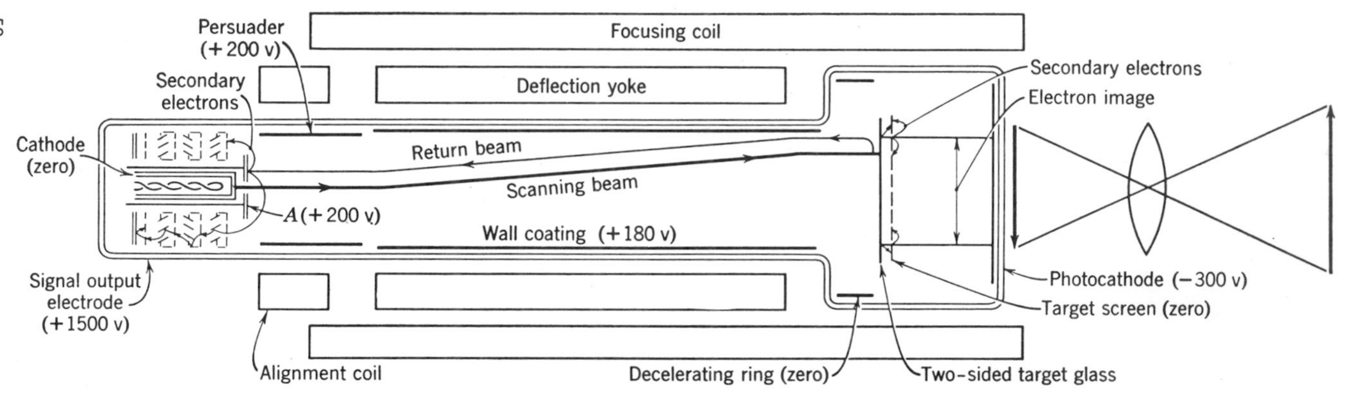

Fig. 3.5. The image orthicon. (From Zworykin and Morton, *Television*, Wiley, New York, 1954.)

such as to direct the secondary electrons ejected from the disk to a second, pin-wheel-shaped, target electrode or dynode, at which the incident electron current is once more amplified by secondary-emission multiplication. Altogether five such stages of secondary-emission amplification are provided. This results in an output current which is some 500 times as large as the incident return beam current. The varying component of this output current corresponds to the charge stored on the target by the photoelectrons and thus constitutes the picture signal.

At low light levels the charge stored on the target, and hence the picture signal, is directly proportional to the picture brightness (Fig. 3.6). However, as the brightness is increased the target potential eventually reaches the potential of the target screen, and secondary electrons from the target are turned back instead of being collected by the screen. This corresponds to the "knee" of the response curve. It might be expected that for light levels beyond this critical point no brightness differences would be recorded in the transmitted picture. This is incorrect. Although the photoelectrons no longer contribute to the total charge deposited on the target, a differential charge image is built up at boundaries between areas of different brightness by electron redistribution: A larger number of secondary electrons from the more heavily bombarded area is returned to the less heavily bombarded area than vice versa, making the more heavily bombarded area positive with respect to the less heavily bombarded area. Thus the image orthicon transmits a satisfactory picture of the scene over an extraordinarily wide range of illumination.

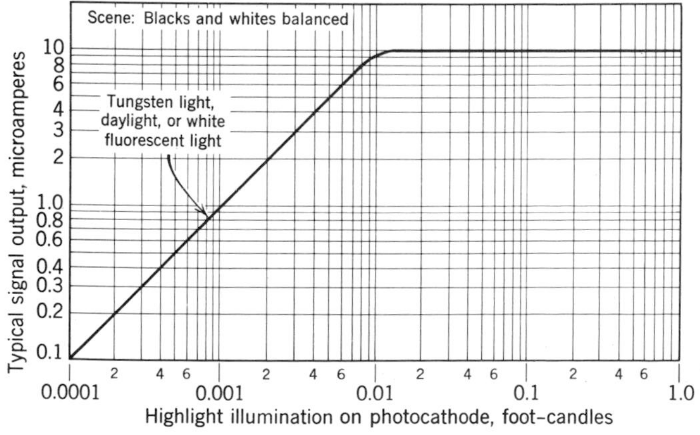

Fig. 3.6. Typical light transfer characteristic of a 5820 image orthicon. (Courtesy of RCA.)

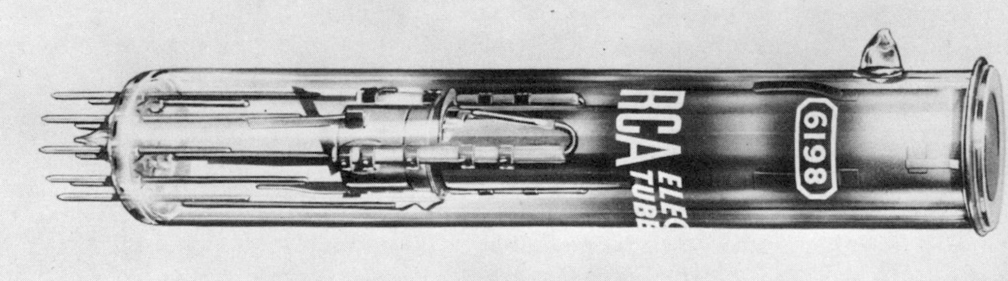

Fig. 3.7. A Vidicon camera tube, Type 6198. (Courtesy of RCA.)

Normally, the target screen is made at most a few volts positive with respect to the gun cathode. Thus instability resulting from driving the target to a potential at which the secondary-emission ratio for the scanning-beam electrons exceeds unity is out of the question. Furthermore, the maximum beam current required may readily be inferred from the target-screen voltage and the capacitance between the target and the target screen. It is of the order of 0.01 microampere.

As expected, the sensitivity of the image orthicon has been found to be close to that of an ideal storage pickup system with a photosensitivity equal to that of the photocathode. Recognizable pictures can be transmitted for a scene brightness of the order of 0.02 foot-lambert, which corresponds to light objects in bright moonlight. Normally, the tube is operated at very much higher light-levels, and some of its extraordinary sensitivity is traded for an improved signal-to-noise ratio. The image orthicon is now, indeed, the universal camera tube for broadcast television in the United States.

In closed-circuit work, on the other hand, the image orthicon finds employment primarily where the ultimate in sensitivity is needed and skilled operating personnel is available. It is obviously a costly and complex tube, requiring numerous adjustments and auxiliary circuits. The tube is preferably maintained within a relatively narrow range of temperature to assure the desired degree of conductivity in the glass target. Finally, the bulk of the tube itself and of the associated equipment limits the compactness of the image-orthicon camera.

The *Vidicon* (Fig. 3.7) differs from the image orthicon in many respects. It is small, simple, and rugged. Apart from the tip-off, its maximum diameter is 1⅛ inches, its maximum length, 6¼ inches. Except for the target, it resembles the orthicon with magnetic deflection. The target of the Vidicon is a photoconductive layer deposited on a transparent signal plate which is biased positively with respect to the gun cathode by 15 to 50 volts. In darkness the photoconductive layer acts as an insulator. As the low-velocity beam sweeps over its back surface, it drives it to cathode potential, depositing just enough electrons to compensate the current which has leaked through the layer in the preceding frame period. When the target is illuminated the current flow from the front surface to the back surface increases, since the resistance of the layer is reduced by the light. The number of electrons deposited by the scanning beam on the target increases correspondingly. This increase in deposited electrons induces current pulses in the signal lead which constitute the picture signal. As in the simple orthicon, the return current is not utilized.

Unlike the orthicon, the Vidicon presents no stability problem. Even when a signal bias of 125 volts is employed and a high-brightness picture is projected on the target, the secondary-emission ratio of the photoconductor does not attain a value exceeding 1. On the other hand, if the scanning beam current is insufficient to return the target surface to cathode potential, the highlights will appear washed out. Since the entire beam will be able to land, the picture signal will be independent of brightness in the highlight range.

Under these circumstances the potential in the highlights will rise continuously, approaching the signal-plate potential as a limit. Consequently, if a highlight is changed to a lowlight because of the motion of the subject, many scans may be needed to bring the surface potential of the photoconductor down to cathode potential as is required for the generation of the appropriate picture signal. This "sticking" of the highlights in moving objects and the loss of detail within them is commonly known as "bloom." For satisfactory operation, the scanning-beam current in the Vidicon should be chosen large enough to drive the brightest portions of the target to cathode potential in each scan. At the same time, it should not be chosen appreciably larger than this, since an excessive beam current results in spot enlargement and consequent loss in resolution.

Of quite different nature from the sticking observed with inadequate beam current is the persistence of the picture resulting from the finite time constant of the photoconductive process itself. The photocurrent requires a definite time after onset of illumination to build up to its maximum value and, similarly, decays gradually after the illumination is cut off. The typical decay curve for a commercial Vidicon is shown in Fig. 3.8. The decay constant depends both on the material and its preparation. Furthermore, it decreases as the illumination of the photoconductive target increases. Thus, in applications in which picture lag

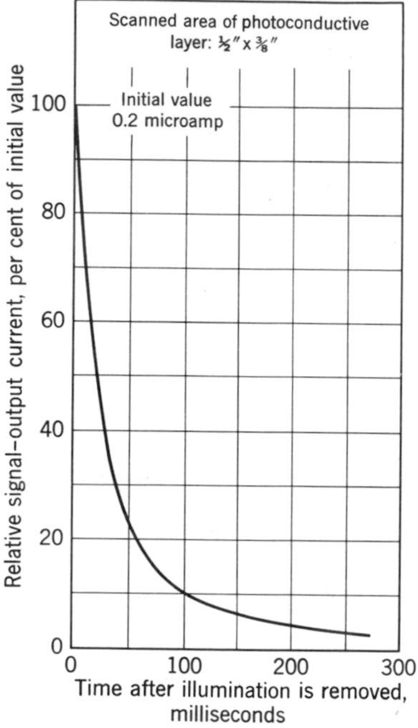

Fig. 3.8. Persistence characteristic of type 6198 Vidicon. (Courtesy of RCA.)

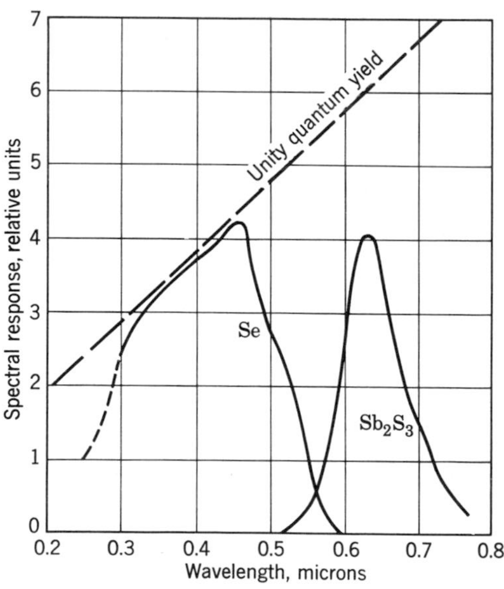

Fig. 3.9. Typical spectral responses of photoconductive layers compared with unity quantum yield. (Courtesy of *Encyclopedia of Chemical Technology.*)

is particularly objectionable it is advisable to work with relatively high levels of illumination.

This also prevents sticking arising from a second source: As the target current is reduced to low values, the equilibrium potential of the scanned surface becomes negative with respect to the gun cathode. Under the circumstances several transits are needed to neutralize stored charge, since only a small fraction of the beam electrons can land.

The Vidicon owes its high sensitivity to the fact that photoconductive films can be given quantum efficiencies (ratios of number of electrons transferred to number of light quanta or photons incident on the target) close to unity (Fig. 3.9), whereas photoemissive targets rarely attain quantum efficiencies exceeding one-fifth. The output noise of the Vidicon is essentially the same as that of a diode with a current equal to the

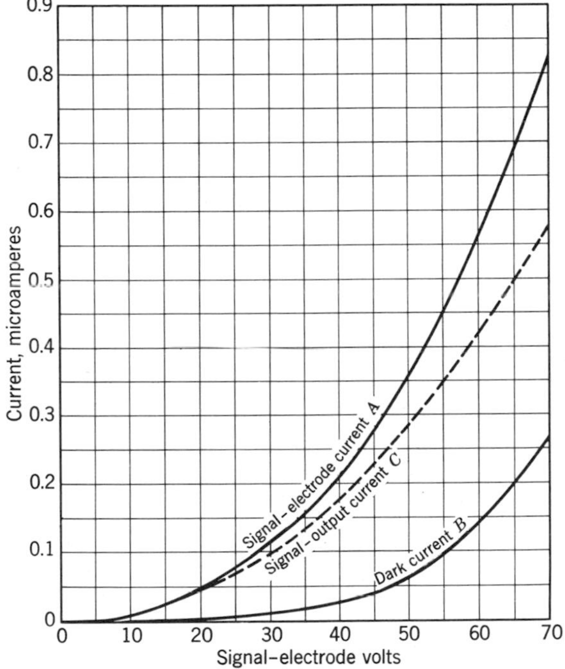

Curve *A*: With 8 ft-c of 2870°K tungsten illumination incident on tube face
Curve *B*: With no illumination incident on tube face
Curve C = curve *A* minus curve *B*
Scanned area of photoconductive layer: ½″ x ⅜″

Fig. 3.10. Variation of signal current and dark current with target voltage for type 6198 Vidicon. (Courtesy of RCA.)

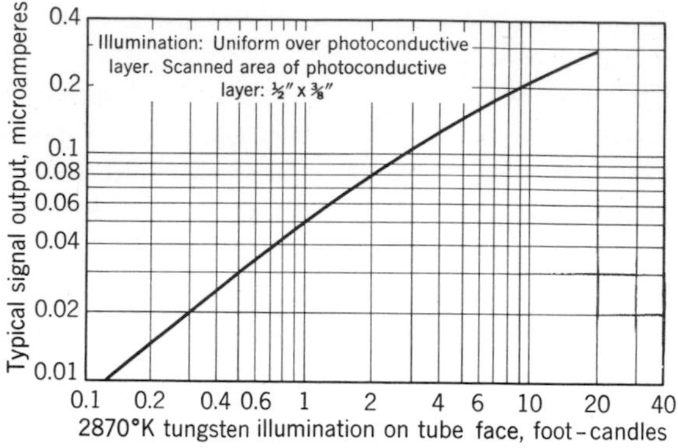

Fig. 3.11. Signal as function of illumination for type 6198 Vidicon. (Courtesy of RCA.)

conduction current through the photoconductive film. By increasing the target voltage the signal current can be increased. Since the noise contributed by the succeeding amplifier is constant, this increases the signal-to-noise ratio in the highlights. However, the dark current through the photoconductive layer increases even more rapidly with the target voltage than the signal current (Fig. 3.10). Consequently, high target voltages lead to excessive background noise contributed by the dark current. At the most favorable value of the signal electrode voltage the noise contributions of the amplifier and of the dark current are of the same order. In most practical cases, however, the limit in target voltage is set by shading signals and "flare" introduced by non-uniformities in dark current rather than by the random noise in the target current.

The variation of signal with target illumination depends on the nature of the photoconductive layer. Figure 3.11 shows a typical curve for a Type 6198 Vidicon with an antimony trisulfide target. The "gamma"[4] of this tube is approximately 0.65. Since the gamma of the kinescope reproducing the picture is generally 2 or more, a low value of the camera gamma is desirable, as it facilitates the attainment of correct contrast reproduction ($\gamma = 1$) for the entire television chain.

For the amorphous selenium targets employed in special ultraviolet-sensitive Vidicons the response is more nearly linear; a typical measured value of the Vidicon gamma is here 0.9.

[4]The gamma, or contrast ratio of the output signal and the input signal (here, the transmitted scene), is defined by

$$\gamma = \frac{d[\log\text{ (output signal)}]}{d[\log\text{ (input signal)}]}$$

The spectral response for a Type 6198 Vidicon is shown in Fig. 3.12. Curve C shows that the reproduction of a scene illuminated by a 2870°K tungsten source should resemble closely, in tonal gradation, the directly viewed scene illuminated with an equienergy source (curve B). The fact that the spectral response of the Vidicon is considerably broader than that of the human eye is advantageous for the employment of the Vidicon in color cameras. The falling-off of the sensitivity toward shorter wavelengths results from the incomplete penetration of the photoconductive layer by this radiation.

The amorphous selenium target, unlike the antimony trisulfide target, shows no sharp drop-off of the sensitivity toward the shorter wavelengths where the radiation is absorbed in a small fraction of the thickness of the target. The electric carriers ("holes") liberated by the radiation ap-

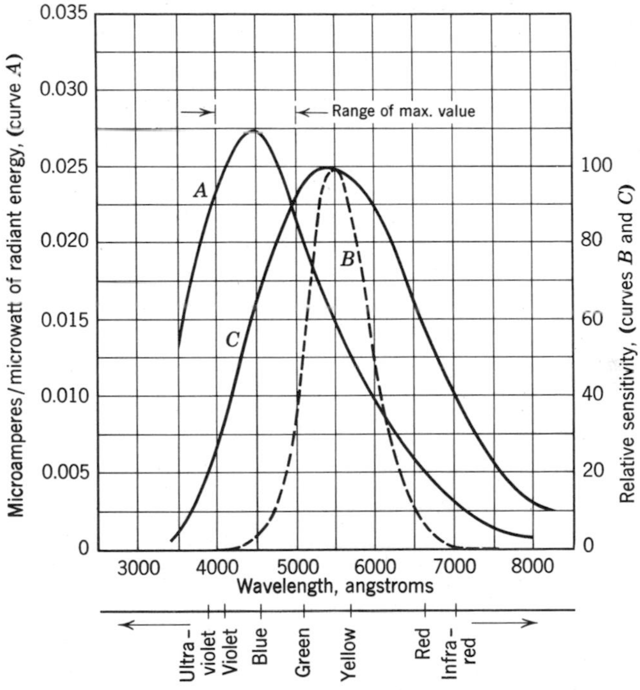

Curve *A*: For equal values of signal — output current at all wavelengths
Signal — output microamperes from scanned area of ½″ x ⅜″ = 0.02
Curve *B*: Spectral characteristic of average human eye
Curve *C*: For equal values of signal — output current with radiant flux from tungsten source at 2870°K

Fig. 3.12. Spectral response of type 6198 Vidicon. (Courtesy of RCA.)

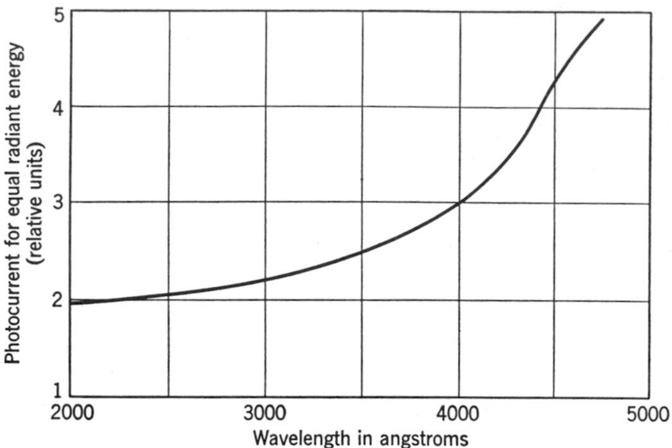

Fig. 3.13. Spectral response of an experimental ultraviolet-sensitive Vidicon camera tube. (From Zworykin and Morton, *Television*, Wiley, New York, 1954.)

parently are drawn through the unilluminated material to the opposite surface by the applied field. The spectral response of a tube with a selenium target deposited on an ultraviolet-transmissive signal plate and window is shown in Fig. 3.13.

The resolving capacity of the Vidicon target is such that a tube with dimensions scaled down by a factor of 2 can still provide an acceptable picture. Such a ½-inch Vidicon is shown, compared in size with an image orthicon and a 1-inch Vidicon, in Fig. 3.14; Fig. 3.15 is a picture received with a ½-inch Vidicon.

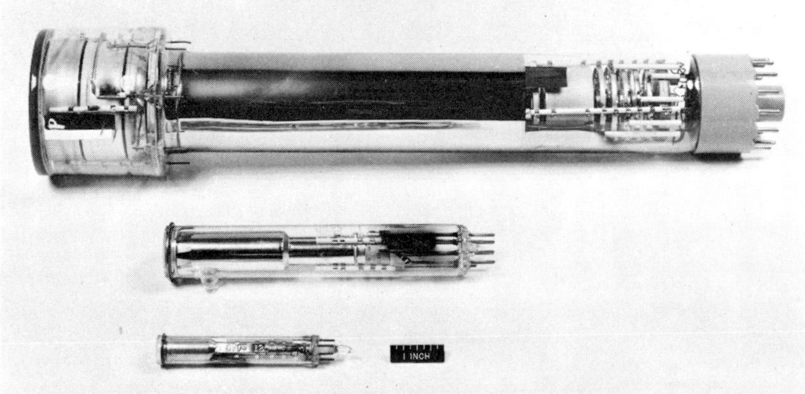

Fig. 3.14. Size comparison of image orthicon, 1-inch Vidicon and experimental ½-inch Vidicon.

Referring to the diagram of a standard 1-inch Vidicon in Fig. 3.16, the electron current emitted by an indirectly heated cathode is limited by a negatively biased control grid (grid No. 1) and is accelerated by the anode (grid No. 2), normally maintained at about 300 volts. A 0.002-inch defining aperture in the anode disk selects an electron beam with a current of the order of 0.2 microampere. From this point almost up to the target the beam travels at a velocity defined primarily by the voltage of the focusing electrode (grid No. 3). The fixed longitudinal magnetic

Fig. 3.15. Photograph of picture transmitted by ½-inch Vidicon, as seen on monitor.

focusing field, provided in many industrial television cameras by four Alnico rods placed symmetrically about the tube (Fig. 3.17), causes the electrons diverging from the defining aperture to travel along helical paths about the magnetic field lines. The "pitch" of these helical paths is given by the ratio of the electron velocity to the magnetic field intensity. Normally, the magnetic field intensity is about 40 gauss. With the focusing electrode voltage at about 250 volts, the pitch of the helices becomes just equal to the distance between the defining aperture and the target, so that all electron paths leaving a given point of the defining

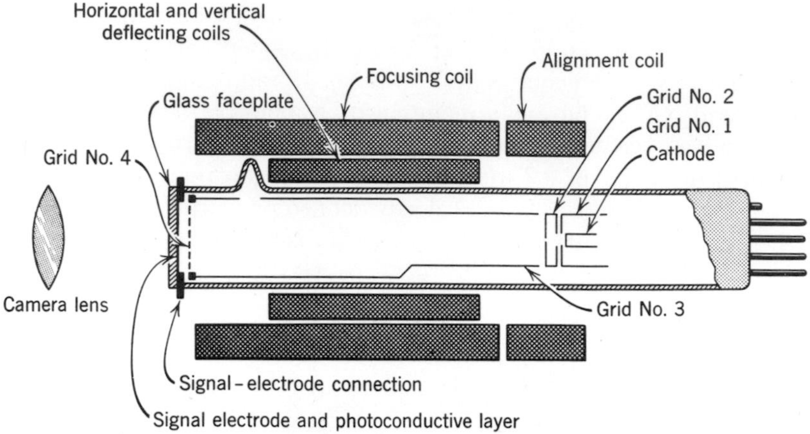

Fig. 3.16. Diagram of Vidicon with electromagnetic focusing.

aperture intersect once more at a point on the target—in brief, the defining aperture is imaged by the magnetic field on the target. The superposition on the longitudinal focusing field of the transverse magnetic deflection fields, provided by sets of coils enveloping the tube, produces a slant in the resulting magnetic field lines and a corresponding displacement of the image point (or scanning spot) on the target.

A high-transparency, 500-mesh screen terminates the focusing electrode in proximity to the target. This screen results in a strong, uniform

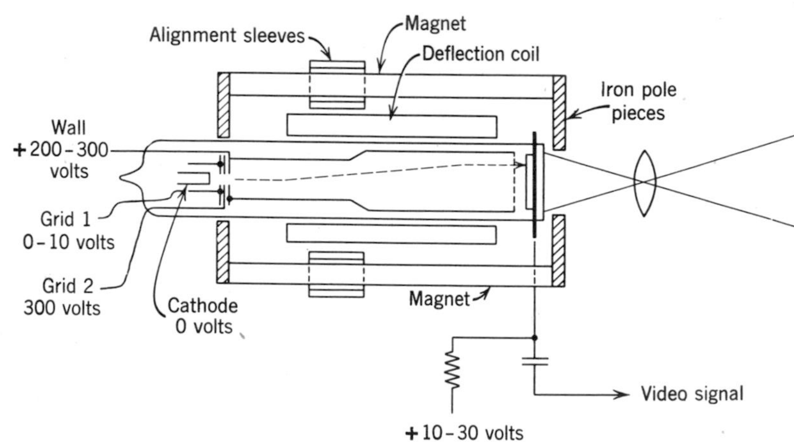

Fig. 3.17. Vidicon with permanent-magnet focusing. (From Zworykin and Morton, *Television*, Wiley, New York, 1954.)

decelerating field, which causes the beam to be incident on the target perpendicularly for all deflections. In addition, the screen prevents the charge distribution on the photoconductive layer from affecting the point of incidence of the beam on the target. A typical thickness of the photoconductive layer is 0.0002 inch.

Standard Vidicons can tolerate temperatures up to 60°C without permanent adverse effects on their operating properties. However, operation close to the upper temperature limit results in some sacrifice of performance, arising from the increased dark current. Operation between 25 and 35°C is recommended.

The Objective. Next to the camera tube, the objective may be regarded as the most important element of the television camera. The

Table 1. Focal Lengths of Television Camera Lenses Required to Cover Various Field Angles

Field angle (diag.)		6°	9°	12°	18°	36°	54°
Field angle (hor.)		4.8°	7.2°	9.6°	14.4°	29.1°	44.3°
Field angle (vert.)		3.6°	5.4°	7.2°	10.9°	22.1°	34.0°
Camera Tube	Target Area, in.						
Iconoscope, 1850-A	4.6 x 3.45	54.8 in.	36.5 in.	27.4 in.	17.1 in.	8.8 in.	5.65 in.
Iconoscope, 5527	1.12 x 0.84	13.3	8.9	6.7	4.2	2.14	1.37
Image orthicon	1.28 x 0.96	15.3	10.2	7.6	4.8	2.45	1.57
Image dissector	2.2 x 1.65	26.2	17.5	13.1	8.2	4.20	2.70
Vidicon	0.5 x 0.375	6.0	4.0	3.0	1.86	0.96	0.61 in.

objective serves to form an image of the scene to be transmitted on the light-sensitive target of the camera tube. The two important parameters of the objective are its focal length and its aperture.

The ratio of the diagonal of the useful picture area of the camera tube target to the focal length of the objective determines the angular field of view covered by the camera. Thus a camera tube with a larger target area requires a lens of greater focal length. Table I shows the target areas of various camera tubes and the objective focal lengths required to cover various field angles. An aspect ratio of 4 : 3 is assumed throughout. Figure 3.18 represents graphically the significance of the various field angles.

The field angles most commonly employed in industrial television lie in the range 18 to 36°; for these two values the Vidicon requires 2- and

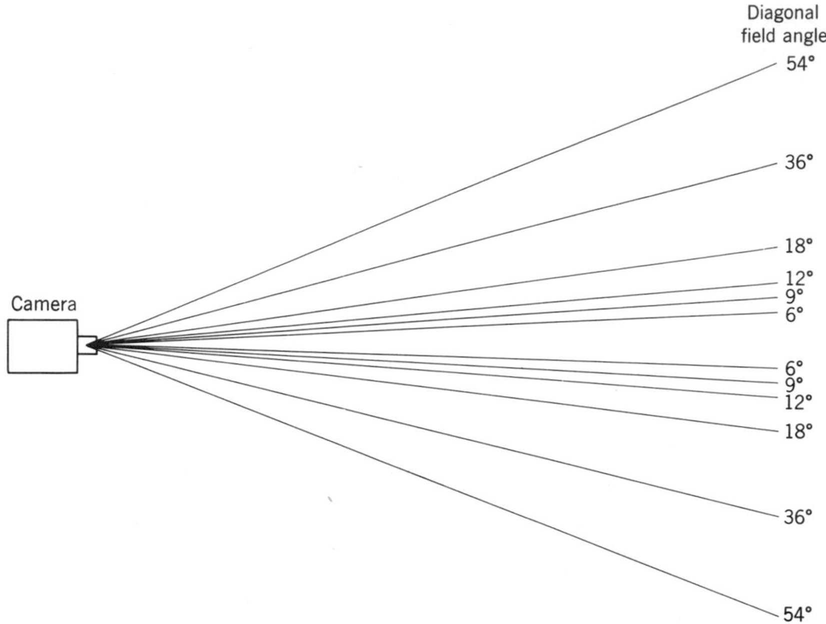

Fig. 3.18. Horizontal extent of viewing cones accepted for various diagonal field angles.

1-inch focal-length lenses, whereas the dissector demands 8- and 4-inch lenses. Lenses of much longer focal length (and smaller field coverage) become useful in applications in which the camera cannot be brought close to the object to be observed.

It will be noted that the target area of the Vidicon is approximately equal to the area of a 16-mm motion-picture frame. Accordingly, a large choice of high-quality, low-cost objectives developed for the 16-mm motion-picture camera is available for use in Vidicon cameras. Similarly, for a ½-inch Vidicon camera the even less expensive 8-mm motion picture camera objectives would be applicable.

The second important parameter of the objective, the aperture, determines the ratio of the camera-tube target illumination to the scene brightness. It is customary to indicate the value of the aperture by the so-called f-number N of the lens; N denotes the ratio of the focal length f to the aperture diameter D.[5]

The total amount of light which reaches the target is given by the

[5] More precisely, $N = 1/(2 \sin \theta)$, where θ is the angle of convergence on the axis of a cylindrical parallel beam of light filling the aperture of the lens (Fig. 3.19). Furthermore, if B is the scene brightness in foot-lamberts (lumens emitted per square foot),

product of the target illumination and the target area. If the target area is expressed by $\pi f^2 \alpha^2$, where α is the effective field angle, we can write.

$$L = \frac{\pi f^2 \alpha^2 B}{(2N)^2} = \frac{\pi D^2 \alpha^2 B}{4}$$

For given field angle α, the total amount of light which reaches the target and, for given resolution, the amount of light per picture element is seen to depend not on the f-number N, but on the absolute aperture area $\pi D^2/4$. Thus the signal current obtained with a ½-inch Vidicon and a 1-inch, $f/1$ lens may be expected to be the same as that obtained with a 1-inch Vidicon and a 2-inch, $f/2$ lens. On the other hand, for

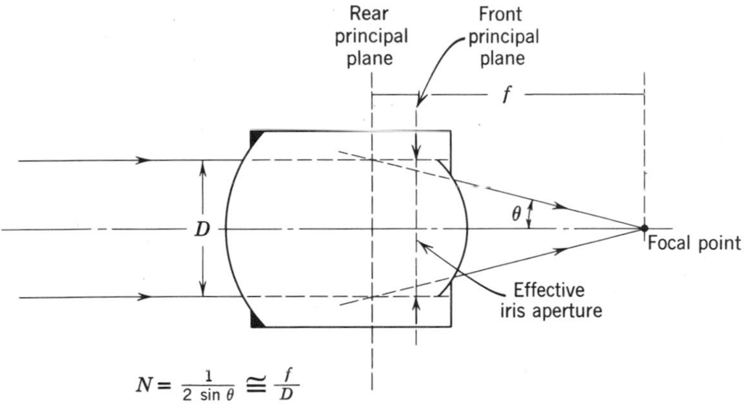

Fig. 3.19. Relationship between the f-number N, the angular aperture θ, the focal length f, and the aperture diameter D of an objective.

fixed target area or a given camera tube, the signal current is simply proportional to the reciprocal square of the f-number N. Thus, in passing from a wide-angle shot with a short-focus objective to a close-up with a long-focus objective the f-number setting of the lenses should remain the same.

The aperture also determines the depth of focus of the objective. The depth of focus is defined as the range ΔL in object space, measured

the target illumination I, in foot-candles (lumens incident per square foot), is given by

$$I = B/(2N)^2$$

neglecting absorption and reflection losses within the lens. This assumes that the focal length f is small compared to the distance L between the lens and the object. More generally the relation becomes

$$I = \frac{B}{(2N)^2} \frac{(L - f)^2}{L^2}$$

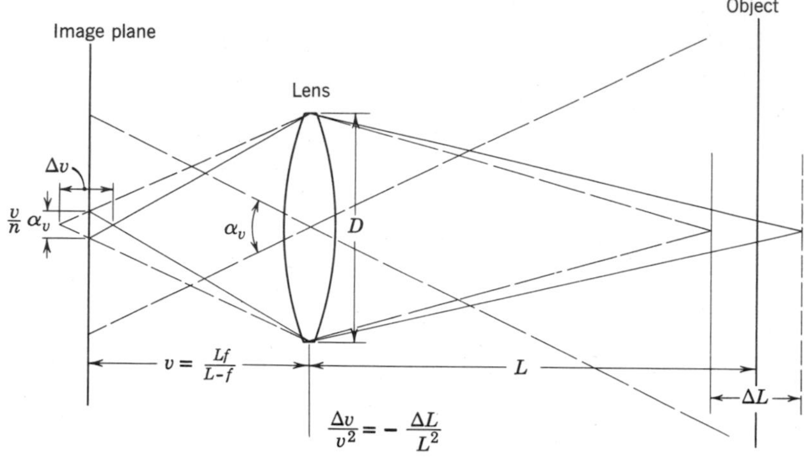

Fig. 3.20. Depth of focus.

along the optic axis of the objective, for which objects are imaged sharply on the target (Fig. 3.20). It is simply inversely proportional to the diameter D of the objective aperture. More precisely, if an image point is regarded as sharp provided its diameter does not exceed the separation of two successive scanning lines, the depth of focus is given by

$$\Delta L = \frac{2L^2\alpha_v}{nD}$$

where L is the distance of the object from the lens, α_v the vertical field angle, and n the number of scanning lines in the picture. For example, for a 1-inch Vidicon camera with a 2-inch, $f/2$ lens and 500-line raster, the depth of focus is 3.6 feet for an object distance L equal to 20 feet. To attain the same depth of focus with an image dissector camera, with an 8.8-inch lens, the f-number would have to be made $N = 8.8$.

Cameras with large-aperture, long-focus objectives are applicable primarily to relatively flat object fields or distant objects. For instance, an image-dissector camera with a 4-inch, $f/1.4$ lens trained on a gage panel 2 feet away has a depth of focus (for a raster of 300 lines) of the order of 0.5 inch. For a Vidicon camera with a 1-inch, $f/1.5$ lens and a raster of 500 lines, covering the same field, the depth of focus would be more than twice as large. On the other hand, for the observation of distant objects, such as the discharge of smokestacks, depth of focus would not be a serious consideration in any case.

General Arrangement of the Camera. The great majority of industrial television cameras on the market today are designed for use with the RCA 6198 Vidicon or an equivalent photoconductive tube. Exceptions are the Diamond Power Specialty Corporation's earlier Utiliscope cameras, which employ a Farnsworth image dissector. The Vidicon cameras quite generally have an electromagnetic deflection yoke which slips over the tube and a *fixed-field* magnetic focusing system. The longitudinal magnetic focusing field may be supplied either by a solenoid with fixed current or by a set of four Alnico bars surrounding the Vidicon, which is provided with shunting sleeves for aligning the magnetic field with the tube axis. Both the yoke and focusing magnets are clearly visible in the interior view of the RCA-ITV-6 camera shown in Fig. 3.21. The focusing and deflection system of the dissector is essentially similar to that of the Vidicon, although the coil dimensions are, of course, much larger.

The remaining equipment of the camera depends on the purposes for which it is designed. The RCA-ITV-6 camera is part of a high-definition system with a passband of 7 megacycles and camera adjustments remotely controlled from a control monitor. Thus its complement consists of a focusing motor for displacing the lens mount and three tubes representing a blanking amplifier, a preamplifier, and a cathode follower which delivers a 0.15 volt, peak-to-peak, video signal across a 53.5-ohm cable. The Kay Lab Model 1984A Camera, the Farnsworth Model 600A Camera, and the Philco ITV cameras are comparable both in their functions and in their complements.

Fig. 3.21. RCA-ITV–6 camera. Interior view showing yoke and focusing magnets.

The RCA TV Eye camera is simplified by the omission of the lens-focusing motor; this permits a reduction of the weight of the camera to approximately 4½ pounds, without the objective. Apart from the lens setting, camera adjustments are remotely controlled from a small control unit, which also contains the power supply and deflection circuits for the camera. Since the horizontal resolution is limited by the pass-band of the standard receiver on which the picture is viewed, it is less than for the RCA-ITV-6 system with special monitor. A division of functions between the camera and the control unit similar to that in the RCA TV Eye and comparable dimensions of these two components are to be found in the Blonder-Tongue Laboratories TVC-1 system.

The Utiliscope camera, which is also remotely controlled, contains a 2000-volt divider for the electron multiplier of the dissector and, in addition, just two tubes, a twin triode serving as black-level setter and cathode follower and a pentode functioning as preamplifier. Since the output level of the dissector is high, this provides an entirely adequate signal across the output cable (0.3 volt, peak-to-peak). A special monitor must be employed with the camera, since a nonstandard scanning rate (350 lines, 60 frames per second, noninterlaced) is used.

Finally, in the Dage Model 60-A Television Camera and the Diamond Utilivue Model 400-A Camera the power supply, camera deflection circuits, synchronization generators, video amplifiers, and radio frequency modulator are all contained in the camera. Thus the camera is a completely self-contained unit; the camera controls are mounted on the camera box, which delivers a radio-frequency signal on a channel 2 to 6 very-high-frequency carrier to a coaxial cable joining it to one or several standard receivers. Even so, the Dage 60-A Camera is comparable in dimensions (10 x 6½ x 4½ in.) to the previously mentioned Vidicon camera and weighs only 8½ pounds. The Utilivue Camera is considerably larger (21 x 10 x 7¼ in.). The Kay Lab Unitized System may be used in a manner similar to the TV Eye or with additional units as a more elaborate system.

INDUSTRIAL TELEVISION CIRCUITRY

Since in the several industrial television chains the circuits are distributed in various ways between the camera, the monitor, and, eventually, one or two additional units, it is convenient to consider the entire circuitry linking the camera tube and the picture tube as a unit. The principal circuits are (1) the video amplifier, (2) the deflection and synchronization circuits, and (3) the power supplies.

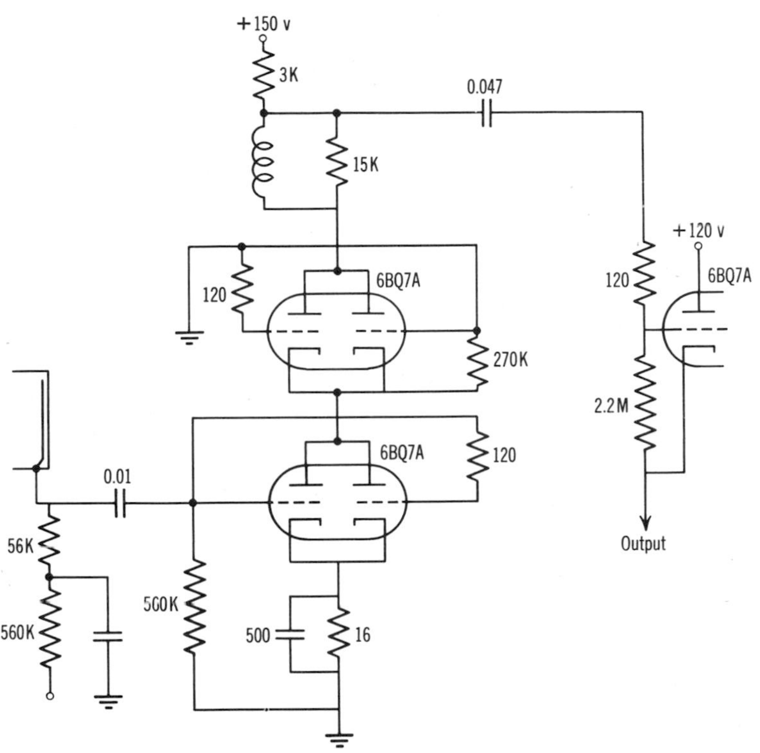

Fig. 3.22. RCA-ITV-6 camera preamplifier.

The Video Amplifier. In the Vidicon chains employing auxiliary control units, the video amplifier is divided into a preamplifier terminated in a cathode follower, contained in the camera, and a line amplifier in the control unit. In a completely self-contained camera the video amplifier chain commonly has two terminations: a radio-frequency-modulating stage to deliver a very-high-frequency signal to be applied to the antenna terminals of a standard receiver and a cathode-follower stage to deliver a video signal for use with a special video monitor.

Since the noise level of the Vidicon output is very low, the noise level in the transmitted signal is determined by the input stages of the succeeding video amplifier. Accordingly, a cascode input stage, consisting of a low-noise, high-mutual conductance, grounded-cathode triode driving a grounded-grid triode, is favored. Here the noisc introduced by the amplifier is determined almost entirely by the noise figure of the input tube, leading to the lowest noise injection attainable with tubes

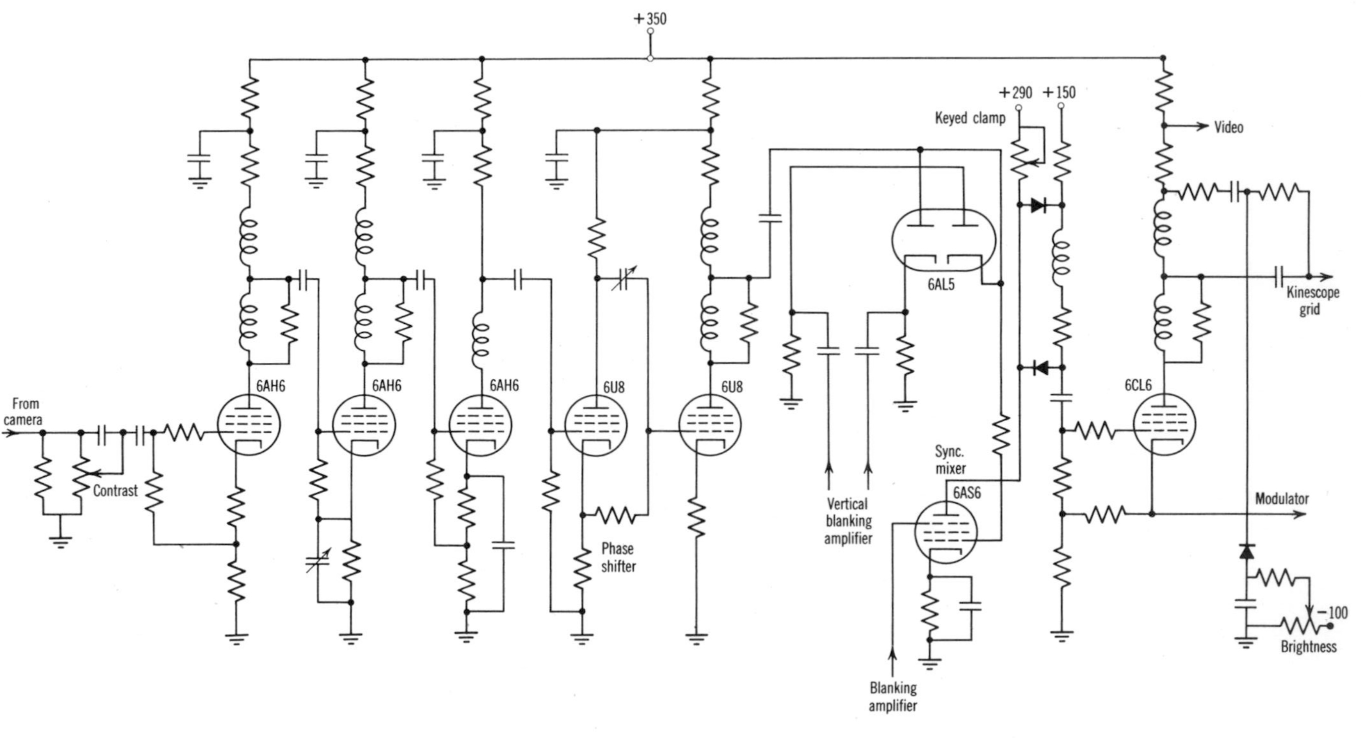

Fig. 3.23. Video amplifier in control monitor (RCA-ITV–6.)

of a given type.[6] Figure 3.22 shows the cascode amplifier succeeded by a cathode-follower impedance-matching stage which is employed in the RCA-ITV-6.

The remaining video amplification in the RCA-ITV-6 system is provided by six pentode stages in the control monitor, giving an overall response which is flat to 7 megacycles (Fig. 3.23) by proper adjustment of the peaking coils in the coupling networks. An adjustable capacitor in the cathode circuit of the second stage compensates the effect of the Vidicon target capacity on the response. A cathode capacitance in the third stage provides aperture correction. The finite size of the scanning spot in the Vidicon results in a reduction in the amplitude response at high frequencies which must be compensated by a rising amplitude response in the amplifier. Since, however, this compensation results in an undesired variation of phase shift with frequency, a phase shifter consisting of a phase splitter with resistance-capacitance voltage divider across the two outputs is provided. A keyed clamping circuit sets the black level at the beginning of each scanning line. Furthermore, horizontal and vertical blanking pulses are added to the video signal in the mixer stage. The final video stage supplies the signal to the kinescope grid and a video signal output jack. In addition, the cathode output of the same stage is applied to the grid of a triode modulator in which the cathode is electron-coupled to a very-high-frequency Hartley oscillator making use of the pentode section within a common 6U8 envelope. This circuit provides a modulated radio-frequency carrier adjustable to any of the lower five very-high-frequency channels for operation of standard receivers as auxiliary viewers.

The circuits of the RCA-ITV-6 system are characteristic of a maximum-performance industrial television chain. In the RCA TV Eye the employment of 6U8 triode-pentodes makes it possible to attain adequate video amplification in two envelopes (Fig. 3.24). Shunt-peaking is employed to attain the desired flat response. A crystal diode establishes black level and a second diode, after the mixer stage, clips the horizontal and vertical blanking pulses to uniform height, so as to assure stable monitor synchronization. The radio-frequency modulator is similar to the modulator in the ITV-6 system. The two video amplifiers described above may be regarded as characteristic of Vidicon camera systems, though others may differ in various details. For instance, the Dage Model 60-A Camera has a video amplifier (Fig. 3.25) which, in general, resembles that of the RCA TV Eye. However, double triodes are employed throughout and one stage serves as phase corrector. Furthermore, the oscillator is not isolated from the modu-

[6] See Valley and Wallman (reference 13).

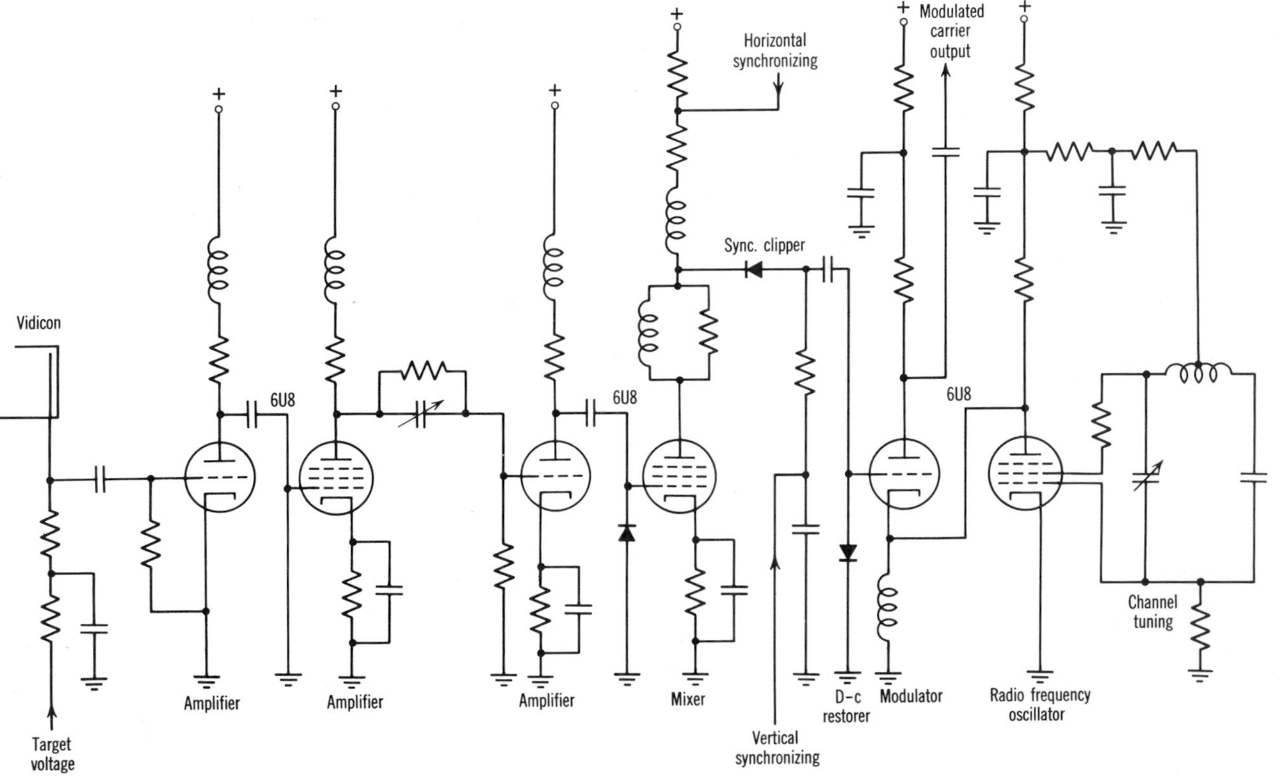

Fig. 3.24. Camera circuits of RCA TV Eye.

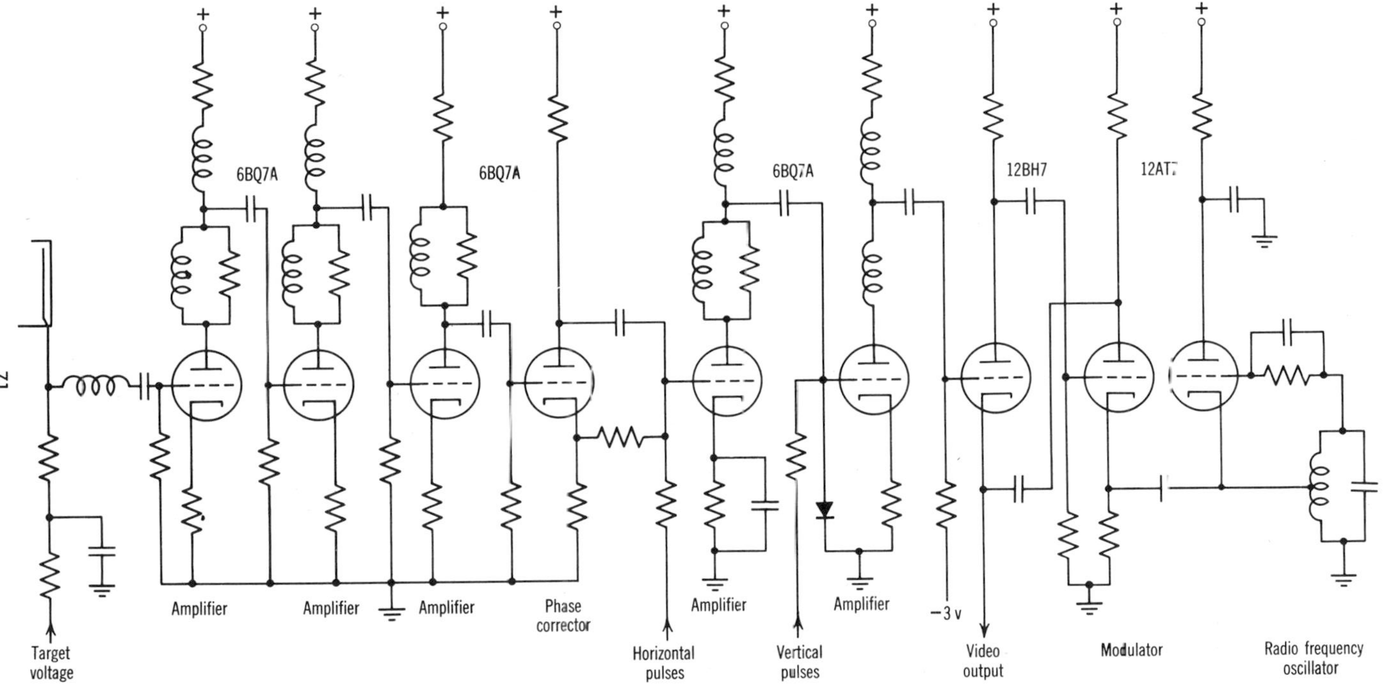

Fig. 3.25. Video amplifier of Dage Model 60–A Camera.

lator by electron coupling; instead, direct cathode coupling is employed.

In the Utiliscope camera the high signal output level of the dissector makes amplifier noise of secondary importance. Accordingly, a pentode input tube is employed, followed by a cathode-follower stage to match the impedance of the amplifier to that of the cable connecting it with the monitor. A black level setter clips off any noise pulses which correspond to "blacker than black." In the monitor two further video stages bring the signal up to the level required for the monitor kinescope.

Deflection and Synchronization. In the more elaborate industrial television systems, such as the RCA-ITV-6, the synchronization and deflection circuits are separate; furthermore, the frequency and phase relations between the horizontal and vertical synchronizing signals are rigidly maintained, and both are locked to the power-line frequency or a crystal. With the above conditions satisfied, interlace can be satisfactorily maintained.

In the simpler systems, examplified by the RCA TV Eye and the Dage Model 60-A Camera, the synchronizing pulses are commonly byproducts of the deflection circuits. Whereas the vertical deflection and synchronization is usually locked to the power-line frequency, the horizontal pulses are derived from a free-running oscillator. Under these circumstances a certain amount of drift in the relative phase of the vertical and horizontal deflection and a corresponding drift into and out of interlace are to be expected. The effective vertical resolution then becomes intermediate between that of a perfectly interlaced system and that of a sequential system with half the number of scanning lines. In a purely sequential system, such as is used in the Utiliscope, phase drift results simply in an overall upward or downward motion of the scanning pattern.

The synchronizing circuit of the RCA-ITV-6 system is shown in Fig. 3.26. Two frequency-dividing stages resembling the "phantastron"[7] generate, in turn, a pulse sequence at a rate of 1260 per second and 60 per second from an initial pulse sequence at twice horizontal frequency (31.5 kilocycles per second) supplied by a class-C master oscillator. In these frequency dividers the sharp negative and positive voltage spikes derived from the leading and trailing edges of the original pulse sequence by differentiation are applied through a diode to the plate and grid of the counter tube. When the circuit is in its stable state, with plate current cut off by the suppressor grid, a negative pulse initiates plate current flow through cathode-follower action. Herewith

[7] See Puckle (reference 14, p. 172).

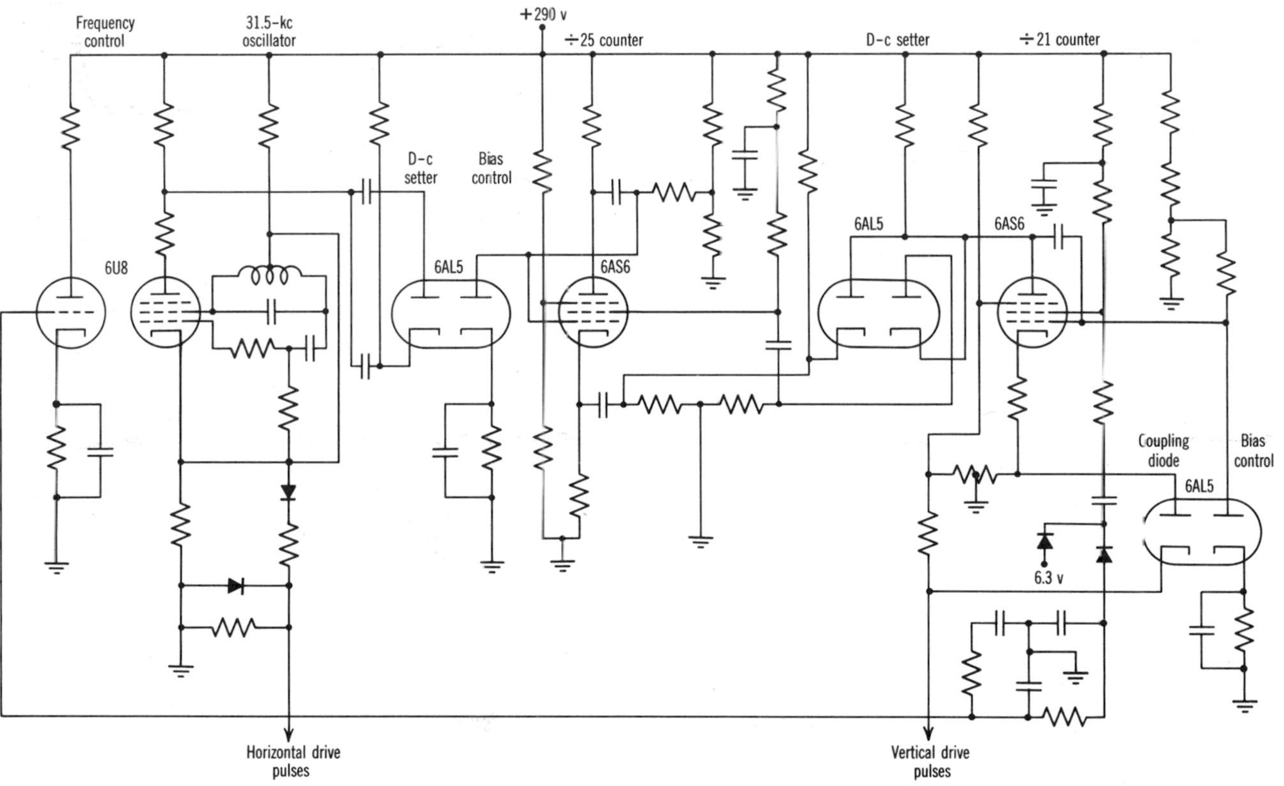

Fig. 3.26. Synchronizing generator of RCA-ITV-6 system.

the diode is blocked, and further pulses are without effect until the circuit has passed through a discharge cycle in which the time constant is determined by cicruit capacitances and resistances. When, in the final stage of the cycle, the circuit rapidly returns to its stable condition the diode is unblocked, and a negative pulse is in a position to start a new cycle. Square-topped pulses of the reduced frequency and of opposite polarity appear at the cathode and screen of the counter tube. The leading edge of these pulses corresponds to the trailing edge of one of the original pulses and the trailing edge to the leading edge of a later original pulse. In the second divider stage the positive spike obtained by differentiating the trailing edge of the screen pulse output of the preceding counter tube initiates the return to the stable condition and gives rise to the leading edge of a 60-cycle pulse. The next discharge cycle is initiated by the negative pulse corresponding to the trailing edge of the succeeding 1260-cycle pulse appearing at the cathode of the counter tube. Accordingly a vertical blanking pulse with leading and trailing edges corresponding to leading edges of the 31.5-kc pulses appears at the cathode of the second counter tube and is transmitted through a coupling diode to the vertical blanking amplifier. The width of the vertical blanking pulse is $^{1}/_{1260}$ second, or approximately 5 per cent of frame time. The sharply deflned time at which the dividing circuits become sensitive to the triggering pulses assures accurate operation.

The 60-cycle pulses from the screen grid of the second counter tube are applied, along with the sinusoidal voltage variation from the power line, to a phase comparator consisting of two crystal diodes. The d-c output of the phase comparator modifies the conductance of a frequency control tube and thus affects the resonant frequency of the 31.5-kc master oscillator in such fashion as to establish the proper phase relation between the line and the vertical pulses. As an alternative to locking the synchronizing generator to the line, the 31.5-kc master oscillator may, of course, also be stabilized by a quartz crystal resonant at this frequency.

The above-described synchronization circuit is highly stable, and circuits of this general type are used in high-quality industrial television equipment, such as, for instance, the RCA-ITV-6 and the Kay Lab Model 1984A Camera System. A somewhat less stable synchronization generator, which is more economical in its tube and power requirements, is employed in the earlier RCA-ITV-5 equipment and in the Dage Model 60-A Camera. It consists essentially of a series of blocking oscillators. The first of these is tuned to twice horizontal frequency (31.5 kilocycles per second). It controls, on the one hand,

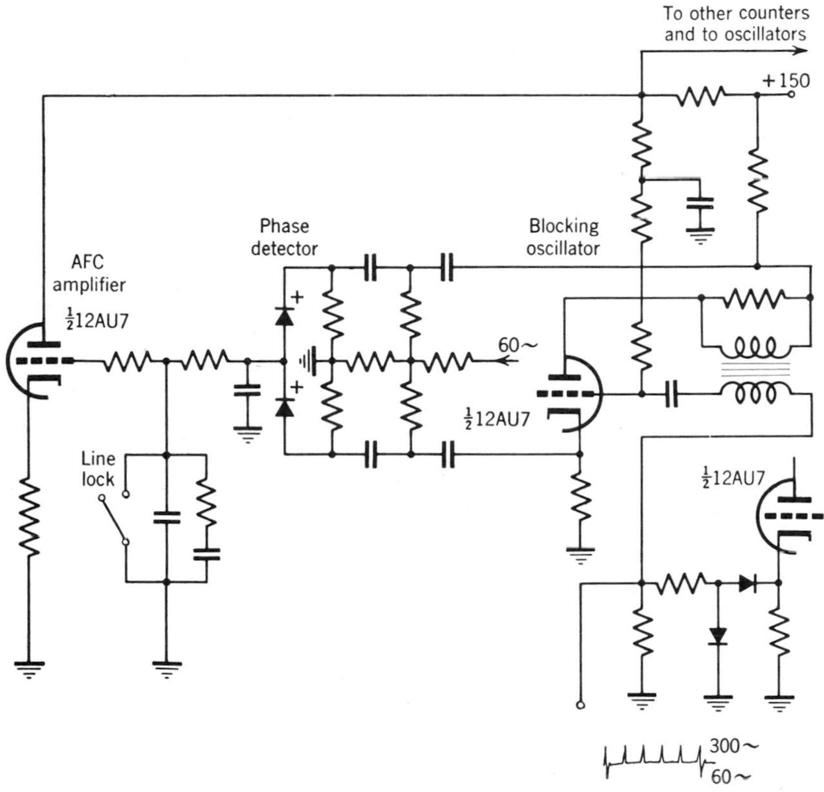

Fig. 3.27. Last frequency divider stage and phase detector of blocking-oscillator type synchronizing generator. (From Zworykin and Morton, *Television,* Wiley, New York, 1954.)

through a buffer amplifier, the horizontal pulse generator; on the other, a succession of blocking oscillators tuned to one-fifteenth, one-seventh, and one-fifth the frequency of the preceding oscillator. Thus the final oscillator generates pulses at 60 cycles, the vertical frequency. The triggering pulses are derived from the cathode resistor of the preceding stage and are applied to the grid resistor; feedback is prevented by a pair of crystal rectifiers connected with the proper polarity (Fig. 3.27). Finally, a phase detector consisting of two selenium diodes generates a d-c bias for the preceding oscillators which depends on the phase difference between the vertical pulses and the power-line alternations. This bias modifies the oscillator frequency so as to bring the vertical frequency into synchronism with the power-line frequency.

The kinescope horizontal deflection circuit in the RCA-ITV-6 system

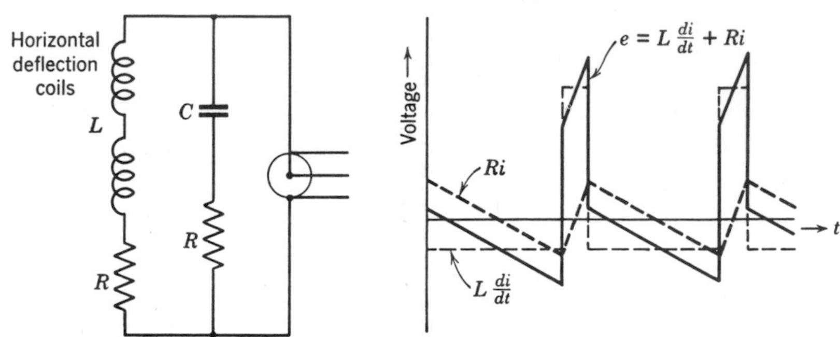

Fig. 3.28. Constant-resistance network incorporating horizontal deflection coil in camera and required deflection voltage transmitted over cable. (From Zworykin and Morton *Television*, Wiley, New York, 1954.)

is essentially conventional. A blocking oscillator triggered by every second 31.5-kc pulse controls the discharge tube of a sawtooth generator. The 15.75-kc sawtooth is applied to the grid of the horizontal deflection output tube, which, together with a damper diode, produces a uniformly varying sweep current through the output transformer and kinescope deflection coils. Fly-back voltage from the transformer is utilized to supply both screen voltage and focusing voltage for the kinescope.

The 15.75-kc pulses from the blocking transformer also trigger a separate sawtooth-generating circuit for the camera deflection. The output of the circuit is amplified and matched by a transformer to a 50-ohm cable, terminated at the camera in a constant-resistance network (Fig. 3.28). With this termination the current wave-shape through the camera deflection coils is undistorted for cable lengths up to 500 feet.

The vertical deflection circuit also employs a blocking oscillator, controlled by the 60-cycle pulses from the synchronizing generator. The sawtooth, generated in conventional manner, is amplified and applied in series to the deflection yokes of the kinescope and the camera. Pulse voltages from both the horizontal and vertical deflection circuits control the application of the target voltage to the Vidicon target. If either pulse voltage is absent, a diode forming a bridge between the power supply and the target is blocked, and the target voltage drops to zero. In this manner damage to the Vidicon target by burn-in of the scanning spot is prevented whenever horizontal or vertical deflection fails.

Finally, the amplified and mixed blanking signals are transmitted by 50-ohm cable to the blanking amplifier in the camera which applies the signals to the Vidicon cathode and cuts off the scanning beam during

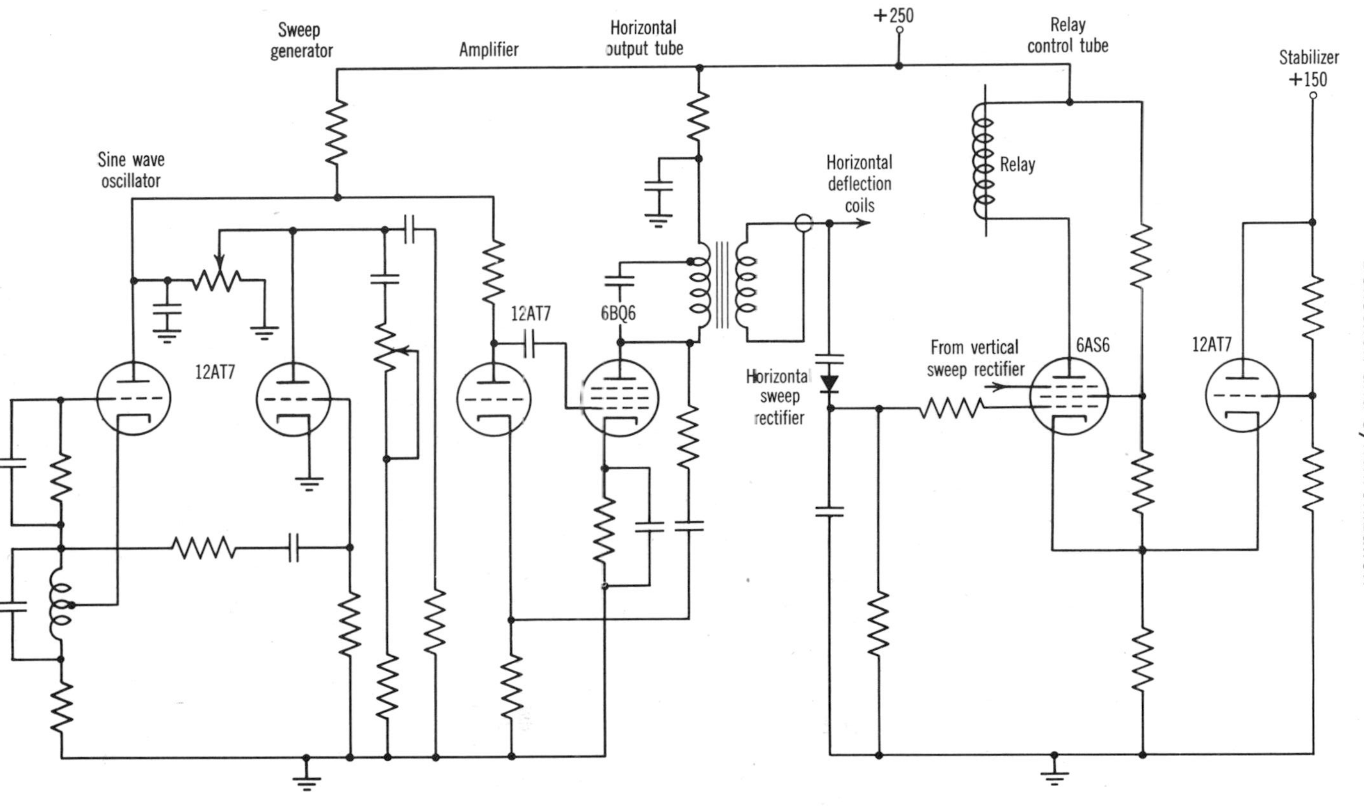

Fig. 3.29. Horizontal deflection circuit in RCA TV Eye control unit.

vertical and horizontal fly-back. The addition of the blanking signals to the video signal has already been indicated.

The synchronization and deflection circuits of the RCA TV Eye are, of course, much simpler (Fig. 3.29). The output of a free-running, 15.75-kc, sine-wave oscillator is applied to a grid bias clipper which transmits current only at the peaks of the sine waves. The clipper triode serves as discharge tube in a sweep generating circuit. The sweep waveform is amplified in two stages and applied by an impedance-matching transformer to a cable terminated, at the camera, in a constant-resistance network such as that shown in Fig. 3.28. The vertical deflection circuit of the RCA TV Eye consists simply of a blocking oscillator synchronized to the 60-cycle line voltage by connecting the cathode of the oscillator tube to the heater, a sweep circuit, vertical output tube, and impedance-matching transformer. The outputs of the vertical and horizontal deflection circuits are furthermore rectified and applied to the suppressor and control grids of a relay control tube, which causes the circuit supplying the Vidicon accelerator voltage to be disconnected whenever either sweep circuit fails. A stabilizing triode in cathode-follower connection minimizes the sensitivity of the relay control tube to supply voltage changes. Finally, a vertical pulse from the grid circuit of the vertical blanking amplifier is amplified to provide a vertical blanking pulse on the control grid of the Vidicon, as well as to add vertical blanking to the video signal. The horizontal blanking pulse, applied to the Vidicon cathode and inserted in the video signal, is derived directly from the horizontal deflection circuit in the camera.

The deflection circuitry of the Dage Model 60A Camera (Fig. 3.30) is even simpler, in part because it dispenses with output transformers and a Vidicon protection circuit. The horizontal deflection circuit employs two triodes in a cathode-coupled multivibrator connection, one serving as sweep discharge tube and the other as output tube. Horizontal blanking is obtained from the voltage developed across the horizontal deflection coils and, for the Vidicon grid, from the plate of the discharge tube. Vertical pulses are obtained by clipping line-voltage alternations and differentiating the result. They control the sweep discharge tube which supplies vertical blanking signals to the Vidicon cathode and the video amplifier. The cathode-follower vertical output tube supplies current to the vertical yoke of the Vidicon.

In the Utiliscope system (Fig. 3.31) all voltages for the camera are derived from a separate power unit. A "beam relaxor" circuit employing a single 6L6 constitutes a 21.5-kc horizontal deflection oscillator, which supplies both horizontal deflection voltages and synchronizing pulses for the monitor (Fig. 3.31). The horizontal deflection yokes

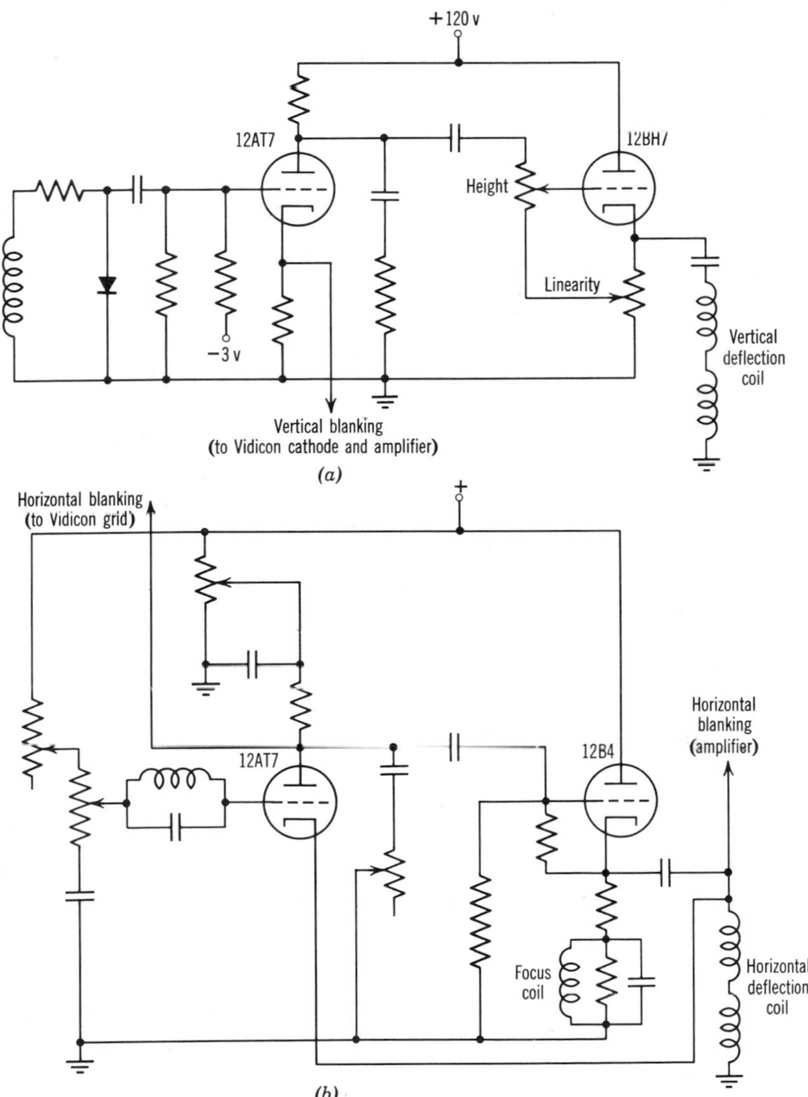

Fig. 3.30. Vertical (*a*) and horisontal (*b*) deflection circuits of Dage Model 60–A Camera.

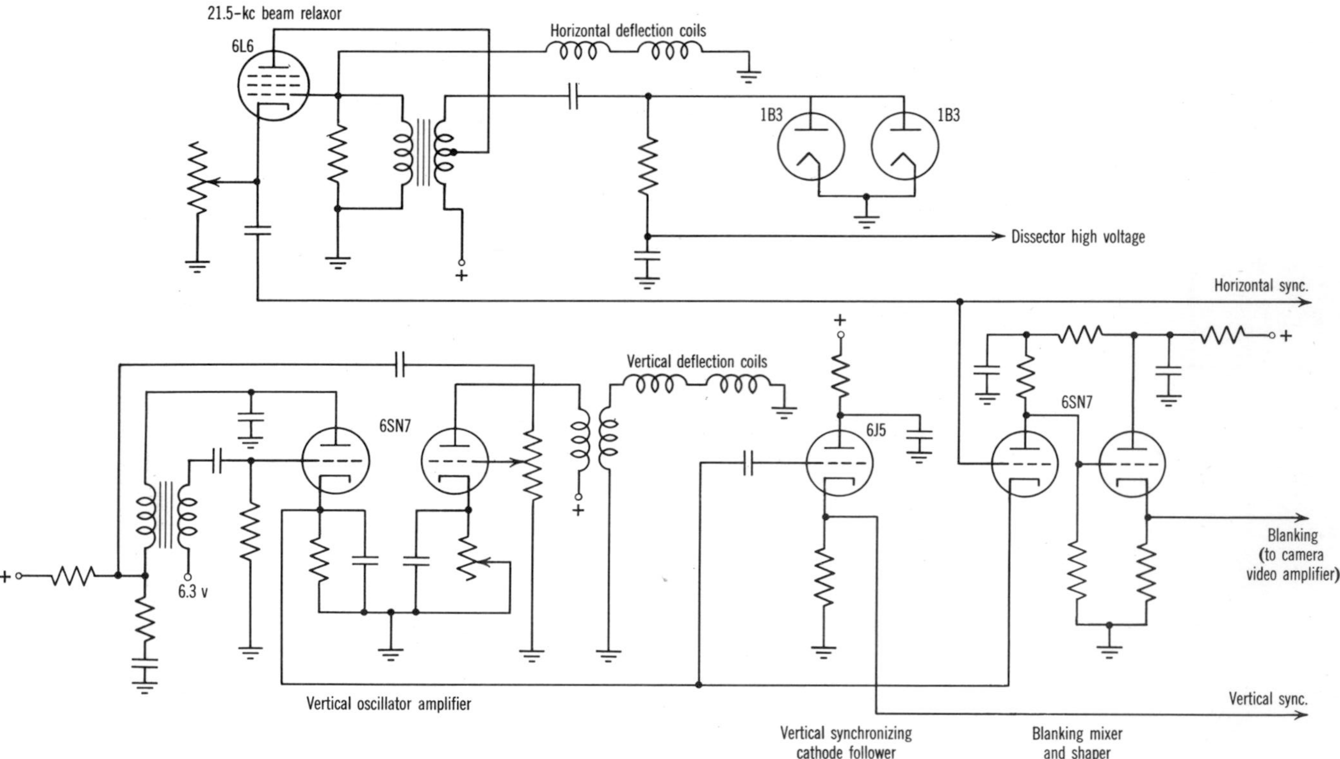

Fig. 3.31. Utiliscope camera deflection circuits and synchronizing generator.

are in the grid circuit, whereas the synchronizing pulses are obtained from the cathode circuit. The fly-back pulses across the horizontal deflection transformer are rectified to provide −2500 volts for the dissector multiplier. The vertical deflection circuit consists of a blocking oscillator, output tube, and impedance-matching transformer; a resistance in the cathode circuit supplies blanking and monitor synchronizing pulses.

Power Supplies. A considerable number of different d-c and a-c voltages are required for operating the camera and its auxiliary circuits. Some of these exhibit greater sensitivity to voltage variation than others. Examples of sensitive circuits are the Vidicon target voltage supply, the Vidicon protective circuits, the vertical oscillator, and the preamplifier. In the RCA-ITV-6 system such voltages are obtained from a vacuum-tube regulator employing the potential drop across a glow tube (OA2) as reference voltage; in the RCA TV Eye they are obtained directly from voltage dividers across the glow tube (Fig. 3.32). In these two systems, as well as in the Dage Model 60-A Camera, both the d-c voltages and the heater voltages are derived from different windings of a power transformer. A selenium rectifier with resistance-capacitance filter supplies the negative voltage for the Vidicon grid. The positive voltages are obtained in all cases from diode rectifiers (in voltage-doubler circuits in the TV Eye and the Model 60-A Camera) followed by ripple filters. Alternating-current voltage for the lens-focusing motor, where employed, is obtained either directly from the line or from a primary winding of the power transformer. Finally, the high voltage for the monitor kinescope is in all instances generated by rectification of the horizontal fly-back pulses, amplified by a high-voltage winding on the horizontal output transformer.

In the Utiliscope approximately 2500 volts obtained by rectification of the horizontal fly-back pulses in the camera power unit provide accelerating voltage for both the dissector and its 11-stage multiplier. Provision is made for modifying the voltage applied to the sixth stage; this provides a multiplier gain control by "defocusing" the intermediate stages of the multiplier and permits adjustment to prevent overloading of the final multiplier stages. The remaining d-c voltages are provided by a power transformer with a selenium rectifier bridge and ripple filter. The monitor has its own power supply and deflection circuits independent of the power unit. The deflection circuits are synchronized with those of the camera by vertical and horizontal pulses supplied by the power unit to the monitor.

Whenever the line voltage is subject to considerable fluctuation the employment of a voltage-stabilizing transformer between the line and

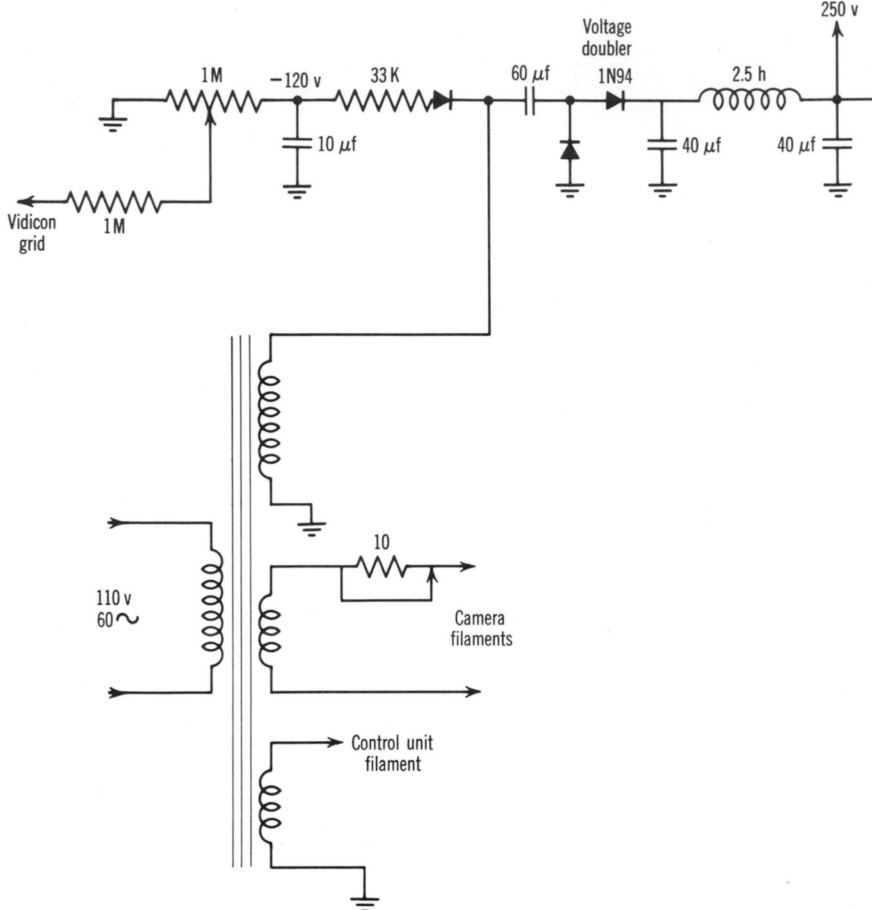

Fig. 3.32. RCA TV Eye power supply.

the power supply of the unit is advantageous. This is particularly true of systems which do not include voltage-stabilizing circuits for the more sensitive portions of the equipment.

Multiple Connections. Any of the Vidicon systems lend themselves to multiple connections between cameras and video monitors or standard television receivers. In the RCA-ITV-6 system a video and radio-frequency outlet is provided on the control monitor, both with a 75-ohm impedance. The RCA TV Eye is specifically designed for use with standard receivers; hence it has only a radio-frequency outlet, with 300-

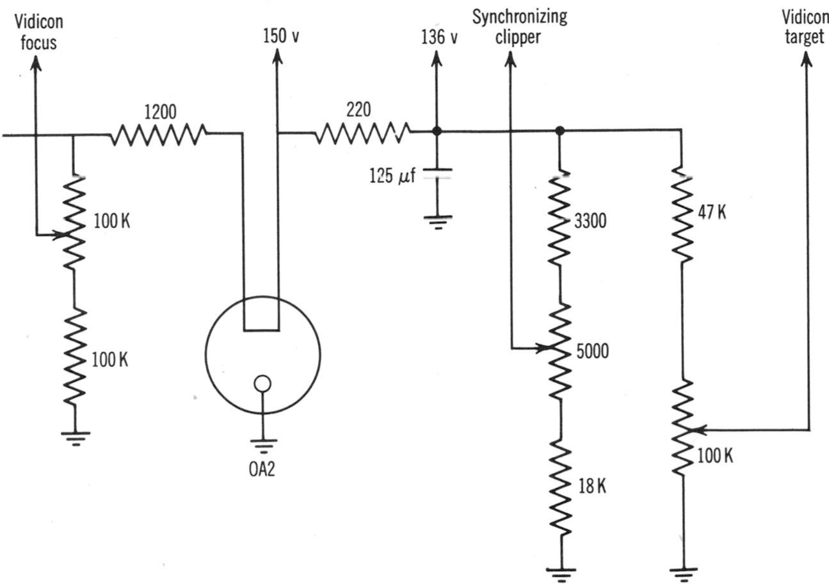

ohm impedance, corresponding to the usual input impedance of the receiver antenna terminals. In the Dage Model 60-A Camera the radio-frequency and video outputs are superimposed at the 75-ohm outlet. It follows that in the ITV-6 system separate groups of video monitors and standard receivers may be fed in parallel by a single camera and control monitor. Impedance transformers or matching networks (Fig. 3.33) are required to match the antenna connections of the receiver to the coaxial cable from the control monitor. In the TV Eye a 300-ohm line may be used to join camera and receiver without matching circuits. In the Dage camera video monitors and standard receivers may be employed in the same chain, with appropriate impedance-matching networks for the standard receivers.

The advantage of using video monitors in the place of standard re-

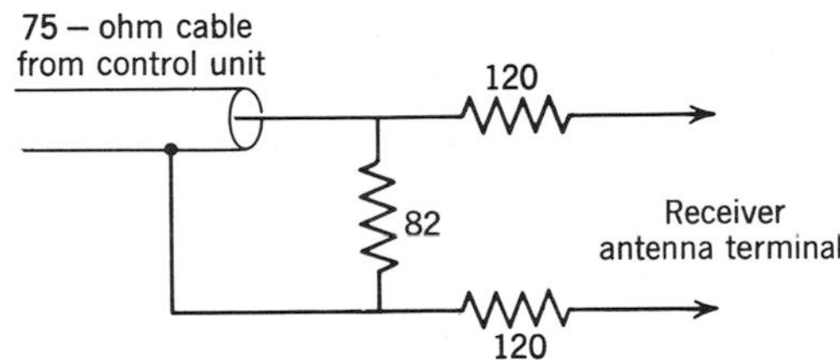

Fig. 3.33. Network for matching 75-ohm cable to 300-ohm receiver input.

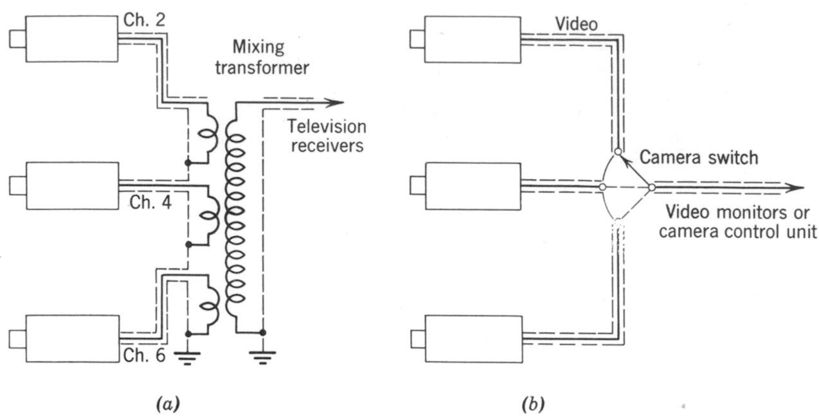

Fig. 3.34. Signal selection from several cameras with radio frequency (*a*) and video (*b*) signal transmission.

ceivers is, of course, that they permit the full use of the resolution capability of the camera. This may correspond to a video passband of the order of 7 megacycles, whereas the passband of a standard receiver is limited to less than $4\frac{1}{2}$ megacycles (usually about $3\frac{1}{2}$). In addition, it avoids possible signal deterioration in tuner, intermediate frequency, and detector stages. On the other hand, the standard receiver is inexpensive and readily available. Finally, with several cameras feeding into a common receiver or group of receivers, the radio-frequency oscil-

Fig. 3.35. RCA camera switching unit. (Courtesy of RCA.)

lators of the cameras may be tuned to different channels and the signals superposed in a single cable by a mixing transformer. The several cameras (and, eventually, programs taken from the air) may then be tuned in at will by the station selector on the receiver (Fig. 3.34). With video monitors, a special camera switch must be provided.

This may conveniently take the form of a switching unit, such as that shown in Fig. 3.35, inserted between the cameras and the camera control unit. The switching unit continuously supplies filament voltages to as many as three cameras and has separate beam, target, and focus controls for each. Blanking, deflection, and plate voltages are switched along with the video signals.

If a number of receivers or monitors are employed simultaneously, all except that farthest away from the camera or control unit are connected to the coaxial cable, or 300-ohm line, by high-impedance bridging trans-

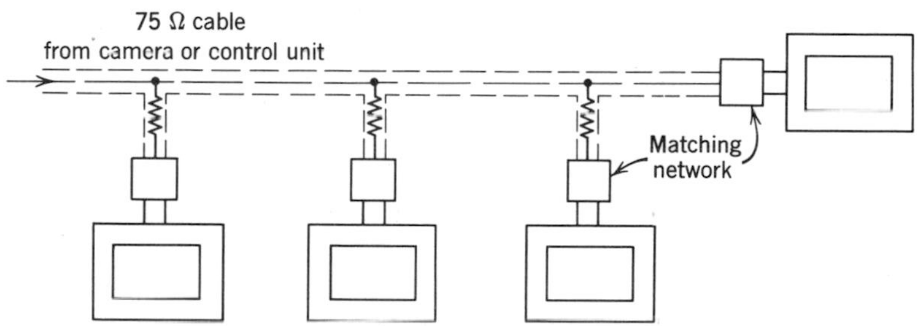

Fig. 3.36. Signal distribution to several receivers or monitors.

formers or networks; the last unit is matched to the line (Fig. 3.36). As the attenuation of the signal along the line is increased, by the receivers connected to it as well as by line loss, beyond the value for the specified maximum length of line, booster amplifiers must be provided. The usual maximum line length specified is of the order of ½ mile for RG-11/U, 75-ohm cable.

THE RECEIVER

As brought out repeatedly, the great majority of the industrial television systems at present in use permit reception with standard television receivers. These are amply described in a number of textbooks on television.[8] Whereas the simplest and least expensive systems commonly

[8] See Zworykin and Morton (reference 1).

Fig. 3.37. Video monitor. (Courtesy of Conrac, Inc.)

rely entirely on standard receivers, others, by preference, utilize video monitors with an increased video passband. An example is the RCA-ITV-6 system, which has been considered in some detail. Here the video monitor, using a 10-inch kinescope with aluminum-backed screen, is combined with the control unit. Accordingly, its circuits have already been discussed. In other cases the video monitor differs from a standard receiver primarily in the absence of the radio-frequency, intermediate-frequency, and detector circuits and the greater passband of the video amplifier. Thus, Conrac Video Monitors, with 17- or 21-inch screens, may be employed as auxiliary viewers (Fig. 3.37). Video monitors serving similar purposes are supplied by most manufacturers of industrial television equipment. The Utiliscope monitor is still further simplified, since the synchronizing pulses and the video signal are transmitted to the monitor by separate cables. Thus the synchronizing-signal selector and separator circuits are also omitted.

Under certain circumstances it becomes advantageous to project the television picture on a large screen for simultaneous viewing by larger audiences. This applies, for example, to the teaching of large classes and the presentation of television reports at stockholders' meetings. Theater projection equipment suitable for such purposes consists, in general, of a control rack containing video amplifier and deflection circuits, a separate high-voltage supply, and an optical barrel containing a high-voltage projection kinescope.

The optical barrel of the RCA PT-100 Ultraspeed Projection System (Fig. 3.38) is opened up to show the internal construction. The optical system employed to project the image on the kinescope face onto the screen is a reflective, Schmidt-type system, with an effective *f*-number 0.82. It consists of a 26-inch spherical mirror, with a 15-inch focal length, visible at the left end of the barrel, and an aspheric correction plate placed at the center of curvature of the mirror, at the right end. The face of the 7NP4 projection kinescope, operated at 80 kilovolts, may be seen near the center, at the approximate focal plane of the mirror. The tube screen is spherical and concentric with the mirror. The concentric arrangement of the screen and mirror, combined with the weak aberration-correcting lens at their common center, permits high-quality

Fig. 3.38. Optics of RCA PT-100 Ultraspeed Projection System. (From Zworykin and Morton, *Television*, Wiley, New York, 1954.)

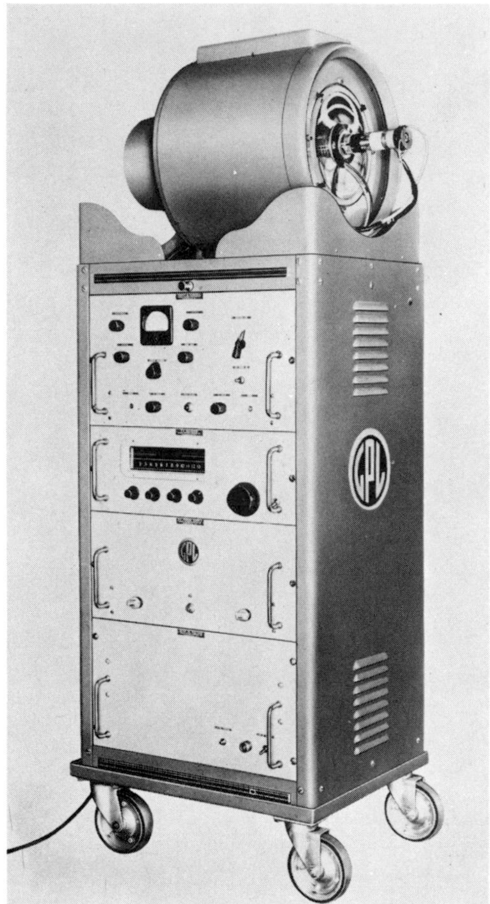

Fig. 3.39. General Precision Laboratory Model PB-611B Television Projection System. (Courtesy of General Precision Laboratory, Inc.)

imaging over large field angles with aperture ratios unattained by other means.

Both the 80 kilovolts for the kinescope anode and 18 kilovolts for its focusing electrode are obtained from a 40-kilovolt transformer by a voltage doubler employing two rectifiers. Apart from the higher signal levels and deflection powers demanded by the kinescope, the operating circuits must include a number of kinescope protective circuits, particularly for deflection failure or excessive positive grid bias. X-ray protection, which is also of importance at the higher operating voltages and currents used, is provided by a lead lining in the optical barrel and an optically polished lead glass disk closing off the end with the correction plate.

For smaller groups more compact projection equipment based on the same principle becomes adequate. Figure 3.39 shows, as an example, General Precision Laboratory's Model PB-611B equipment, which operates at 40 kilovolts and has been found satisfactory for projecting pictures from 7 x 9 to 12 x 16 feet in dimension. Here the optical barrel with the kinescope is mounted directly on top of a mobile control rack 66 x 22 x 18 inches in size; the high-voltage supply forms a separate unit. The weight of the control console is 250 pounds.

A still more compact and flexible unit is the RCA Telemural Projector, illustrated in Fig. 3.75. This employs three separate Schmidt projectors placed side-by-side. For monochrome pictures, three 2½-inch, black-and-white projection kinescopes yield a 6 x 8-foot picture on a viewing screen placed a distance of 17 feet from the projector. The unit, which contains complete video and audio equipment, is 52 x 25 x 30 inches in size and weighs 300 pounds. The same unit serves to project color pictures when the black-and-white kinescopes are replaced by yellow, blue, and green projection kinescopes and appropriate filters are inserted.

NEWER DEVELOPMENTS IN EQUIPMENT

While equipment previously described has been confined to systems and components in a commercial stage of development, there are at this writing several new developments which in a short time will take their place and add to the usefulness and flexibility of closed-circuit television.

Among these developments two of the most outstanding are the use of transistors and miniature camera tubes. Transistors are very attractive in industrial television because of their small size and even more because of their extremely low power consumption.

It was demonstrated several years ago[9] that transistors could be made to perform all the functions of vacuum tubes in a television receiver. Problems encountered in a camera chain are similar in that pulse circuits, sawtooth generators, and deflection amplifiers are required. The chief difference is in the amplifier. The receiver requires an amplifier to pass the video bandwidth at intermediate frequency (in conventional receivers usually about 20 or 40 megacycles) while in the camera the band extends from near direct current to 4 or more megacycles. Recent development in high-frequency transistors has made it possible to obtain the necessary amplification with the high input impedance required by the Vidicon signal level. A gain of 15 to 20 decibels per transistor stage over a band of 4 megacycles has been achieved with commercially

[9] See Sziklai, Lohman, and Herzog (reference 22).

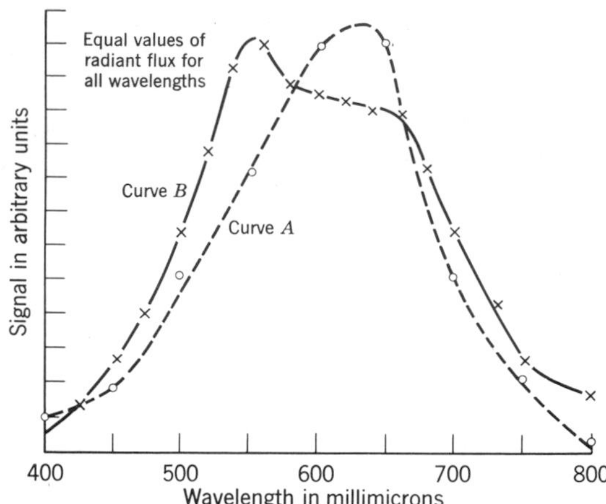

Fig. 3.40. Spectral responses of two high-sensitivity photoconductive materials for the ½-inch Vidicon. (Cope, reference 12.)

available transistors. In view of the low power required for deflection in the Vidicon the design of the deflection circuits does not pose difficult problems.

The miniature Vidicon offers several advantages of its own and when considered in conjunction with transistor circuitry it becomes even more attractive. Figure 3.14 shows an experimental miniature Vidicon in comparison with the image orthicon and a 1-inch commercial Vidicon.

All of the parameters of the miniature Vidicon, with the exception of the voltages and the beam current, are scaled down from the 1-inch size. It is necessary to operate with essentially the same maximum beam current if the maximum signal level (and the signal-to-noise ratio) is to be maintained. With a lens of the same *f*-number the illumination per unit area of the target would be the same, and with the same sensitivity of the target material the working sensitivity of the tube would be reduced by the ratio of areas, or about four times for a ½-inch Vidicon, as compared with that of the 1-inch tube. However, for the same target thickness the target capacitance is reduced by the same amount, and, in addition, the current density in the beam is increased (the beam diameter being reduced by scaling down the gun length). The result is a reduction in the time constant of the photoconductive material which shows up as reduced lag. Thus, when working sensitivity is limited by time lag, the ½-inch tube may equal the larger tube in performance. With illumination adjusted for a maximum white signal of 0.2 microampere the horizontal resolution at which the signal-to-noise ratio in a system with a cascode amplifier input becomes unity is greater than 600 lines. This permits a fully aperture-corrected picture to at least 450 lines with good signal-to-noise ratio.

Special photoconductive materials of very high sensitivity have been developed for the miniature Vidicon which raise its sensitivity well beyond that of the standard Vidicon.[10] With them, satisfactory pictures can be transmitted with 10 foot-candles incident illumination on the scene and a camera objective aperture of $f/1.9$. The spectral responses of two different target materials of this type are shown in Fig. 3.40. At very low signal levels the gamma is found to be unity, whereas at higher levels, of the order of 0.05 microampere, it is approximately 0.5. The lag which accompanies the very high sensitivity (1000 to 2000 microamperes per lumen) is too high for general application in standard Vidicons. However, in the miniature Vidicon the target-size reduction decreases the lag of the high-sensitivity target to a point comparable with that of the 6198 and 6326 Vidicons.

Fig. 3.41. A completely self-contained transistorized ½-inch Vidicon camera with personal television receiver.

The small size of the tube and the ease with which it may be handled in manufacture indicates that it would be well adapted to large-scale production on semiautomatic machines.

Because of its small diameter the miniature Vidicon demands only about one-third the current required for beam deflection by the standard tube. This makes it extremely attractive for transistor use. A complete, experimental transistor camera built around the miniature Vidicon is seen in Fig. 3.41.[11] This camera contains all the circuitry for operating

[10] See Cope (reference 12).

[11] See Flory, Gray, Morgan, and Pike (reference 23).

Fig. 3.42. Interior view of transistorized camera.

the Vidicon, including deflection, video amplifier, blanking circuits, a 300-volt supply for the Vidicon, and a modulated 60-megacycle oscillator so that the signal can be supplied to a standard receiver. In short, the operation duplicates that of the RCA TV Eye or the Dage Model 60-A Camera. The camera may be operated on batteries or on a built-in regulated power supply. Bandwidth is better than 4 megacycles, which is sufficient to make full use of a standard receiver. The weight of the camera is four pounds. Total power consumed by the camera is 2.9 watts, somewhat less than that required by the heater of the 6198 Vidicon alone. A photoelectric "iris control," which decreases the Vidicon target voltage in response to an increase in light level, preserves picture quality as the illumination is varied over a wide range. An interior view of the transistor camera is shown in Fig. 3.42. One pound of silver cell batteries will operate the camera for about five hours. As an alternative, shown in Fig. 3.41, the 60-cycle power required to operate the camera may be transmitted from a junction box directly over the video wire; the separation of video signal and 60-cycle current is effected by condensers and chokes (Fig. 3.43).

An extremely lightweight camera containing the miniature Vidicon and transistorized preamplifier circuits (the JTV-1) has been built by the Radio Corporation of America for military purposes. It weighs less than 1 pound and measures 1⅞ x 2⅜ x 4½ inches; it is provided with photoelectric iris control, as in the camera described above.[12]

TRANSMISSION OF CLOSED-CIRCUIT TELEVISION SIGNALS

The methods which may be employed in the transmission of closed circuit television signals are familiar from broadcast practice. The relaying of signals from the studio to the transmitter, as well as their distribution from an originating station to other stations of the same network, represent important applications of these methods. Of possibly even more immediate interest are the practices developed in community television installations in which the number of receivers involved and the permissible outlay are more nearly of the same order as in industrial, commercial, and educational television applications. It need occasion no surprise that the engineering firms which have specialized in the

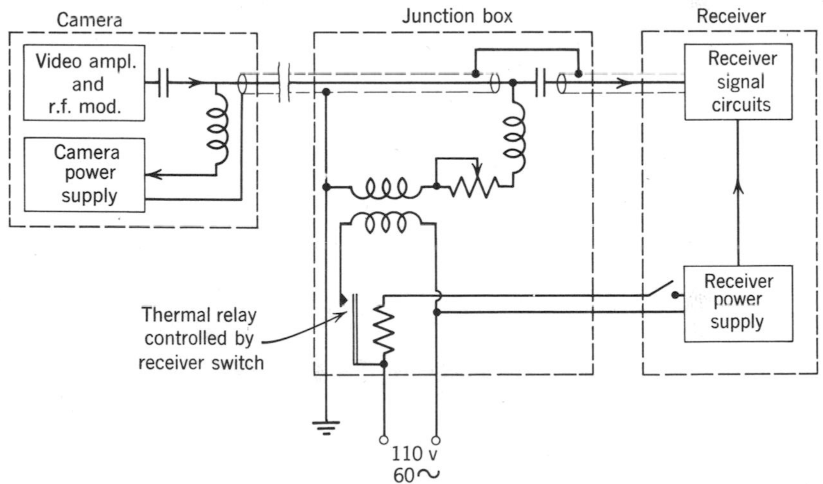

Fig. 3.43. Transmission of power to camera over signal wire.

construction of community-distribution systems for entertainment television have also taken a leading part in the establishment of distribution networks for industrial and educational purposes.

There are, essentially, three different methods for the closed-circuit transmission of television signals. These are (1) the direct transmission of the video signals by wire or cable; (2) the transmission by coaxial

[12] See reference 24.

cable of high-frequency carriers modulated by the video signals; and (3) the air transmission of video signals on microwave carriers. Each of these has its specific advantages and drawbacks which mark out for it an area of preference. This is brought out more clearly in the succeeding paragraphs.

The Direct Transmission of Video Signals by Wire or Cable. With direct video transmission only one video signal can be transmitted over a line at a time. Furthermore, while the cable attentuation is relatively low because of the low top frequency of the transmitted signal (4 to 8 megacycles), any line amplifiers which may have to be employed to maintain the signal at a level well above noise must have substantially flat transmission and constant time delay for frequencies ranging from approximately one kilocycle to several megacycles; clamping circuits controlled by the horizontal blanking signals will then permit the proper transmission of still lower frequency components, including the d-c level. Direct video transmission hence will be employed only if a single signal need be transmitted over a line at a time, if the points of transmission and reception are fixed or otherwise such that they can be connected by cable or wire, and if the distance between them is small enough to require few or no repeater amplifiers. An excellent example for the fulfilment of all these conditions is the transmission of television signals from an underwater camera to a monitor on shipboard. The airborne television system manufactured by the Davies Laboratories, Inc., and shown schematically in Fig. 3.44 represents another instance; here seven Vidicon cameras, installed at various points on the plane, derive their camera-control voltages from a single generating unit and deliver their signals to a single monitor through a switching unit, or "camera station selector." When the necessary requirements of direct video transmission are fulfilled, it presents the advantage of a certain simplification and the reduction of possible sources of signal deterioration resulting from the absence of modulation and demodulation stages.

In urban centers the Bell Telephone System maintains video circuits for the transmission of video signals from studios to transmitters, as well as for theatre television.[13] These are, in large part, cable circuits which provide direct transmission of the signals. A brief examination may serve to point out some of the problems encountered in direct video transmission over greater distances.

The signal derived from a studio, or from an industrial television camera, is commonly delivered by a 75-ohm coaxial cable, unbalanced to ground. While such a cable is highly satisfactory for short-distance transmission of video signals, it is not suitable for great distances, par-

[13]See Morrison (reference 25) and Cowan (reference 26).

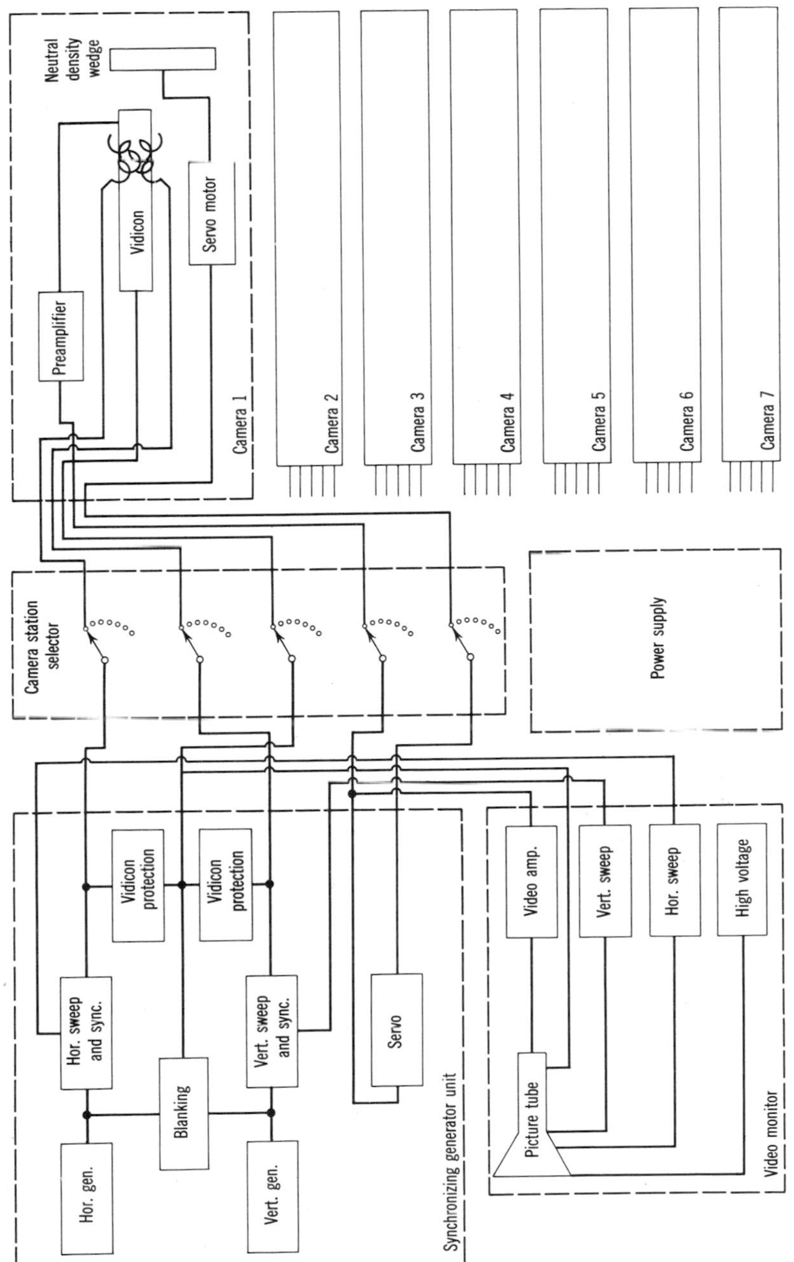

Fig. 3.44. A direct video transmission system: airborne television system designed by Davies Laboratories, Inc.

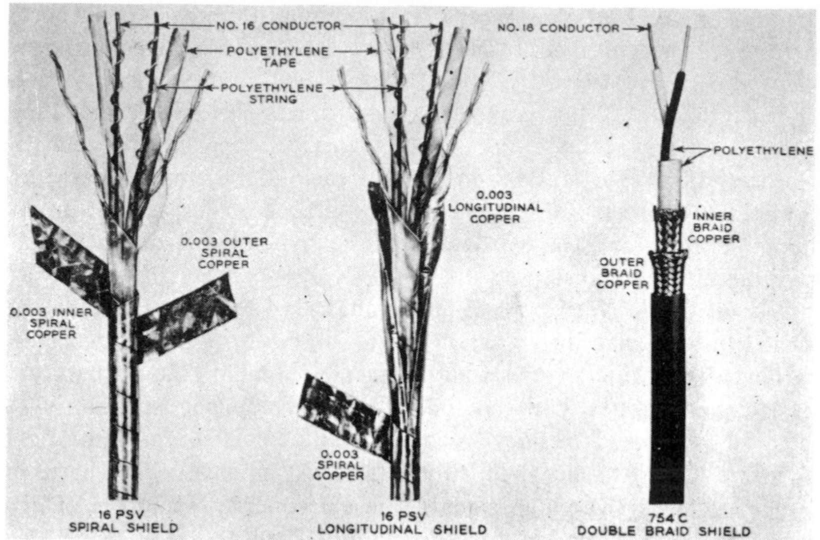

Fig. 3.45. Shielded pairs suitable for the transmission of video signals. (Courtesy of American Telephone and Telegraph Company.)

ticularly if the television line is in close proximity (e.g., within the same lead shield) to other message carriers. Although the coaxial cable provides excellent shielding against high-frequency fields, in view of the skin effect at the external shield, low-frequency fields corresponding, for example, to switching transients in adjoining lines readily penetrate the shield and produce interference. Hence the Bell Telephone System generally converts the unbalanced signal to a balanced signal by means of a repeater coil and transmits the balanced signal on a "shielded pair." The shielded pair consists of two closely adjoining wires, commonly insulated with respect to each other and the external, tubular, metal shield by polyethylene in tape, string, or extruded form. Interfering signals induce equal voltages in the two wires, which cancel out in the balanced output.

A typical shielded-pair cable (Fig. 3.45), such as 16 PSV (16-gage wire, polyethylene-shield, video cable), has an attenuation of about 17 decibels per mile at 4 megacycles and a characteristic impedance of 110 ohms. Repeaters placed at a separation of three to four miles maintain the input signal to each cable section at a level of about 2 volts, peak-to-peak. By comparison, the attenuation at 4 megacycles of ordinary, paper-insulated, twisted pairs ranges from 25 to 95 decibels per mile for wire thicknesses ranging from 10 to 26 gage.

The Transmission by Coaxial Cable of High-frequency Carriers Modulated by the Video Signals. For transmission over greater distances the Bell Telephone System employs 75-ohm coaxial cable. Interference difficulties are circumvented and amplification is simplified by modulating a high-frequency carrier with the video signal and transmitting the modulated carrier. The carrier is given a relatively low value—0.311 and 4.139 megacycles in the L1 and L3 systems, currently employed for relaying television programs—so as to minimize the attenuation of the signals in the cable. As shown in Fig. 3.46, this attenuation varies approximately as the square root of the frequency. Furthermore, vestigial side-band transmission is employed to make the transmission bandwidth only slightly greater than the television bandwidth. Figure 3.47 indicates the disposition of the television channel in the earlier, narrow-band, L1 system and the more recent, broad-band, L3 system. The total bandwidth transmitted by the former is 3 megacycles, that transmitted by the latter, 8 megacycles. Physically, the difference between the two systems rests in a different spacing of the repeater stations (eight and four miles, respectively for the L1 and L3 systems) and in differences in the repeater circuits and the terminal equipment. A gradual conversion of the narrow-band into broad-band circuits has been in process for some time.

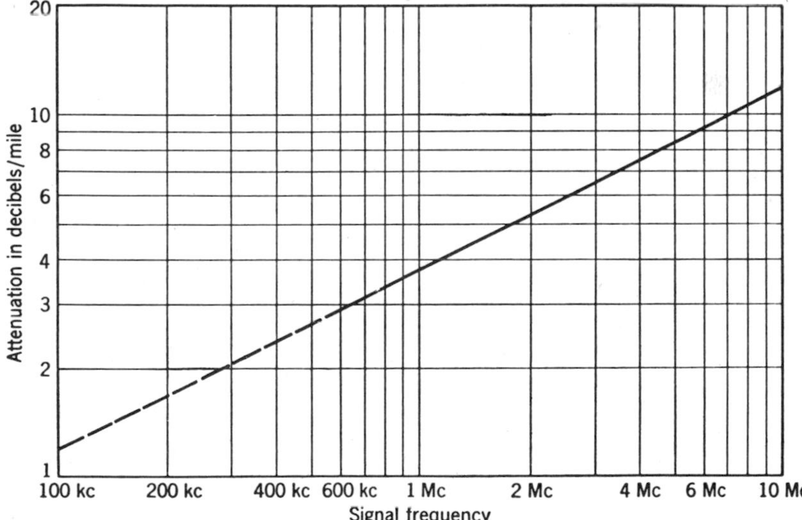

Fig. 3.46. Attenuation of a typical $\frac{3}{8}$-inch coaxial cable as function of frequency. (From Zworykin and Morton, *Television*, Wiley, New York, 1954.)

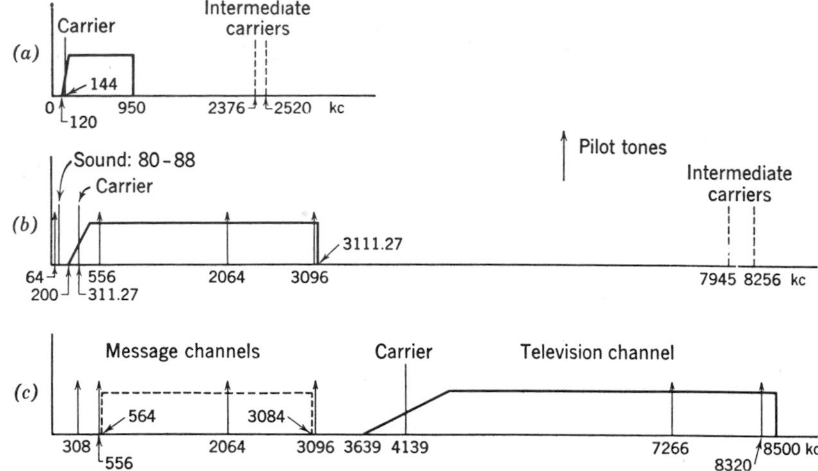

Fig. 3.47. Frequency allocations in coaxial cable systems: (*a*) New York-Philadelphia cable (1937); (*b*) L1 system; (*c*) L3 system. (From Zworykin and Morton, *Television*, Wiley, New York, 1954.)

The amplification control circuits for these coaxial-cable routes are exceedingly complex. A series of pilot tones, indicated in Fig. 3.47, are transmitted along with the signal and may be separated out by means of sharp crystal filters. Feedback circuits maintain the amplitude of these pilot tones, hence the gain over the transmitted bandwidth at a constant value. These and other precautions are required in view of the great distances over which the signals are transmitted and the enormous total amplification needed to overcome the attenuation. They are not necessary in most closed-circuit applications.

Although in the relay system only a single television signal is transmitted over a cable and a relatively low-frequency carrier is employed to minimize the number of line amplifiers required, most closed-circuit networks utilize standard, very-high-frequency television carriers, preferably in the range of 55 to 83 megacycles (channels 2 to 6), and transmit several signals over a single cable. The higher television channels are usually avoided, since amplification costs rise rapidly with frequency. The use of standard television carriers has the obvious advantage that it permits the use of the station selector in standard commercial receivers to select the desired closed-circuit signal without the interposition of any special modulation or demodulation equipment.

Figure 3.48 shows schematically a rather large-scale, closed-circuit installation for Fort Monmouth, N. J.,[14] made by the Jerrold Elec-

[14]See Kraus (reference 28).

tronics Corporation. Here over 100 classrooms, various theatres, and the field house are served by programs derived from live and film studios, spot-pickup transmitted by microwave, and commercial broadcast stations. The desired programs are transmitted on television channels 2, 4, and 6. The use of channels spaced apart in this fashion makes the frequency cut-off characteristics of the parallel amplifiers less critical.

The method of combining amplifier outputs is indicated in Fig. 3.49; the inductances L of the coils between amplifier outputs are matched to the output capacities C, so that $\sqrt{L/C} = R$, where R is the characteristic impedance of the line. Similarly, in a distribution amplifier which serves to distribute signals to a number of secondary cables, pentodes are bridged across the line, with their input capacities matched to the series inductances in the same manner (Fig. 3.50). An alternative arrangement for adding amplifier outputs, which utilizes series-resonant

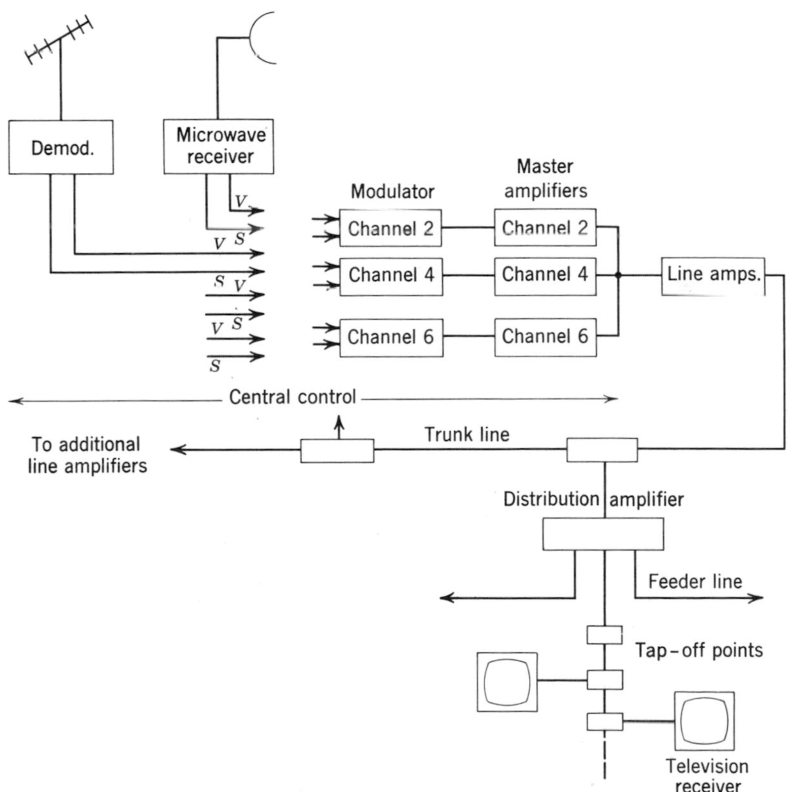

Fig. 3.48. Block diagram of a closed-circuit television distribution system.

circuits and half-wave transmission line sections to achieve isolation and prevent signal loss in the load circuits of the paralleled amplifiers, is shown in Fig. 3.51. Individual receivers are connected to the cable by passive resistive or capacitative tap-offs.

It should be noted that sound may be added to the locally originated television program in two different ways (Fig. 3.52). First, the output of a microphone or tape or disk phonograph may be employed to

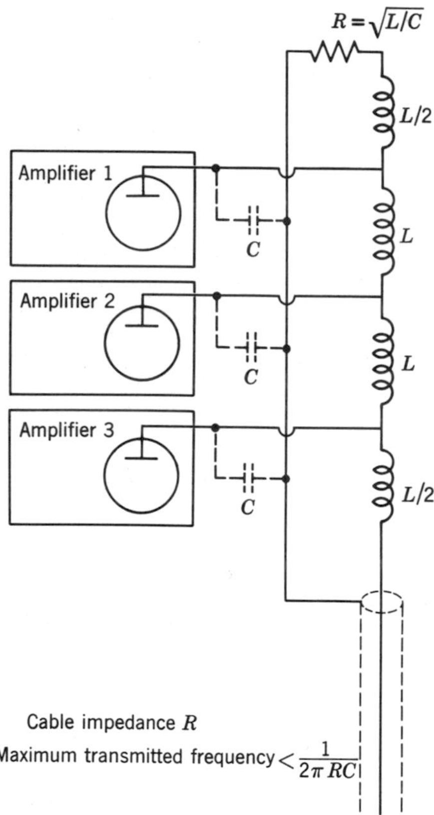

Fig. 3.49. Addition of amplifier outputs.

frequency-modulate an audio carrier 4.5 megacycles above the video carrier, and this modulated carrier may be added to the video signal. Any standard receiver to which the resultant signal is applied will then provide both picture and sound. As an alternative the sound may be transmitted over a separate telephone line which parallels the video cable. The second procedure has the advantage that it lends itself

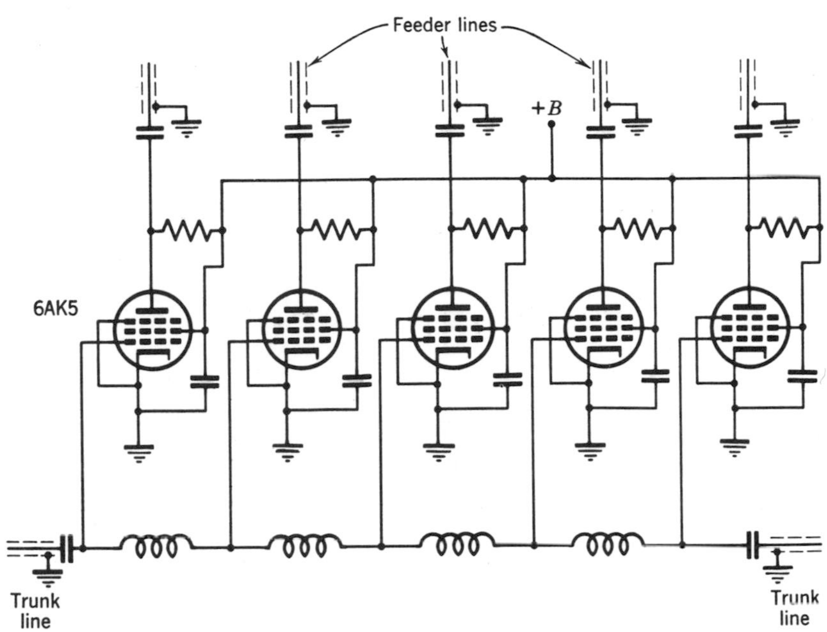

Fig. 3.50. Distribution amplifier. (From Zworykin and Morton, *Television,* Wiley, New York, 1954.)

readily to two-way communication between the operator of the camera and the viewers of the transmitted picture.

Both methods are illustrated in the schematic diagram of a closed-circuit television installation made by the Jerrold Electronics Corporation at the Electrical Engineering Building of the Case Institute of Technology (Fig. 3.53). Unlike the installation shown in Fig. 3.48, the

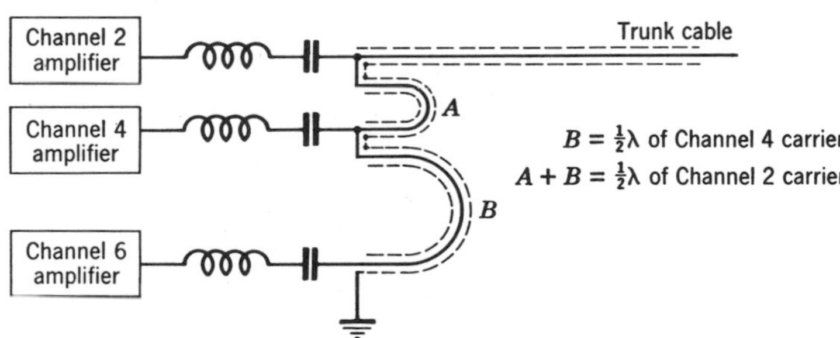

Fig. 3.51. Alternative form of signal-adding network. (From Zworykin and Morton, *Television,* Wiley, New York, 1954.)

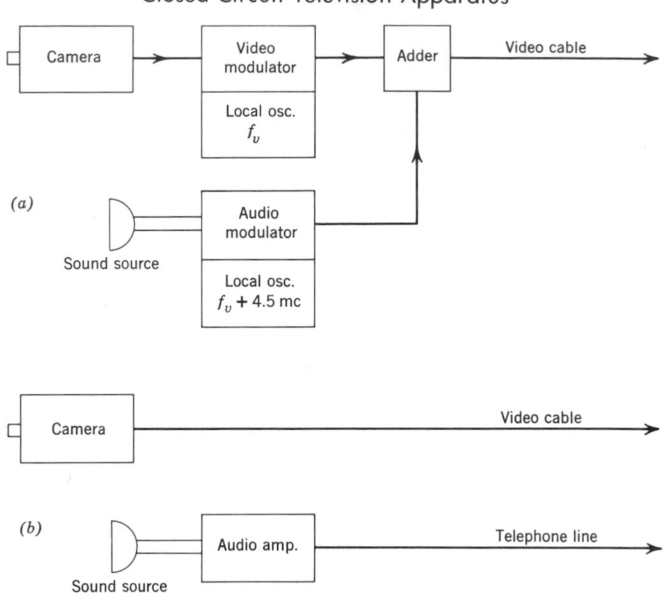

Fig. 3.52. The addition of sound to a locally originated program by (*a*) the addition of an audio-modulated carrier to the video signal and (*b*) sound transmission over a separate line.

arrangement shown in Fig. 3.53 provides for the origination of local television programs in any one of the classrooms of the building. For this purpose, three parallel lines in a single conduit are provided. One of these is the television distribution cable, which carries three commercial-station channels (3 [converted to 2], 5, and 8) and one locally originated program, on channel 4. A second video cable carries the locally originated program from any classroom or laboratory to the master amplifier from which it is distributed by means of the first cable. The third line is a twisted-pair telephone circuit which permits two-way voice communication between all the rooms of the building. Wall connections for the three lines are provided in every room.

It has already been pointed out, in the discussion of the coaxial-cable television relay system, that, for long-distance transmission, the conversion of the television channels to low frequencies (e.g., from 1 to 7 megacycles) becomes profitable. The fact that a separate cable is required for every channel is outbalanced by the saving in line amplifiers and associated electronic equipment. At the same time, in shorter-distance systems, the need for a separate origination and distribution cable may be avoided by employing different frequency bands for the transmission of the video signals from the local camera to the master amplifier and for their distribution. For instance, the original video signal modulator may operate with a carrier frequency of 45.25 megacycles and the sound carrier be chosen at 40.75 megacycles, 4.5 *below* the video carrier. By mixing the resulting signal with a 106.5-megacycle oscillation at the master amplifier and applying appropriate filtering, the local video program is transferred to channel 3 (60 to 66 megacycles) and may be transmitted, along with a number of broadcast programs, to receivers connected to the cable which also carries the lower-frequency signals from the cameras.

Microwave Transmission of Video Signals. Microwave transmission is employed both for long-distance and local relaying of television signals. For long-distance relaying, the Bell Telephone System's TD-2 microwave system employs a frequency band from 3700 to 4200 megacycles. This accommodates six channels in each direction, spaced 40 megacycles apart. At each repeater the channel frequencies are shifted by 40 megacycles to prevent feedback from the transmitter to the re-

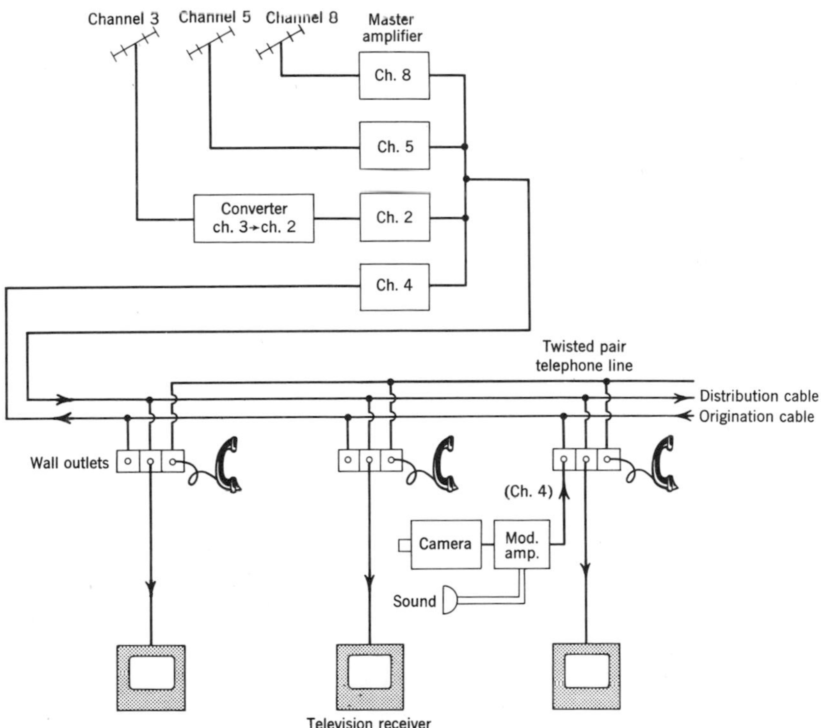

Fig. 3.53. Two-way television distribution system.

ceiver; the prevention of feedback dictates the relatively large frequency separation between channels.

Microwave wavelengths are in the centimeter range; thus a wavelength of 7.5 centimeters corresponds to a frequency of 4000 megacycles. This makes it possible to construct microwave mirrors and lenses in which the linear dimensions are large compared to the microwave wavelength. Under these circumstances microwave mirrors and lenses act upon microwaves essentially as conventional mirrors and lenses act upon light. Thus microwaves can be concentrated in relatively narrow beams directed at a distant receiver, the degree of concentration attainable depending on the ratio of the lens or mirror diameter to the wavelength λ. It may be shown from simple diffraction theory that the maximum gain to be achieved by the use of a parabolic reflector or lens of area A, fully intercepting the radiation from a small horn-antenna at its focus, is $8.4\ A/\lambda^2$, if the radiation from a short dipole with the same total radiated power is taken as a standard of comparison. In practice, the gain may be expected to be less; in particular, the expression assumes that the effective source size is very much smaller than the ratio of the wavelength to the aperture angle of the lens or mirror and that the radiation from the source is uniformly distributed over the lens or mirror area.

If a lens or mirror of equal area A is employed at the receiver, the received intensity is seen to be proportional to $(A/\lambda)^2$. Thus, for equal range, the lens or reflector area required is proportional to the wavelength, or inversely proportional to the frequency, employed for the carrier. However, atmospheric absorption, as well as increasing difficulties in the generation and amplification of microwaves, fix a practical upper limit to the frequency. At the present time frequency bands near 4000 and 6000 megacycles are used for network relaying of television programs, and 7000-megacycle carriers are commonly employed for spot-pickup studio links. As yet no frequencies are assigned for general commercial or industrial use in the private transmission of closed-circuit television signals.

The 7000-megacycle equipment has also found application outside the broadcast field. In a self-contained mobile television system built by the Radio Corporation of America for the U.S. Army Signal Corps,[15] a microwave link is employed to transmit pictures from the training ground to the classrooms. The microwave signal is generated by a 100-milliwatt klystron oscillator, which is frequency-modulated by the video signal varying the voltage on the repeller plate. A 4-foot parabolic reflector provides a directional gain of 5000, so that the field strength at the receiver corresponds to that provided by a 500-watt nondirectional transmitter.

[15] See reference 31.

Fig. 3.54. Vidicon camera with backpack transmitter. (From Zworykin and Morton, *Television*, Wiley, New York, 1954.)

The sharply directional radiation pattern obtained with the aid of a parabolic reflector or microwave lens is not always desirable. Thus, if the distances between transmitter and receiver are relatively small and their relative locations vary widely, or if the signal is to be picked up at several points at once, an omnidirectional antenna, such as a vertical dipole, is preferable. Even then, however, a parabolic reflector at the receiver can frequently contribute materially to the signal strength.

A backpack-carried television station represents a good example of such an application. Units of this type were first developed for the National Conventions of 1952.[16] The camera and transmitter pack, which weighs approximately 50 pounds, are shown in Fig. 3.54. Figure 3.55 is a block diagram of the complete transmitting unit. The camera is a typical 1-inch Vidicon camera with a lens turret and kinescope view-finder. Its video output is further amplified in the pack unit, where

[16] See Flory, Pike, Dilley, and Morgan (reference 32) and Ohler (reference 33).

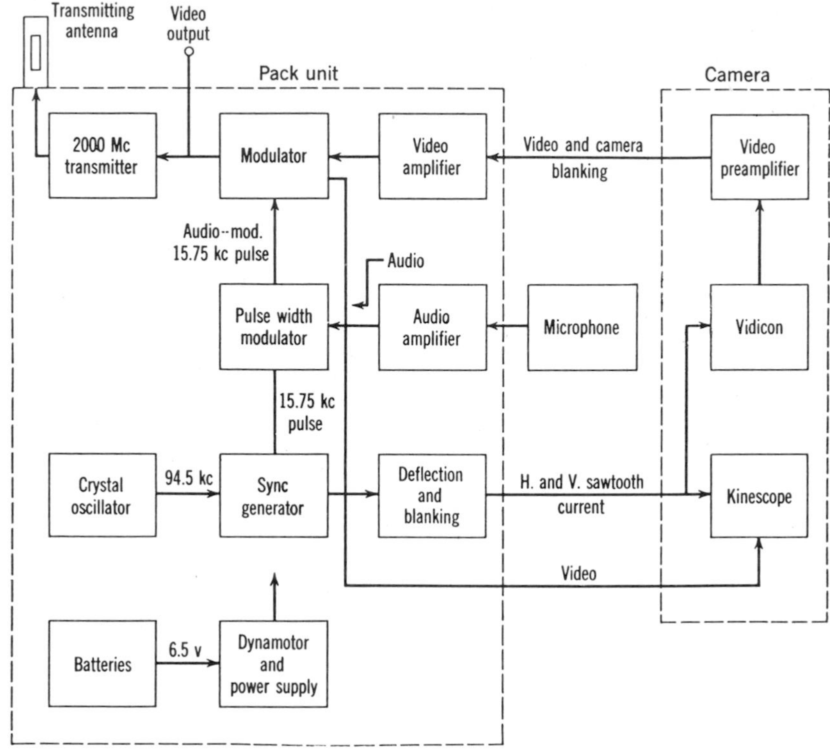

Fig. 3.55. Block diagram of pack unit and camera. (From Zworykin and Morton, *Television,* Wiley, New York, 1954.)

the horizontal synchronizing signal and the audio information are added. The composite video signal amplitude-modulates a 2000-megacycle cavity-oscillator employing a 5893 pencil triode. The oscillator output is applied to an antenna, which may be the slot type or a vertical dipole. The vertical dipole has the advantage of a more uniform radiation pattern.

The synchronizing and deflection and blanking circuits are essentially conventional, with special emphasis placed on miniaturization; the synchronizing generator is stabilized by a 94.5-kc crystal oscillator, the 15.75-kc line frequency being derived from it by frequency division. The sound information is added to the video signal by modulating the duration of the horizontal synchronizing pulses, leaving the front edge, which carries the synchronizing information, fixed.

In greater detail (Fig. 3.56), short pulses at horizontal line frequency are used to trigger a multivibrator which generates pulses of a length determined by its time constant and the electrode potentials. By applying audio voltages derived from a microphone to one of the grids of the multivibrator, the pulse length can be varied at an audio rate. At the receiver the audio signal is recovered by first separating the synchronizing pulses from the video signal and then passing them through a low-pass filter. The instantaneous amplitude of the filter output, which has a high-frequency cut-off at about 7000 cycles, corresponds to the pulse width and hence to the original audio amplitude.

In the National Convention application the signal was transmitted by microwave to a fixed base station, where it was converted into a standard video signal in conformity with broadcast standards. This involved recovery of the video and audio signals and insertion, in the former, of a standard synchronizing signal. A microwave relay receiver with wide-band (18-megacycle) intermediate-frequency amplifiers was modified for 2000-megacycle operation by replacing the usual 6000-megacycle klystron waveguide and mixer by a coaxial antenna feed and a commercial crystal mixer and providing a 2000-megacycle cavity for a 2K28 klystron local osciallator. A standard field synchronizing generator locked in with the leading edge of the transmitted horizontal synchronizing pulses by a commercial "Genlock" provided the synchronization signals. Since the transmitted signal had no vertical synchronizing signal, the vertical phase was adjusted manually by a continuous phase

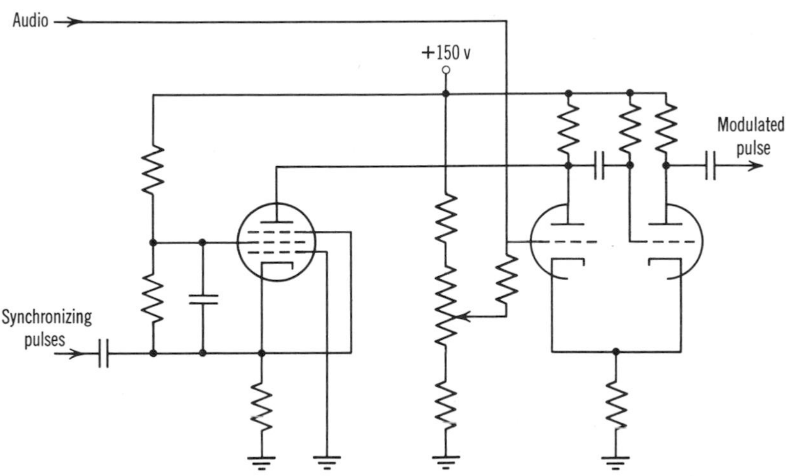

Fig. 3.56. Circuit for audio modulation of horizontal synchronizing pulse width.

shifter inserted between the local oscillator at twice horizontal frequency and the first counter of the synchronizing generator.

In the equipment just described the power for the camera and pack transmitter was supplied by five Yardney Silvercels delivering 30 amperes at 6.5 volts. These cells, which are very light and compact in comparison with conventional lead batteries of equal capacity and maintain the voltage at an almost constant level during operation, permit 1½ hours of continuous operation without recharging. The higher d-c voltages required by the equipment were provided by a dynamotor, driven by the storage cells, at the bottom of the pack.

Many variations are possible in the construction and operation of this equipment. Thus, an earlier version employed not only a microphone mounted on the camera to transmit the cameraman's comments, but provided, in addition, a narrow frequency-modulation link operating at 154.49 megacycles to transmit instructions from the base unit to the cameraman. These were converted by a fixed-tuned frequency-modulation receiver and applied to a headphone set. The same link

Fig. 3.57. Transistorized backpack transmitter.

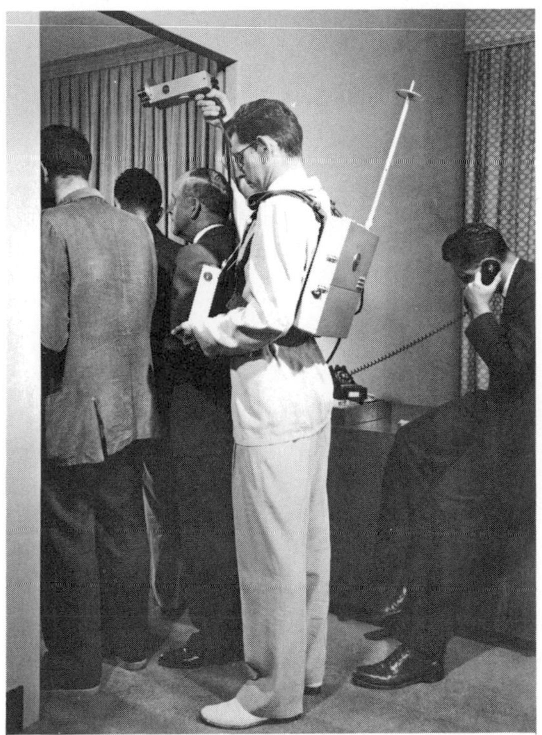

Fig. 3.58. Backpack transmitter in use, with operator observing image on detached viewfinder.

transmitted a 60-cycle note to lock the synchronizing generator in the pack to the power lines, thereby rendering the local crystal oscillator unnecessary.

Of greater importance are the changes, in particular with respect to weight, bulk, and power consumption, which have been made possible by the replacement of tubes by transistors. Figure 3.57 shows the completely transistorized pack unit.[17] Its flexibility in use is illustrated by Fig. 3.58.

In this unit all of the circuitry is designed around transistors, except for the transmitter itself (Fig. 3.59). The transmitter is a 2000-megacycle, self-excited oscillator with special cavities designed for wide-band operation. It is grid-modulated, requires less than a volt of video for full modulation, and can be driven by a transistor amplifier. Peak power is of the order of ½ watt.

The camera, built around the experimental ½-inch Vidicon, con-

[17] See Flory, Gray, Morgan, and Pike (reference 23).

Fig. 3.59. Interior of backpack unit, with battery case removed. The transmitter is on the right.

tains the Vidicon deflection circuit and most of the video amplifiers (Fig. 3.60). A monitor unit, or view-finder, containing its own deflection circuits and a video driver stage, is detachable from the camera; if the camera is inaccessible to the operator he may attach the monitor to the pack unit.

The pack contains the batteries, a transistor oscillator power supply to transform power for the transmitter and for other high-voltage requirements, the synchronizing and pulse generator, and mixing stages of the video amplifiers.

The camera with view-finder weighs about five pounds and the pack unit with batteries for five hours operation, about fifteen pounds.

COLOR AND STEREO TELEVISION APPARATUS

In many instances the information conveyed by a television picture is materially enhanced if the presentation is in natural color or three-dimensional. In fact, closed-circuit color television demonstrations, in particular of surgical operations, preceded the adoption of color television standards for broadcasting by a considerable period. The equipment employed in these early demonstrations was field-sequential: picture signals for the entire field viewed through a red, a blue, and a green filter were transmitted in turn. The pictures reproduced with these signals on a black-and-white kinescope in the receiver were viewed through similar filters whose displacement was synchronized with the transmitter filters (Fig. 3.61). In order to avoid intolerable flicker, it was necessary to make the field frequency much higher—of the order of three times higher—than in black-and-white television. Consequently, a standard black-and-white receiver could not translate field-sequential color television signals into an intelligible picture. The field sequential color television system was, and is, "incompatible."

By contrast, in the compatible color television systems complying with the standards prescribed by the Federal Communications Commission the field and frame rates are the same as for black-and-white television. The three red, blue, and green component pictures of the scene, separated

Fig. 3.60. Interior of camera and detached viewfinder.

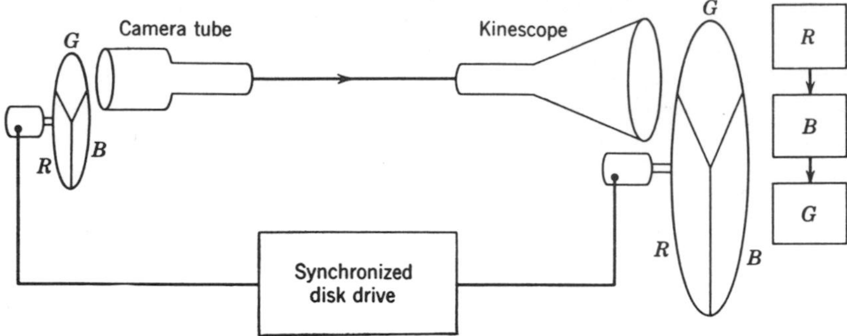

Fig. 3.61. Field-sequential color television system. (From Zworykin and Morton, *Television*, Wiley, New York, 1954.)

by a "beam splitter" generally consisting of a system of dichroic mirrors, are projected simultaneously on the photosensitive targets of three camera tubes. The signals derived from the three camera tubes are added together in such proportion as to form a luminance signal, of an amplitude proportional to the brightness of the picture element scanned simultaneously in the three camera tubes (Fig. 3.62) In addition, a chrominance signal is generated by forming suitable linear combinations of the three camera signals and modulating a subcarrier at different phase angles (e.g., at 120° with respect to each other or in phase opposi-

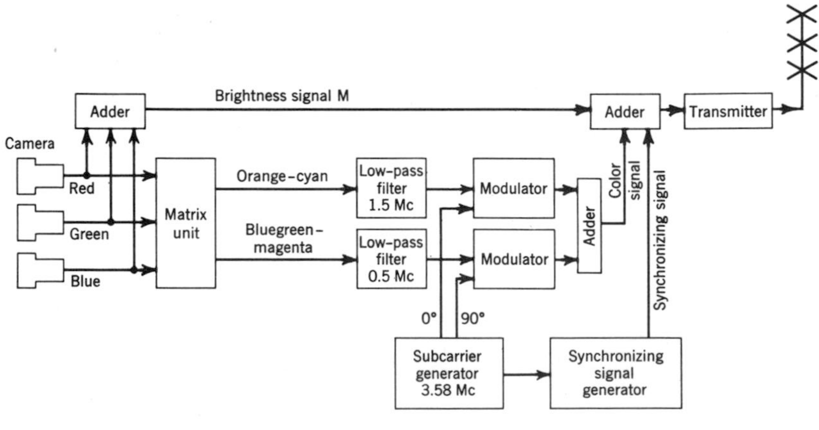

Fig. 3.62. Simplified block diagram of a compatible color television transmitter.

tion and phase quadrature with respect to a reference subcarrier oscillation). The subcarrier itself is chosen as an odd-integer multiple of half the line frequency, approximately equal to 3.58 megacycles. With such a choice, the chrominance signal, when added to the luminance signal, superposes in a black-and-white receiver a fine dot pattern on the picture, the phase of which reverses in successive frames. But for receiver nonlinearity, persistence of vision would render such a pattern quite invisible. In practice the attenuation of the video signal near 3.58 megacycles minimizes the visibility of the residual dot pattern in the average standard black-and-white receiver. The resultant chrominance signal is a high-frequency oscillation in which the phase determines the hue of the picture and the amplitude its saturation or degree of departure from black and white to a pure spectral color (or purple) (Fig. 3.63).

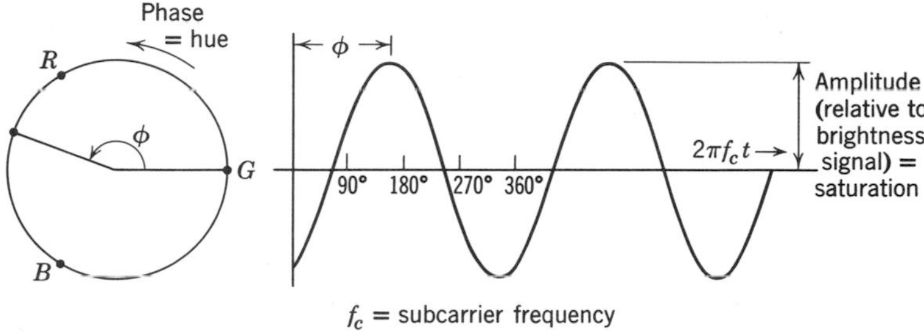

Fig. 3.63. The chrominance signal for a field of uniform color.

In a color receiver (Fig. 3.64) the chrominance signal is selected from the compound video signal by a band-pass filter and is decoded into linear combinations of the red, blue, and green component signals. These are then combined with the luminance signal (with the high-frequency chrominance signal superposed on it) so as to recover the original red, blue, and green signals. The red, blue, and green signals modulate three beams in a color kinescope, which reproduce the component pictures in superposition on the screen of the kinescope.

The disturbance produced by the superposition of the chrominance signal on the luminance signal is minimized by the employment of a high-frequency subcarrier and by limiting the frequency range over which color reproduction of the original scene is provided. This is possible without any loss in color fidelity as perceived by the eye, since the perception of color detail is much more limited than that of

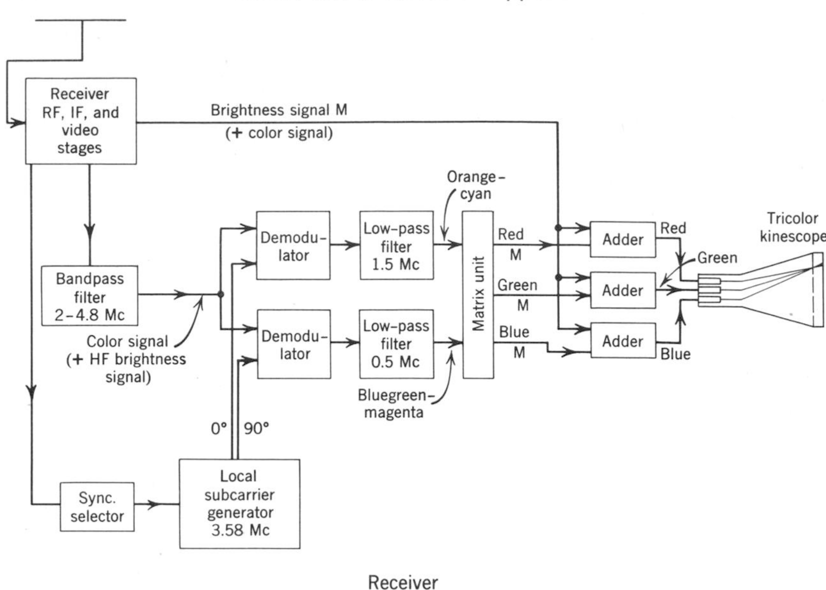

Fig. 3.64. Simplified block diagram of a compatible color television receiver.

brightness detail. Full color discrimination is possible only for relatively coarse structures. For finer detail the eye has effective two-color vision, and for the finest detail the eye discriminates differences in brightness only. Thus a pattern of red and blue dots will, from a certain distance on, appear uniformly purple, with dots of different brightness. This will occur long before the dots disappear altogether. The compatible color standards are carefully adapted to these properties of the human eye.

The ultimate resolution achieved with a compatible color system having a standard video passband is approximately equal to that obtained with black-and-white television. In a field-sequential system the horizontal resolution is reduced to approximately 58 per cent of that obtained with black-and-white television, even when the complete picture frequency is reduced from 30 to 24 per second and the line number is reduced from 525 to 405.

However, although the adoption of compatible color television standards has ruled out the use of field-sequential equipment in broadcasting, it has not had this effect in closed-circuit applications. There are several reasons for this, apart from the fact that Federal Communications Commission decisions find no application here. First, compatibility is of minor basic importance, although nonstandard operation has the material drawback of preventing the use of mass-produced and, consequently, highly developed, inexpensive color receivers in the video chain. Second, adequate resolution can be obtained by increasing the video passband to 10 to 12 megacycles. Third, the field-sequential camera can be made more compact and simpler than a compatible color camera with three camera tubes; this was particularly true before the advent of the Vidicon. Finally, the field-sequential system requires no registration of the three component pictures.

On the debit side, rainbows on the leading and trailing edges of moving objects, resulting from the time difference between the component pictures, and color break-up, or bright color flashes noticeable when the observer moves his head, frequently prove annoying in field-sequential color television. Furthermore, the camera sensitivity is reduced, since with interlaced scanning proper color rendition does not permit the use of full signal storage; the light level must be maintained near the knee of the response curve so that essentially only line storage is employed. It is true that, with the high intrinsic sensitivity of the image orthicon, this is a minor limitation. Finally, compared with simultaneous operation of a receiver employing similar components, field-sequential operation materially reduces the brightness of the picture viewed on the receiver.

Field-Sequential Color Television System with Image Orthicon Camera. A three-unit industrial field-sequential color television system was designed by the Columbia Broadcasting System,[18] and a similar system was marketed in 1956 by the General Electric Company. The system operates with 144 fields per second, interlaced, corresponding to 24 complete pictures per second. The line number is 405.

The camera (Fig. 3.65), measuring 23 x 7½ x 7½ inches and weighing only 43 pounds, is compact. It contains an image orthicon, a remotely controlled and focused lens turret, and a motor-driven filter drum surrounding a 45° mirror between the lens and image-orthicon photocathode. In addition, a small high-frequency power supply, a preamplifier, and a blanking amplifier are mounted within the camera envelope. The drum rotates at 1440 rpm, so that one rotation of the six-sided drum corresponds to one complete picture.

The control-monitor console (Fig. 3.66) contains the synchronization generator, deflection circuits for the image orthicon and monitor kinescope, a "color mixer" permitting separate adjustment of gain and black level for the three component pictures, and a kinescope and filter disk for observing the color picture. In addition, the control-monitor

[18]See Goldmark, Christensen, and Reeves (reference 36).

Fig. 3.65. Field-sequential industrial color television camera (Goldmark, Christensen, and Reeves, reference 36). (Courtesy of Proceedings of the Institute of Radio Engineers.)

console contains audio amplifying and switching circuits which permit observers at subsidiary monitors to direct questions to and receive answers from personnel at the camera station.

The color mixer contains three gating circuits which switch the incoming video signal at field rate from the "red" to the "blue" amplifier, from the "blue" to the "green" amplifier, etc., in such sequence that the picture signal corresponding to a component picture of a particular color is always amplified by the corresponding amplifier.

Fig. 3.66. Camera control monitor, type TH-1-B. (Courtesy General Electric Company.)

A 48-cycle pulse, marking out every third scanning field, is added to the synchronizing signal as color pulse. A 48-cycle sine wave derived from the color pulse and coupled through a selsyn motor to an amplifier drives the synchronous color-drum motor in the camera. The drum rotation is so phased that the separation between successive filters coincides with the line scanned. In this manner an overlap of color fields is avoided. In the receiver synchronization of the filter-disk drive motor is attained by phase comparison between the vertical synchronizing pulses and a sawtooth wave generated by a generator mounted on the

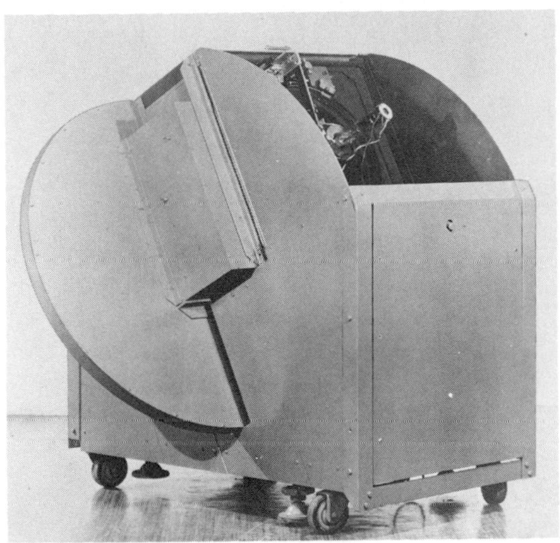

Fig. 3.67. Large-screen color television projector, type TG-2-B. (Courtesy of General Electric Company.)

color-disk shaft. The correcting voltage derived from the comparator serves to adjust the motor field and, hence, the speed of the disk.

The color receivers to which the video signal generated in the control monitor is supplied may employ color kinescopes with special deflection and color-switching circuits. As an alternative, they may be reflective projection units, providing a 4½ x 6-foot picture on a screen at a distance of 10 feet from the spherical mirror of the projection system (Fig. 3.67).

Field-Sequential Color System Using the Vidicon. A simplified field-sequential system can be built around the Vidicon as a pickup tube by incorporating certain specific design features to exploit the properties of

Fig. 3.68. Field-sequential color system using the Vidicon.

the Vidicon. Such an experimental system is shown in the photograph in Fig. 3.68.

In this system standards of scanning were chosen as a compromise between ideal performance and economy of bandwidth. A field frequency of 120 cycles was selected as offering considerable advantage as a multiple of 60 cycles. With a two-to-one interlace, as in broadcasting, the large-area color flicker is reduced to a satisfactory level for most industrial applications.

The storage characteristics of the Vidicon, helpful in many applications, introduce a problem in field-sequential color pickup. The charge pattern produced on the Vidicon target by its illumination in one of the primary colors must be removed before the illumination by the next color begins, or there will be degradation in color reproduction. The charge pattern in one color is removed in the area scanned for the field of that color, but in normal interlaced scanning only alternate lines are covered by a given scan. In this case a residue of charges corresponding to one color would remain in the unscanned alternate lines when the illumination in the next color began.

The problem was solved in this camera by using a 637-line raster.

With this high number of lines there is sufficient overlapping of lines above and below to discharge the spaces between alternate lines in each field. As a result, the vertical resolution corresponds to approximately half the number of lines. The only purpose gained by the use of interlaced scanning is then the reduction of flicker. With the above scanning standards a bandwidth of 12 megacycles is required to obtain a horizontal resolution of 400 lines.

Color carry-over from one field to the next, caused by time lag of the Vidicon target, is minimized by the use of very high levels of illumination and low target voltage.

Color selection in the camera is by means of a filter drum of 72 sections (24 of each color) driven at 100 rpm by a synchronous motor (Fig. 3.69). A magnetic bar placed at the beginning of each set of

Fig. 3.69. Interior of field-sequential camera. The color drum hugs the cylindrical casing.

three filters generates a 40-cycle synchronizing signal in a magnetic pickup circuit. This signal is used to lock the synchronizing generator in the control unit so that camera phasing with the scanning is automatic.

The monitor unit contains the power supply, deflection circuits, video amplifier, and synchronizing generator, as well as a 5-inch monitor with a 6-element, 1200-rpm filter disk. This disk is driven by a synchronous motor and is phased manually. Automatic phasing, as described in the section on the image-orthicon color system, could, of course, be incorporated. Color balance is controlled by applying gain-controlling pedestals, separately adjusted for each color, to a balanced modulator stage in the video amplifier. These pedestals are generated by a ring-of-three counter and are individually adjustable by control knobs.

Video signal output and synchronizing signals are supplied for operating additional viewers. Such a viewer was built by modifying a receiver designed for standard color broadcasts and incorporating a color kinescope. In this way a large picture is obtained with no mechanical parts at the viewing end.

A satisfactory picture with useful color purity is obtained with an incident scene illumination of about 1000 foot-candles. For many industrial applications this would not be an unreasonable amount of illumination, and the simplicity of the equipment would be very attractive.

Compatible (Simultaneous) Color Television System. While the sequential color systems just described give satisfactory operation for some specialized uses in which extreme compactness and simplicity are paramount, they do not produce a picture of highest quality and so are limited in their application.

High-quality, studio-type color pickup equipment designed for broadcasting has been used for closed-circuit work, particularly in the medical field.

The studio equipment utilizes a camera with three image-orthicon tubes, one for each of the primary colors. The objective lens forms an image on a field lens in the front of the camera, and the field lens is in turn imaged on the photocathodes of the image-orthicon tubes by a relay lens. The purpose of the relay lens is to obtain sufficient working distance between the lens and the tubes to insert the beam-splitting device. This beam splitter consists of an assembly of dichroic and plane mirrors which splits the "white" image into its three component red, green, and blue images and projects them onto the corresponding image-orthicon tubes. Such a color camera is shown in Fig. 3.70.

The signals from the three camera tubes are amplified and carried

Fig. 3.70. Image orthicon camera for broadcast use. (From Zworykin and Morton, *Television*, Wiley, New York, 1954.)

by cable to the processing amplifiers which further amplify and balance the signals. From there the signals are passed to the "colorplexer" unit, which performs the operation of modulating the chrominance information on the subcarrier and mixing the result with the luminance information to make up the complete color signal.

This system requires a maximum of one and one-half racks of equipment in addition to the camera. While it is quite satisfactory for large, permanent, industrial or medical applications, there is need for a more compact and simpler system to be used in more restricted and less permanent installations. The Vidicon again forms the basis of such a system.

Three Vidicons have been used in the 3V film camera in a manner analogous to the image orthicons in the studio camera just described. Dichroics are used as beam splitters to obtain the three primary images (Fig. 3.71). The mechanical arrangement of this camera was not suitable for direct pickup; hence special cameras were designed to provide a direct pickup unit with three Vidicons which could be built into a system of a complexity in line with that of black-and-white Vidicon

Fig. 3.71. Three-Vidicon color film scanner (interior view).

equipment. The Dage Model 350-A Color Camera and Model 750-A Color Console are an example of such a system (Fig. 3.72).

Another experimental three-Vidicon color camera system is seen in Fig. 3.73. This consists of a camera and four portable units each weighing about 40 pounds. It is complete with built-in synchronizing generator and colorplexer and radio-frequency generator, so that a complete color carrier is generated which can be used to operate standard home color receivers as viewers.

An interior view of the camera is given in Fig. 3.74. The assembly of the three Vidicons in their focus coils, together with the video preamplifiers and objective lenses, can be seen. Because of the smaller image size of the Vidicon and the shorter focal-length lenses, individual objective lenses were used with the dichroic mirror assembly in front. This greatly simplifies the camera but has the disadvantage of requiring considerable time to change lenses. Optical focus is remote; it is accomplished by moving the entire three-Vidicon assembly by means of a small reversible motor.

Fig. 3.72. Dage Model 350-A Color Camera in servicing position. (Courtesy of Dage Television Division, Thompson Products, Inc.)

Fig. 3.73. Compatible Three-Vidicon Color Television System. (Courtesy of RCA Laboratories.)

Fig. 3.74. Interior of color camera. (Courtesy of RCA Laboratories.)

Fig. 3.75. RCA Telemural Color Television Projector TLS-50. (Courtesy of RCA.)

The other packages contain the black-and-white monitor and processing amplifiers, the camera control circuits and synchronizing generator, and the power supply and colorplexer. A standard receiver or a studio color monitor may be used for monitoring the color picture. For demonstration to larger audiences, the TLS-50 Telemural Color Television Projection System (Fig. 3.75), which forms 6 x 4½-foot pictures on a projection screen, is convenient. The unit employs three Schmidt

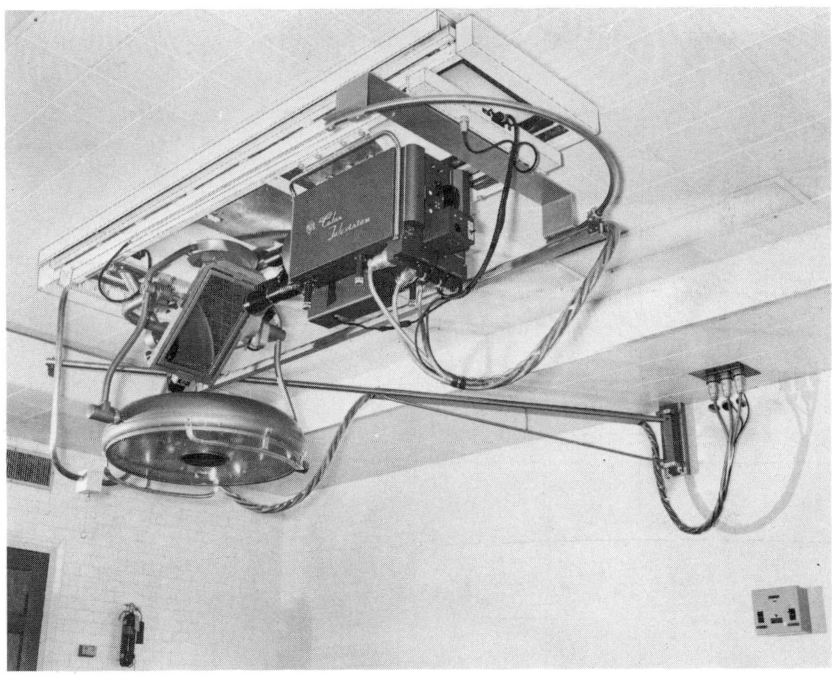

Fig. 3.76. RCA TK-45 Three-Vidicon Medical Color Camera arranged for transmission of surgical operations. (Courtesy of RCA.)

projectors with a 2½-inch kinescopes, side-by-side, and has a power consumption of only 550 watts.

The more highly developed Vidicon camera equipment shown in Fig. 3.76 has been used in several surgical demonstrations and has shown that a Vidicon system is capable of producing a perfectly satisfactory color picture with a minimum of equipment. The amount of illumination normally used by the surgeon is adequate for the Vidicon camera.

In addition to its use as a direct pickup camera the three-Vidicon color camera is extremely convenient for viewing stained microscope specimens, as, for instance, in a biopsy taken during an operation. Its use in this way is very simple. It is necessary only to provide a suitable ocular on the microscope to project the image into the 3V camera (Fig. 3.77). The usual microscope illumination of reasonable quality will suffice.

The commercial designs shown in Figs. 3.76 and 3.77 form part of an installation carried out in 1956 at the Walter Reed Army Medical Center in Washington, D. C.

As a further step in the development of more compact color pickup cameras, Fig. 3.78 shows an experimental camera designed to use three of the ½-inch Vidicons previously described. The control equipment is identical with that of the larger Vidicon camera. The small size of the Vidicon assemblies permits the use of a lens turret and relay lenses in a compact arrangement.

Stereo Television Systems. There are numerous practical applications of industrial television in which the exact relative location in three

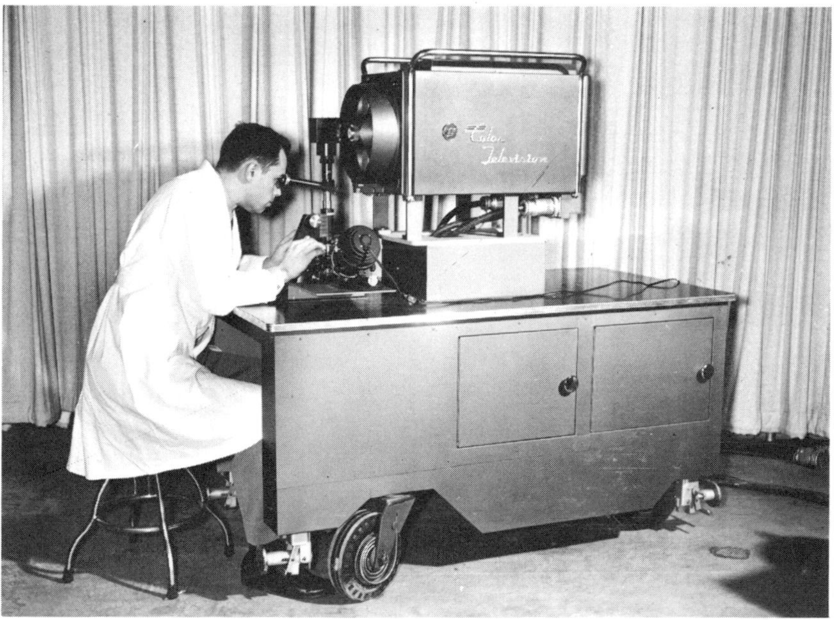

Fig. 3.77. RCA TK-45 Medical Camera employed for transmission of microslides. (Courtesy of RCA.)

Fig. 3.78. Experimental color camera using half-inch Vidicons (side panel removed).

dimensions of various objects in the observed scene is of great importance. The remote handling of reagents in the carrying out of experiments with radioactive materials is a case in point. Pouring substances from one beaker into another without spillage requires more than a picture projected on a plane for guidance.

It is thus not surprising that a detailed study of various stereo television techniques was carried out at the Argonne National Laboratory's Remote Control Engineering Division.[19] The problem consists of presenting to each eye of the observer the image which it would see if the observer were stationed at the camera location. Either a sequential or a simultaneous method may be employed for this purpose. In the sequential method moving mirrors and shutters are used to translate the effective position of the camera lens and to mask one or the other eye of the observer in synchronism. In the simultaneous method the two images are transmitted at the same time and observed individually by each eye through some type of viewing stereoscope.

The sequential method proved unsatisfactory because of flicker and lag effects. Consequently, a simultaneous method was adopted. In one

[19]See Johnston, Hermanson, and Hull (references 39).

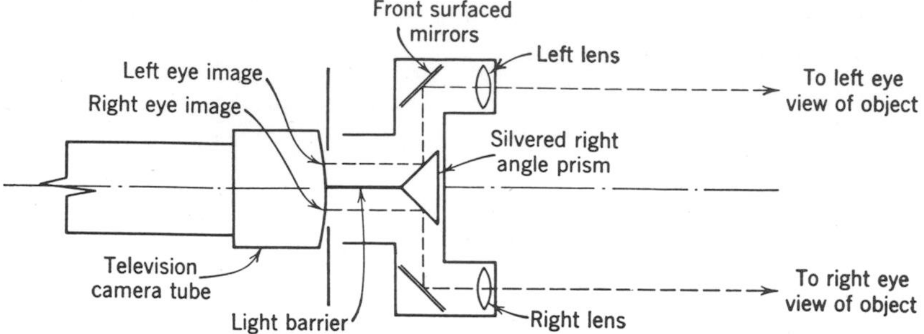

Fig. 3.79. Projection of two images on photocathode of camera tube in stereo system employing single image orthicon (Johnston, Hermanson, and Hull, reference 39). (Courtesy of Electrical Engineering.)

system used at the Argonne National Laboratories a DuMont image-orthicon chain was employed, and the images formed by two objectives were projected, with the aid of a mirror system. (Fig. 3.79), side-by-side on the photocathode of the camera tube.

If the image field is split up in this manner the attainable resolution is materially reduced. In a simultaneous stereo system developed by the

Fig. 3.80. RCA stereo television chain consisting of camera, stereo monitor, and control unit. (From Zworykin and Morton, *Television*, Wiley, New York, 1954.)

Radio Corporation of America the resolving capabilities of the industrial television system are fully utilized by the employment of two Vidicons and two parallel video channels (Fig. 3.80).[20] The figure shows a stereo monitor employing two miniature kinescopes, the camera, and the control unit. The three-dimensional image is viewed preferably through polaroid spectacles on a receiver in which two kinescope images, filtered by complementary polarizing screens, are superposed by a semitransparent mirror. This may be a stereo console receiver with a vertically and a horizontally mounted kinescope. A more compact stereo receiver, formed from two standard industrial television monitors, is shown in Fig. 3.81.

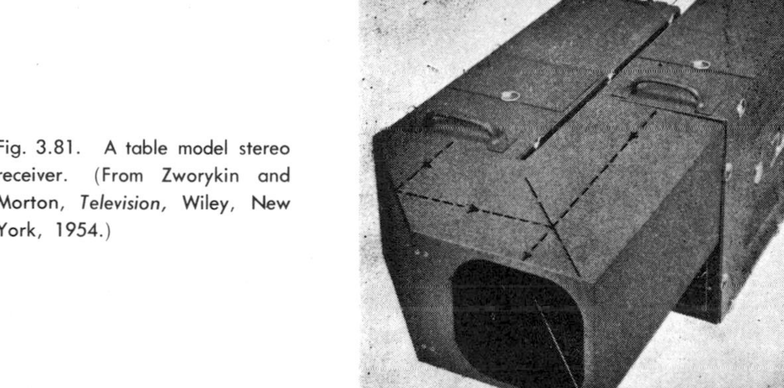

Fig. 3.81. A table model stereo receiver. (From Zworykin and Morton, *Television*, Wiley, New York, 1954.)

THE TELEVISION MICROSCOPE

The effectiveness of conventional light microscopy is limited not only by the finite resolving power of the instrument, set by the wavelength of the illuminating radiation, but also by inadequate contrast between different structural elements of the specimen. This fact applies particularly to the study of organic materials at high magnification. Selective staining and phase microscopy frequently aid in the attainment of the desired differentiation. They are not universally effective, however. Staining with dyes, furthermore, is rarely possible with living specimens.

The television microscope can provide enhanced contrast in two ways: first, by electronic contrast enhancement and, second, by the employment

[20] See Zworykin (reference 40).

Fig. 3.82. The "Electric Microscope" (1933).

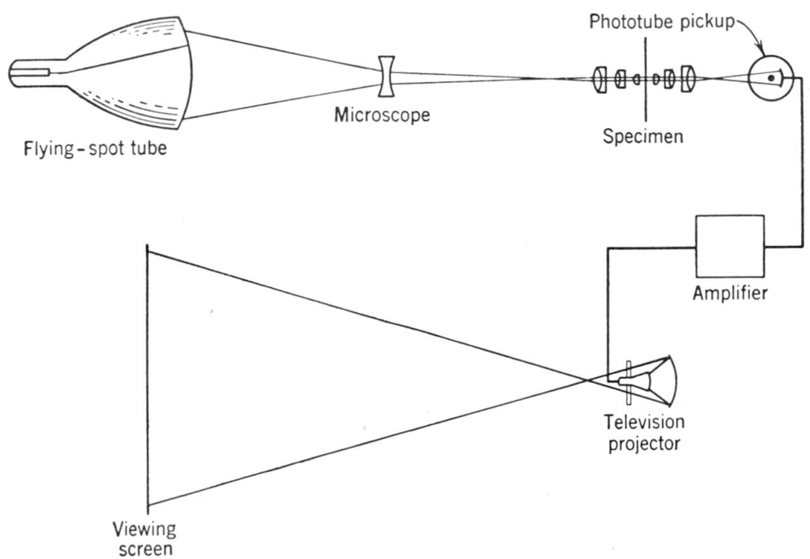

Fig. 3.83. Flying-spot microscope (schematic). (From Zworykin and Ramberg, *Photoelectricity*, Wiley, New York, 1949.)

of invisible radiations, particularly in the near ultraviolet, to which the eye is insensitive. Electronic contrast enhancement in combination with greater ease of viewing and convenient adjustment of the brightness level make it possible to follow closely the changes in living cells at high magnification. The great advantages which this technique offers in the teaching of bacteriology, histology, and other branches of microbiology are obvious.

The second method of contrast enhancement depends on the fact that many organic materials have strong distinctive absorption bands in the near ultraviolet, facilitating differentiation. Photography with high-contrast emulsions or plates sensitive to invisible radiations can, it is true, accomplish the same ultimate end. However, the time delay implicit in the photographic process prevents continuous observation

Fig. 3.84. Flying spot microscope equipment at University College, London. (Courtesy of Dr. F. Roberts.)

and greatly slows the examination of extended specimens. The observation of a fluorescent screen on which the invisible image is projected, on the other hand, is unsatisfactory with respect to resolution and brightness.

A very early realization of a television microscope—for the purpose of studying specimens illuminated by ultraviolet radiation—employed an iconoscope with an ultraviolet-transmissive window (Fig. 3.82).[21] At a later date R. C. Webb developed a flying-spot microscope in which the face of the flying-spot tube was imaged on a microspecimen through the microscope, and the transmitted light was collected by a multiplier phototube (Fig. 3.83).[22] Young, Roberts, and Causley,[23] in England,

[21] See Zworykin (reference 41).

[22] See Zworykin and Ramberg (reference 2, p. 383).

[23] See Young and Roberts (reference 42), Roberts and Young (reference 43), and Roberts, Young, and Causley (reference 44).

have done extensive work with systems of this type and have obtained excellent results. Figure 3.84 shows their apparatus. Figure 3.85 indicates the function of the several components.

For a given intensity of specimen illumination, the flying-spot microscope is in principle capable of yielding a higher signal-to-noise ratio than any other known type of television microscope. Except for light losses in the objective, the entire light transmitted by the specimen is utilized for signal generation. The only significant factor that reduces the signal-to-noise ratio below that of the transmitted light itself is the limited quantum efficiency of the photoelectric effect in the multiplier phototube. In practice the necessity of "aperture correction" (i.e., compensation in the amplifier for the fact that the excitation of the screen of the flying-spot tube persists longer than the time required for the scanning beam to sweep across a picture element) further reduces the signal-to-noise ratio.

The high efficiency in the utilization of the specimen illumination could be of particularly great value in the study of living specimens with ultraviolet illumination, since excessive doses of ultraviolet irradia-

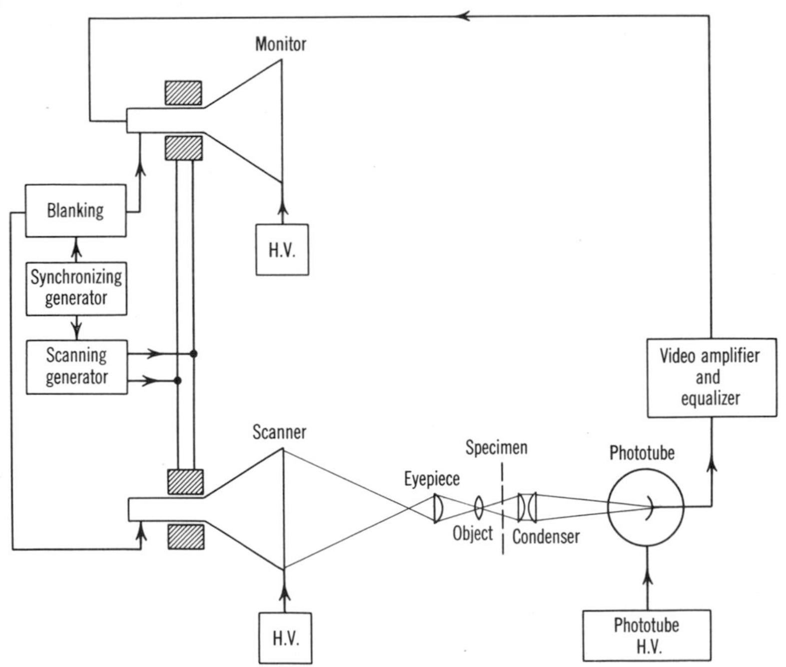

Fig. 3.85. Block diagram of flying-spot microscope shown in Fig. 3.84.

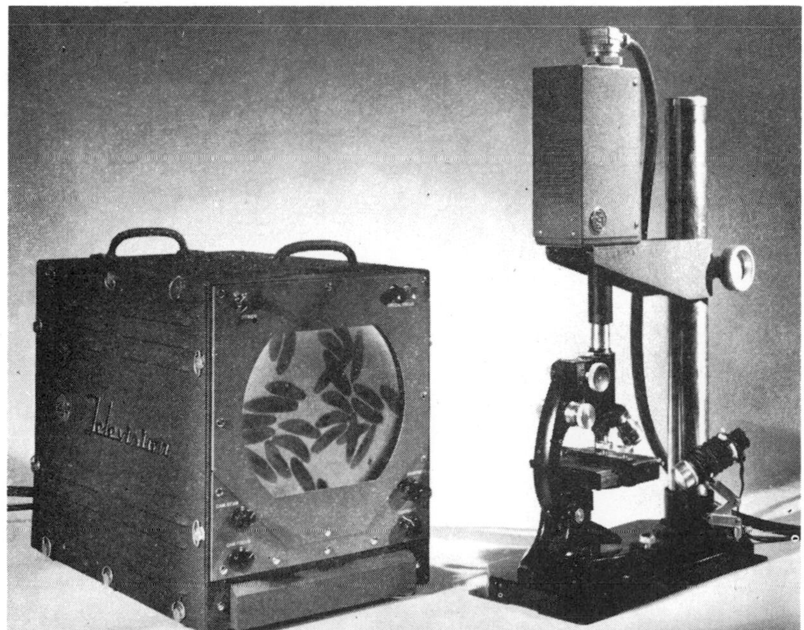

Fig. 3.86. Television microscope. (From Zworykin and Morton, *Television,* Wiley, New York, 1954.)

tion prove lethal. This advantage is offset by the fact that the absolute intensity of illumination of the specimen is limited by the brightness of the face of the flying-spot tube. In particular, high illumination intensities in limited wavelength ranges, such as may be obtained from the principal lines of a mercury arc, are not readily attained with flying-spot tube illumination. For stationary objects the inadequate signal-to-noise ratio resulting from insufficient illumination may be overcome by the use of long-persistence (radar) screens in the receiver.[24]

A more flexible type of television microscope is obtained by combining a standard microscope with a simple Vidicon camera (Fig. 3.86).[25] If the standard optics of the microscope are replaced by quartz-fluorite and/or reflective optics and a simple quartz prism monochromator with a medium-pressure mercury arc source is used as illuminator, it becomes possible to compare images obtained at different selected wavelengths in the ultraviolet and visible (Fig. 3.87). The only modification in the

[24]See Young and Roberts (reference 42), Roberts and Young (reference 43), and Roberts, Young, and Causley (reference 44).

[25]See Zworykin (reference 40).

Vidicon camera is the replacement of the standard Vidicon with a tube provided with an ultraviolet-transmitting face plate and a selenium target. Figure 3.13 shows the spectral response of such a tube in the ultraviolet. It is seen to vary only a little in the entire near-ultraviolet range. In applications requiring complete freedom from lag and very high sensitivity a special image orthicon with ultraviolet-transmitting face plate may be employed as pickup tube—at the expense of considerably increased bulk and of more complex and costly control equipment.

The ultraviolet-sensitive television microscope makes it possible to observe a given microspecimen illuminated in succession with radiation of different wavelengths for which its components have characteristic absorptions. The distribution of these components in the specimen may be inferred from such observations. It is much more convenient,

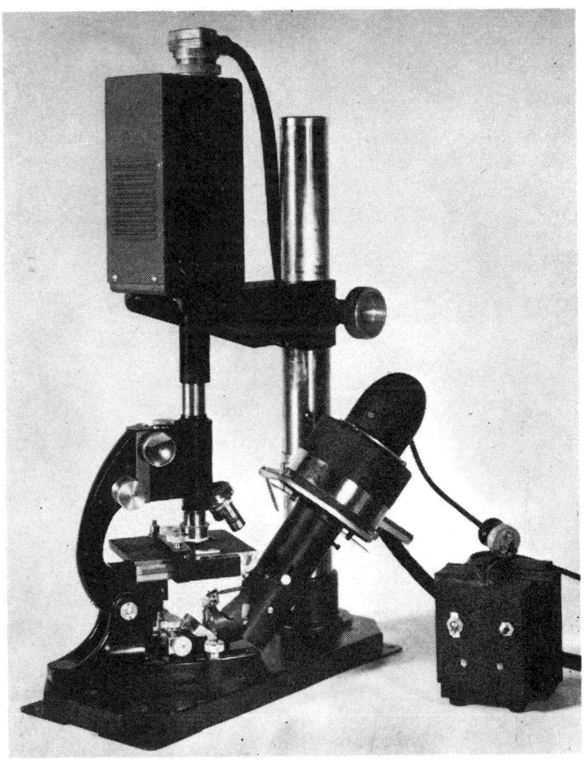

Fig. 3.87. Television microscope with ultraviolet illuminator. (From Zworykin and Morton, *Television*, Wiley, New York, 1954.)

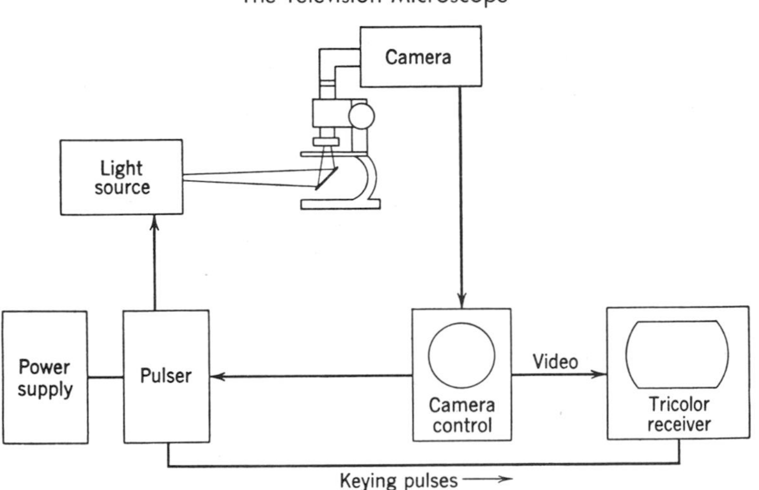

Fig. 3.88. Block diagram of television color translating microscope with single pulsed source. (From Zworykin and Morton, *Television*, Wiley, New York, 1954.)

however, if they are distinguishable in the picture by different colors. A photographic technique for accomplishing this, suggested by Brumberg, has been worked out by E. H. Land and his associates.[26] The principal practical drawbacks of this technique, namely the time delay implicit in the photographic process and the high cost of materials, are overcome by the application of television methods.

A block diagram of an early television color-translating microscope[27] is shown in Fig. 3.88. Ultraviolet illumination is provided by an ultraviolet monochromator with pulsed mercury arc source. A rotating mirror disk with three sectors recessed to different depths selects in turn three different wavelengths from the output of the monochromator, projecting the corresponding radiation on the entrance slit of the microscope illuminating system (Fig. 3.89). The image of the specimen formed with this radiation is projected by a reflective microscope objective on the target of an ultraviolet-sensitive Vidicon, from which the video signal is applied, in turn, to the red, green, and blue guns of a color kinescope. The pulsing of the light source, the rotation of the mirror disk, and the field change of the receiver are synchronized, so that the images formed by the three different wavelengths selected by the mirror disk correspond to the red, green, and blue component pictures whose resultant is viewed on the color-kinescope screen. Char-

[26] See Land, Blout, Grey, Flower, Husek, Jones, Matz, and Merrill (reference 46).

[27] See Zworykin, Flory, and Shrader (reference 45).

Fig. 3.89. Detail of single-source color translating microscope. (From Zworykin and Morton, *Television*, Wiley, New York, 1954.)

acteristic absorptions by the specimen of one or more of the selected wavelengths are translated into characteristic colors in the picture viewed on the receiver.

The system pictured in Fig. 3.89 demonstrated the practicality of indicating differential ultraviolet absorptions by television color-translation microscopy. However, it suffered from several drawbacks. In particular, a change in the wavelengths to be selected by the mirror disk required the construction of a new disk or a complex mechanical adjustment. Furthermore, the angle of incidence of the radiation on the illuminating slit varied slightly with the wavelength selected, which gave rise to spurious color-shading effects in the picture.

Both difficulties are overcome in a more elaborate television color-translating microscope constructed at the Rockefeller Institute For Medical Research in New York. The arrangement of the complete system is indicated in Fig. 3.90. Figure 3.91 shows a more detailed sketch of the illuminating system. Three separate grating mono-

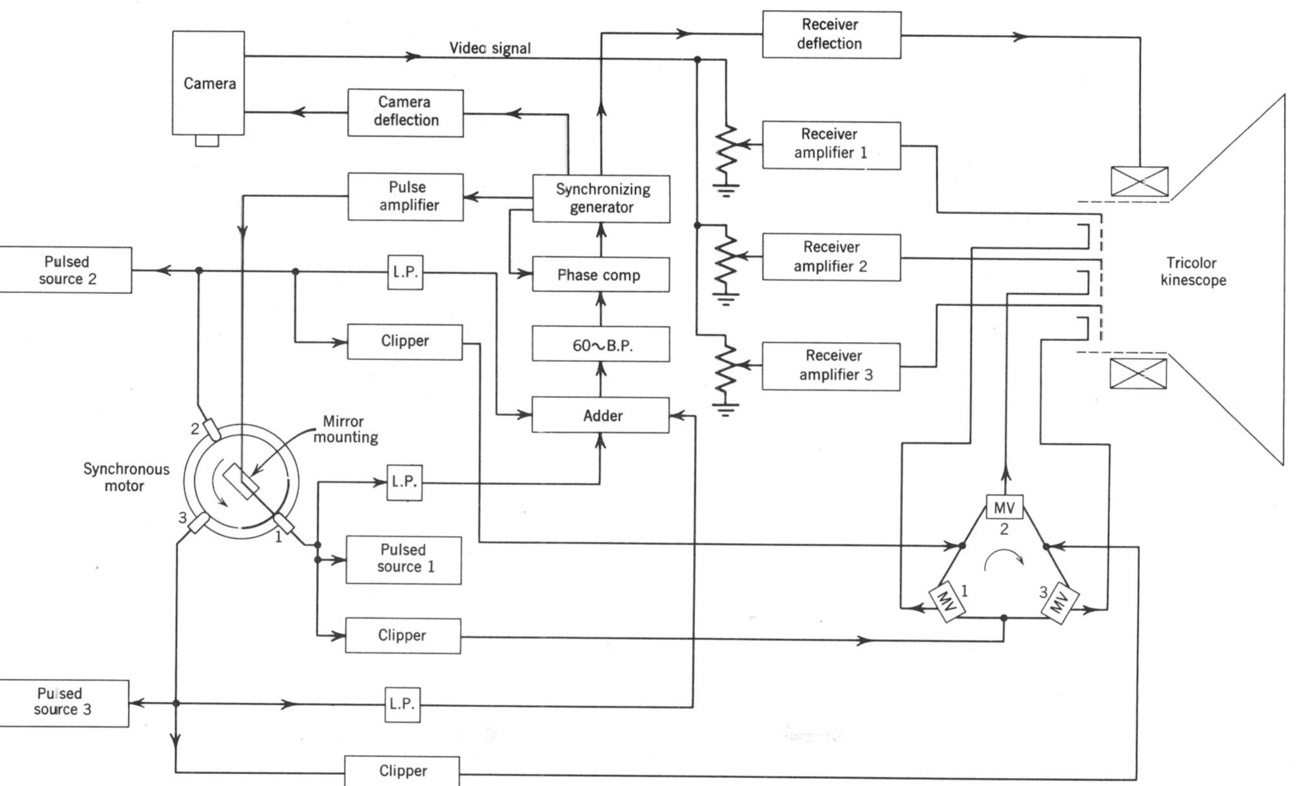

Fig. 3.90. Block Diagram of television color translating microscope with three pulsed sources.

chromators and mercury-arc light sources, pulsed in succession, are employed. Thus the wavelength setting for each component picture can be adjusted at will. The exit slits of the monochromators are imaged in succession by way of a rotating 45° mirror onto the entrance aperture of the microscope illuminating system. Since only the central portion of the slits is utilized, the direction of the illumination on the specimen is identical in the three component pictures, provided that the system is properly aligned optically and the light sources are pulsed at the proper instant. Figure 3.92 gives a general view of the television color-translating microscope. The pulsing circuits and power supplies are in the left portion of the desk; the complete illuminating system is in a drawer compartment directly below the microscope. The viewing

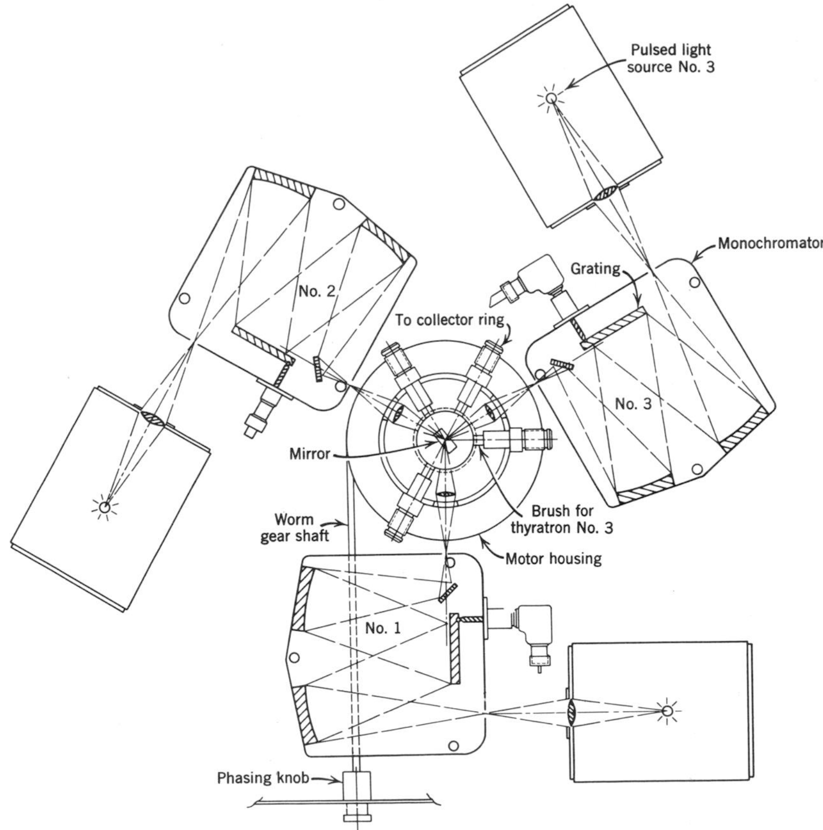

Fig. 3.91. Diagram of illumination system of color translating microscope.

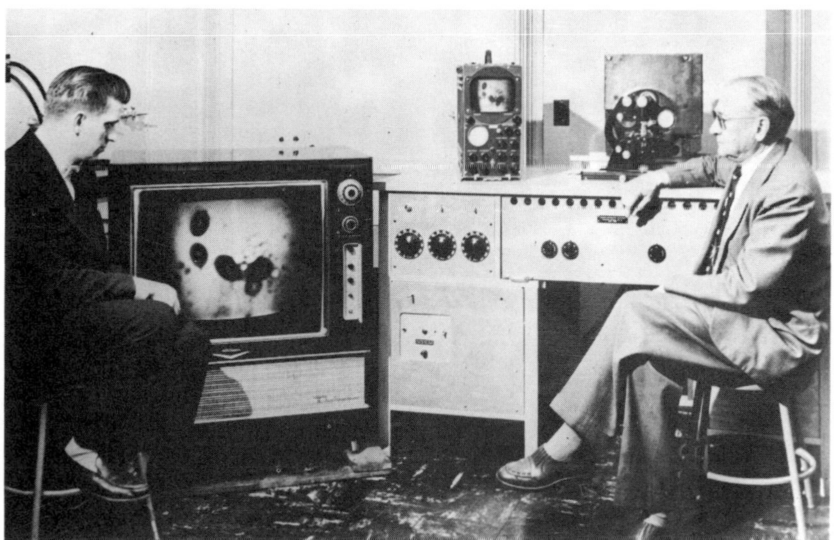

Fig. 3.92. Television color translating microscope. (Courtesy of Rockefeller Institute for Medical Research.)

unit, a modified standard color-television receiver, is to the left of the desk. Since picture lag in the Vidicon camera prevented a complete separation of the colors, it was replaced by an image-orthicon camera employing a tube with ultraviolet-transmitting face plate. Herewith satisfactory operation was achieved.

ACCESSORIES

We have noted a number of accessories which extend the utility of the closed-circuit television chain in describing closed-circuit transmission methods. Switching units, bridging and matching transformers, audio-video mixers for adding sound to the transmitted picture, and microwave transmitting and receiving units are examples. All of these play a role in broadcast television as well. Still other accessories prove useful in very specific applications and are taken up in the next chapter. There are, however, a number of devices of more general utility in the closed-circuit television field which may be properly taken up at this point.

Protective Housings. An important function of the closed-circuit television system is surveillance. When the camera must be placed

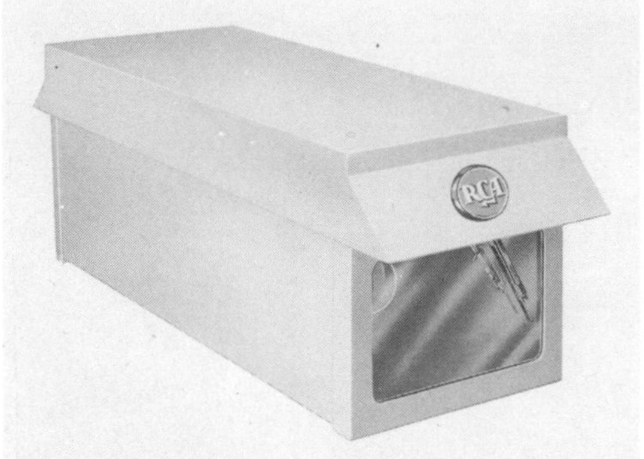

Fig. 3.93. Weatherproof housing for ITV cameras. (Courtesy of RCA.)

outdoors in an unattended location, weather protection becomes essential. This may be provided by a housing such as that shown in Fig. 3.93; it is equipped with blowers and heater strips to prevent overheating of the camera at high ambient temperatures and ice formation at low temperatures, as well as with motor-driven windshield wipers to maintain visibility.

Other applications may demand that the camera be placed in explosive atmospheres or in locations in which an occasional explosion hazard may exist. It is then advisable to employ an explosion-proof housing (Fig. 3.94) which encloses the camera in a sturdy, sealed, aluminum casting. Compressed-air cooling may be provided to prevent overheating.

Fig. 3.94. Explosion-proof housing for ITV cameras. (Courtesy of RCA.)

Whenever the camera is employed to view high-temperature processes, such as the flame conditions in furnace interiors, the interposition of a water-cooled window between the camera lens and the object is recommended. Figure 3.95 shows an arrangement in which water is circulated by a pump between two parallel glass disks also cooled by an air

Fig. 3.95. Water-cooled window for thermal protection of camera. (Courtesy of RCA.)

blower. It is thus possible to prevent the temperature of the camera lens from rising above 65° C, even when the furnace interior viewed by the camera is at 1600° C.

Special Mountings. Various special mountings for both the camera and the monitors are widely employed in practical applications. These may serve to minimize the effects of mechanical shock or, in the monitor, to shield the tube face from ambient lighting. A particularly useful device is the pan and tilt unit shown in Fig. 3.96. It contains two

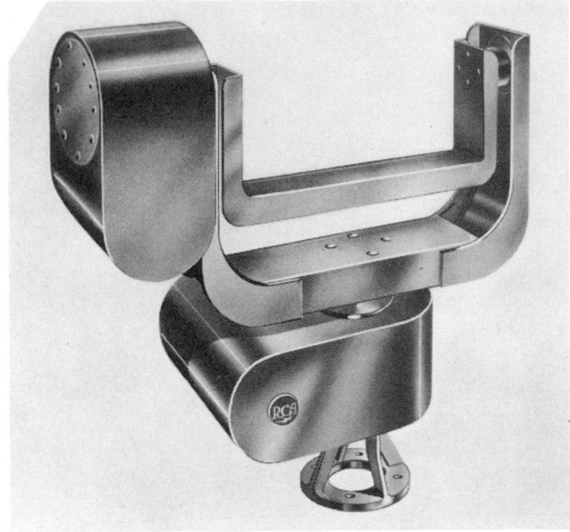

Fig. 3.96. Pan-and-tilt unit. (Courtesy of RCA.)

electric motors with separate speed controls. One of these effects a scan by the camera mounted on the unit through a horizontal arc of 320°, whereas the other can tilt the camera up and down to 45° with the horizontal. Combination of the two movements, controlled at the monitor location, makes it possible for the camera to survey an extraordinarily large solid angle.

Lens Accessories. Remotely controlled lens focus represents standard equipment in a number of commercially available closed-circuit television systems. A remotely controlled reversible motor is geared directly to the focus ring of the lens mount. A second motor may serve to actuate a lens turret; in the case of the Utiliscope Camera shown in Fig. 3.101 both motors are external to the camera, the second serving

Fig. 3.97. Perkin-Elmer Auto-Zoom Lens. (Courtesy Perkin-Elmer Corporation.)

to shift from a 90-mm focal-length lens to a 180-mm focal-length lens or vice versa.

A smoother shift from a wide-angle shot to a close-up is possible with a "zoom" lens. In the zoom lens a continuous displacement of two internal components of an objective effects an increase or decrease of the field angle covered (or of the effective focal length of the objective) without a change in focus. Figure 3.97 shows the Perkin-Elmer Auto-Zoom, especially designed for Vidicon television cameras, in which the focal length can be continuously varied from 1.2 to 6 inches. The lens aperture varies from $f/2.7$ at the short end of the range to $f/4.7$ for the longest focal lengths. Focus, zoom, and iris aperture are all motor driven and remotely controlled at the camera-control position.

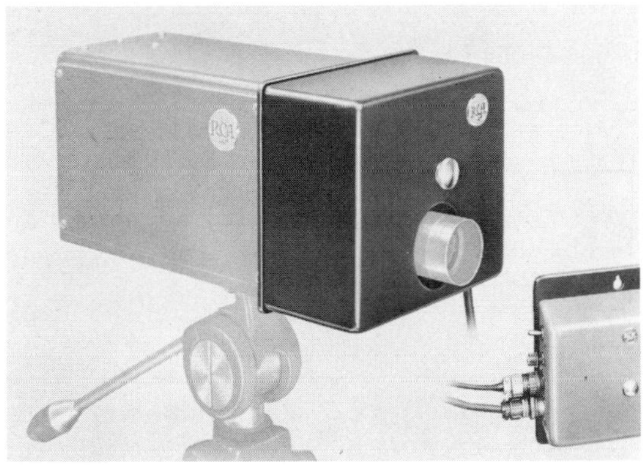

Fig. 3.98. RCA Remote Iris Control attached to ITV camera. (Courtesy of RCA.)

Manually operated zoom lenses weighing less than three pounds are also available and are particularly suitable for hand-held cameras.

Another accessory of great value for unattended outdoor camera installations is an iris controlled by the light level of the transmitted scene. Without this automatic adjustment the detail in the highlights would be "washed out" as the illumination level increased by a large factor and detail in the shadows would be "blacked out" as it decreased. In one form of iris control[28] the integrated video signal is amplified and compared to a fixed voltage level, the signal difference controlling a reversible motor geared to the iris setting. In the RCA remote or automatic iris lens control the function of the iris is assumed by a motor-

[28]See Thomas and Norvell (reference 48).

driven 35-mm film strip with uniformly graded light transmission. The film, between lens and Vidicon, is displaced either in response to signal changes or by actuation of the remote-control switch. An effect similar to iris control can be obtained by varying the Vidicon target voltage in response to the average signal level or the illumination as measured by a separate photocell. Automatic iris controls are supplied as an accessory by most manufacturers of closed-circuit television equipment.

SPECIAL TECHNIQUES: SPIRAL SCAN

Nearly all present-day closed-circuit television systems employ either a sequential or an interlaced scanning pattern of straight, parallel lines. An interesting departure from this practice is realized in equipment manufactured by Laboratoires R. Derveaux, at Boulogne-sur-Seine, France.[29] Here spiral scan is employed throughout. While it has the obvious drawback that it does not permit the employment of standard receivers or other standardized equipment, it also possesses a number of advantages.

Figure 3.99 shows schematically, in block diagram, a wired television system with spiral scan. A 15-kc sine wave modulated with a sawtooth with frame frequency (50 cycles) is applied in quadrature to the pair of deflection coils of both the camera tube and the viewing tube in the monitor. It produces a rotating deflection field which increases gradually in amplitude until, at the end of the frame period, it collapses to zero and returns the scanning spot to the center of the picture.

The scanning is seen to generate 600 scanning lines across any picture diameter. The speed of the scanning spot is slow at the center and high at the periphery. This leads to high resolution at the center of the picture and low resolution at the edge. Since the area of greatest interest is generally in the center, this is probably not objectionable. If both the camera and the viewing tube were perfectly linear in their characteristics, intensities would be correctly reproduced, since the reduction in signal strength near the center resulting from the slower speed of spot travel at the camera tube target would be compensated by the longer dwelling time of the spot in the corresponding area of the viewing tube screen. In practice, receiver nonlinearity will demand modulation of the gain by the frame-time sawtooth.

It is seen at once that the system described dispenses altogether with the "horizontal" blanking signal and the resulting loss in useful transmission time. "Vertical" blanking can be reduced to 2 per cent of the transmission time. The scanning wave itself, which is a narrow-band

[29] See Derveaux (reference 21).

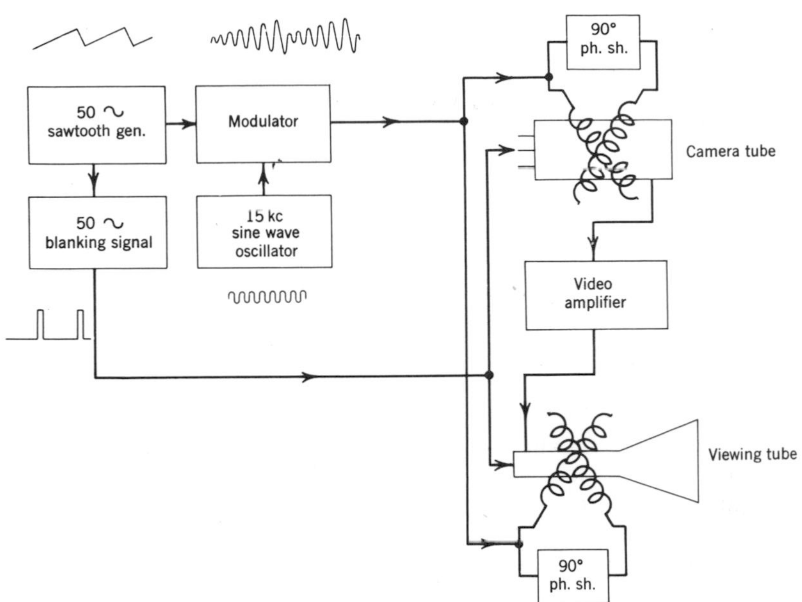

Fig. 3.99. Block diagram of a spiral scan television transmission system.

signal centered about 15 kilocycles per second, may be transmitted as a "synchronizing signal." Furthermore, spiral scanning utilizes in full the circular sensitive area of the camera tube target. Finally, the almost purely sinusoidal character of the scanning wave greatly reduces the power requirements of the scanning generator and permits its transmission over a simple wire from the control unit of the camera.

It might be expected that the starting point of the scanning spiral would be annoyingly apparent in the reproduced picture: it is claimed, however, that this can be successfully avoided. The system has been applied by Derveaux to cameras employing Vidicon-type tubes of standard size (1-inch diameter) and miniature Vidicon-type tubes (½-inch diameter), as well as larger camera tubes.

COMMERCIAL CLOSED-CIRCUIT TELEVISION EQUIPMENT

In the first sections of this chapter the functioning of closed-circuit television equipment has been illustrated largely by reference to a few specific systems, namely the RCA-ITV-6 system and TV Eye, the Dage 60-A Camera, and the earlier Utiliscope system which employs an image dissector. The present section aims to give the reader a somewhat broader view of commercially available equipment by listing the principal manufacturers of closed-circuit television systems and the principal characteristics of their products.

In the compilation of this list equipment designed primarily for broadcast purposes has been omitted from consideration, even though it may have been adapted extensively for closed-circuit applications. This applies not only to the elaborate image-orthicon studio chains developed by the major suppliers of broadcast equipment, but also to the simpler Vidicon cameras which are finding their way into broadcast practice; cameras of this type were marketed, recently, by Kay Lab, Dage, and Compagnie Francaise Thomson-Houston.

With the exception of the earlier Utiliscope cameras of the Diamond Power Specialty Company and a camera developed by EMI Ltd in England, all of the equipment listed below employs Vidicon-type tubes as camera tubes. These tubes are manufactured under the name "Vidicon" by the Radio Corporation of America, the General Electric Company, and the Westinghouse Electric Corporation in the United States and by EMI, the English Electric Company, and Fernseh abroad; under the name "Staticon" by Cathodeon Ltd. in England; under the name "Utilicon" by the Diamond Power Specialty Company; and under the name "Resistron" by the Physikalische Werkstätten Wiesbaden-Dotzheim in Germany. These tubes are similar in structure and operation, although they may differ in the target material.

Superficially, the several systems can be classified as consisting of (1) a self-contained camera connected by a signal lead only to other units (i.e., receivers or monitors); (2) a camera and a control box containing circuits and remote controls for the camera; or (3) a camera and a control monitor which contains a viewing unit in addition to the camera circuits and remote controls. The Dage Model 60A camera, the RCA TV Eye, and the RCA-ITV-6 system, respectively, are representative of these three classes. However, it is clear that it is primarily only a mechanical modification of the Dage 60-A Camera, for example, to separate the remote controls and eventually a portion of the camera circuits to provide a separate control box. A classification on the basis of the bandpass characteristics of the video amplifiers and the nature of the synchronization circuits might be more significant. However, these parameters are not indicated in all instances.

A list of the principal closed-circuit television equipment manufacturers in the United States follows:

Blonder-Tongue Laboratories, Inc., Westfield, N.J. The Observer TVC-1 Camera and Control Generator operate on RETMA standards (525

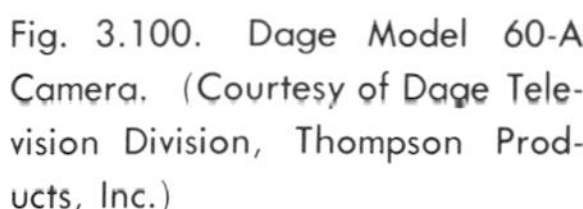
Fig. 3.100. Dage Model 60-A Camera. (Courtesy of Dage Television Division, Thompson Products, Inc.)

lines, 60 fields, 2:1 interlaced) and supply a 0.5-volt, peak-to-peak video signal and a 0.9-volt peak-to-peak radio-frequency signal. Camera tube: Vidicon. Horizontal resolution: 500 lines video, 350 lines radio-frequency.

Curtiss-Wright Corporation, Carlstadt, N.J. Curtiss-Wright industrial television equipment consists of camera control unit and receiver. The camera delivers either a video or a radio-frequency signal. Camera tube: Resistron.

Dage Television Division, Thompson Products, Inc., Michigan City, Ind. The Dage 60-B or the earlier Dage 60-A Camera (Fig. 3.100) is a self-

Fig. 3.101. Utiliscope chain, consisting of monitor, power unit, and camera. (Courtesy of Diamond Power Specialty Corporation.)

Fig. 3.102. Utilivue 400A Camera and Monitor. (Courtesy of Diamond Power Specialty Corporation.)

contained unit delivering 1.0-volt video and 0.1-volt radio frequency on the same outlet. RETMA standards. Camera tube: Vidicon. Horizontal resolution: 400 lines. Separate camera and control monitor also supplied. The Dage Model 350-A Color Camera (Fig. 3.72) and Model 750-A Color Camera control console with Model 850-A Regulated Power Supply provide three simultaneous color signals (1.0-volt output), 525 lines, 60 fields, 2:1 interlaced. Camera tubes: 3 6326 Vidicons. Horizontal resolution: 500 lines.

Diamond Power Specialty Corporation, Lancaster, Ohio. Utiliscope 300B chain consisting of camera, power unit, and monitor (Fig. 3.101) employs an image dissector as camera tube and operates with 350-line, 60-field, noninterlaced scanning. Utiliscope 300BV using Vidicon and RETMA standards may be substituted for image dissector camera. Signal output: 2 volts video. UtiliVue 400A Camera (Fig. 3.102) is a self-contained unit delivering 1 volt video signal. RETMA standards. Camera tube: Vidicon or Utilicon.

Allen B. DuMont Laboratories, Inc., Clifton, N.J. The Tel-Eye TV Camera Type 5359-B supplies both 0.75 volt video and 0.1 volt radio-frequency signals. Transmission bandwidth: 6 megacycles. RETMA standards. Camera tube: Vidicon.

Farnsworth Electronics Company, Fort Waync, Ind. Thc Industrial Television System 600-A (Fig. 3.103) consists of a camera and a control monitor. It delivers 1.4 volt video, 0.1 volt radio frequency. RETMA standards. Camera Tube: Vidicon. Horizontal resolution: 600 lines.

General Electric Company, Syracuse, New York. Industrial Television System consisting of camera and control monitor delivers 1.5 volt video and 0.1 volt radio-frequency output. RETMA standards. Video bandwidth, 8 megacycles. Camera tube: Vidicon. Cameras and monitors are also supplied for a field-sequential (441 lines, 30 color frames, 2:1 interlaced) color television system, using an image-orthicon camera (see Figs. 3.65 to 3.67).

General Precision Laboratory, Inc., Pleasantville, N.Y. PD-150-1 System (Fig. 3.104) consists of camera and control monitor and dclivcrs 1.4 volt video and 0.1 volt radio-frequency signal. RETMA standards. Cam-

Fig. 3.103. Farnsworth Industrial Television System Model 600A. (Courtesy of Farnsworth Electronics Company.)

Fig. 3.104. General Precision Laboratory PD-150-1 Camera and Control Monitor. (Courtesy of General Precision Laboratory, Inc.)

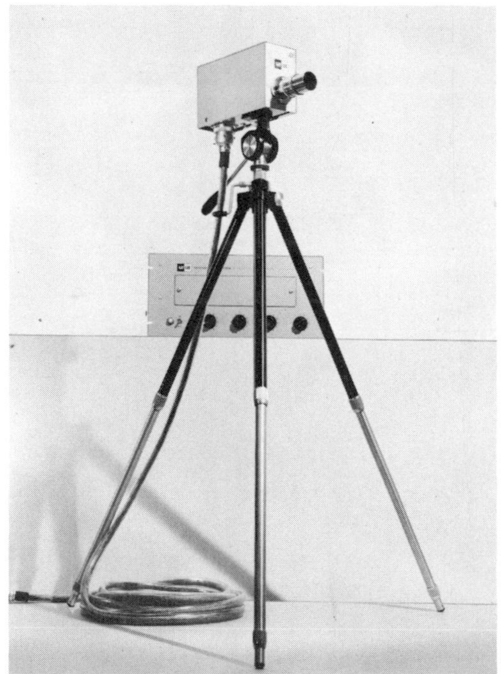

Fig. 3.105. Kay Lab Model 1985A Camera and Camera Control. (Courtesy of Kay Lab, San Diego, Calif.)

era tube: Vidicon. Horizontal resolution: 500 lines. For projection receivers, see Fig. 3.39.

Kay Lab, San Diego, Calif. 1985A Camera and Camera Control (Fig. 3.105) deliver 1 volt video signal. RETMA standards. AFC, locked to line. Camera tube: Vidicon. Horizontal resolution: 600 lines.

Philco Corporation, Philadelphia, Pa. Philco ITV Camera (Fig. 3.106) and rack-mounted control unit and synchronizer deliver 1.4 volt video signal. RETMA standards. AFC, locked to line. Camera tube: Vidicon. Horizontal resolution: 600 lines.

Fig. 3.106. Philco ITV Camera. (Courtesy of Philco Corporation.)

Radio Corporation of America, Camden, N.J. Model ITV-6 Camera and Control Monitor (Fig. 3.107) provide 1.4 volt video signal or 0.1 volt radio-frequency signal. RETMA standards. AFC, locked to line. Video bandwidth: uniform to 7 megacycles. Camera tube: Vidicon. TV Eye Camera and Control Unit (Fig. 3.108) deliver 0.1 volt radio-frequency signal across a 300-ohm line. RETMA standards. Camera tube: Vidicon. In the RCA Compatible 3V Color Television System, the TK-45 camera, control monitor, colorplexer, and power unit de-

Fig. 3.107. RCA Model-ITV-6 Camera and Control Monitor. (Courtesy of RCA.)

liver a standard color television signal which may be applied to color receivers or black-and-white receivers. Camera tubes: 3 6326 Vidicons. Also Telemural projection receivers for color (TLS-50) and monochrome (Fig. 3.75).

It should be noted that the horizontal resolution and bandwidths given above refer, in general, only to the video signal. The resolution obtainable with the radio-frequency signal is quite generally limited by the receiver to about 350 lines. Furthermore, the radio-frequency signal is normally a double-sideband signal, so that the receiver channel directly below the channel employed for closed-circuit transmission

Fig. 3.108. RCA TV Eye Camera and Control Box. (Courtesy of RCA.)

cannot be used. Except where otherwise indicated, the output signals appear across a 75-ohm impedance.

In addition to the American manufacturers listed above, the following foreign firms produce industrial television equipment:

Laboratories R. Derveaux, Boulogne sur Seine, France. Television cameras and control units operating with spiral scan (600 scanning lines across picture diameter, 50 fields per second) deliver video and synchronizing signals to special monitors. Camera tubes: 16-mm and 8-mm Resistrons.

Fig. 3.109. Pye Industrial Camera and Control Unit. (Courtesy of Pye Ltd., Cambridge, England.)

EMI Ltd., Hayes, Middlesex, England. Camera supplies video signal or radio-frequency signal (on BBC broadcast channel) with 405-line, 50-field, 2 : 1 interlaced standards. Camera tube: 5907 CPS Emitron. More recent equipment employs the Vidicon as camera tube.

Fernseh GMBH, Darmstadt, Germany. Industrial television camera and camera control-unit operating on 625 lines, 50 fields interlaced. Camera tube: Vidicon. Also more elaborate equipment for medical and other purposes employing "Rieselikonoskop" as camera tube.

Grundig Radio-Werke, Fürth (Bayern), Germany. Fernauge camera, operates with 16-mm Resistron, also special-purpose cameras with 8-mm Resistron.

Marconi's Wireless Telegraph Co., Ltd., Chelmsford, Essex, England. Marconi Industrial Television Equipment, consisting of camera and control box similar to RCA TV Eye, operates on U.S. RETMA or Continental European standards (625 lines, 50 fields interlaced). Camera tube: Vidicon.

Pye Ltd., Cambridge, England. The Pye Industrial Camera and Control Unit (Fig. 3.109) deliver a 1.4-volt video signal or a 0.1-volt radio-frequency signal. They operate on British standards (405 lines, 50 fields, 2:1 interlaced), RETMA standards, or European standards. Camera tube: Staticon.

Compagnie Française Thomson-Houston, Paris, France. The industrial television camera and control box operate on 637 lines, 50 fields, 2 : 1 interlaced with a Staticon or Orthicon as camera tube. Video output: 1 volt. Bandwidth: 8 megacycles. Simplified microwave links for the carrier frequency range between 960 and 2100 megacycles are also supplied.

Tele-Industrie (La Radio Industrie), Paris, France. Camera and control monitor. Camera tube; Vidicon.

In addition to the indicated equipment, all manufacturers supply video monitors and a variety of accessories.

The list of manufacturers given above is necessarily fragmentary. Thus, no Japanese manufacturers are listed, although it is known that industrial television equipment is manufactured and widely applied in Japan. Furthermore, a number of firms specialize in industrial television installations without necessarily marketing packaged units. These, too, are not listed.

REFERENCES

General

1. V. K. Zworykin and G. A. Morton, *Television*, 2nd Ed., Wiley, New York, 1954.
2. V. K. Zworykin and E. G. Ramberg, *Photoelectricity and Its Application*, Wiley, New York, 1949.

Television Camera Tubes

3. V. K. Zworykin, G. A. Morton, and L. E. Flory, "Theory and Performance of the Iconoscope," *Proc. I.R.E.*, Vol. 25, pp. 1071–92, 1937.
4. A. Rose and H. Iams, "The Orthicon, a Television Pickup Tube," *R C A Rev.*, Vol. 4, pp. 186–199, 1939.
5. A. Rose, P. K. Weimer, and H. B. Law, "The Image Orthicon—A Sensitive Television Pickup Tube," *Proc. I.R.E.*, Vol. 34, pp. 424–432, 1946.

6. R. B. Janes, R. E. Johnson, and R. S. Moore, "Development and Performance of Television Camera Tubes," *R C A Rev.*, Vol. 10, pp. 191–223, 1949.
7. R. B. Janes, R. E. Johnson, and R. R. Handel, "A New Image Orthicon," *R C A Rev.*, Vol. 10, pp. 586–592, 1949.
8. P. K. Weimer, S. V. Forgue, and R. R. Goodrich, "The Vidicon Photoconductive Camera Tube," *Electronics*, Vol. 23, pp. 70–73, May 1950, or *R C A Rev.*, Vol. 12, pp. 306–313, 1951.
9. B. H. Vine, R. B. Janes, and F. S. Veith, "Performance of the Vidicon, a Small Developmental Television Camera Tube," *R C A Rev.*, Vol. 13, pp. 3–10, 1952.
10. W. L. Hurford and R. J. Marian, "Monochrome Vidicon Film Camera," *R C A Rev.*, Vol. 15, pp. 372–388, 1954.
11. L. Heijne, P. Schagen, and H. Bruining, "An Experimental Photoconductive Camera Tube for Television," *Philips Tech. Rev.*, Vol. 16, pp. 23–25, 1954.
12. A. D. Cope, "A Miniature Vidicon of High Sensitivity," *R C A Rev.*, Vol. 17, pp. 460–468, 1956.

Closed-Circuit Television Systems

13. G. E. Valley, Jr., and H. Wallman, *Vacuum Tube Amplifiers*, McGraw-Hill, New York, 1948.
14. O. S. Puckle, *Time Bases*, 2nd Ed., Chapman, London, 1951.
15. R. W. Sanders, "Closed-Circuit Industrial Television," *Electronics*, Vol. 23, pp. 88–92, July 1950.
16. R. E. Barrett and M. M. Goodman, "Simplified Television for Industry," *Electronics*, Vol. 20, pp. 120–123, June 1947.
17. R. C. Webb and J. M. Morgan, "Simplified Television for Industry," *Electronics*, Vol. 23, pp. 70–73, June 1950.
18. L. E. Flory, W. S. Pike, and G. W. Gray, "A Vidicon Camera Adapter for Television Receivers," *Electronics*, Vol. 25, pp. 141–143, January 1954.
19. R. J. Boddy and C. D. Gardner, "An Industrial Television Channel," *J. Television Soc.*, Vol. 7, pp. 248–261, 1954.
20. Allard and Frejaville, "Special Television Equipment of the French Thomson-Houston Company for Use in Science, Industry, and Commerce," *Onde electrique*, Vol. 34, pp. 1006–1012, 1954.
21. R. Derveaux, "A New Television System with Spiral Analysis," *Onde electrique*, Vol. 34, pp. 838–841, 1954.
22. G. C. Sziklai, R. D. Lohman, and G. B. Herzog, "A Study of Transistor Circuits for Television," *Proc. I.R.E.*, Vol. 41, pp. 708–717, 1953.
23. L. E. Flory, G. W. Gray, J. M. Morgan, and W. S. Pike, "Transistorized Television Cameras Using the Miniature Vidicon," *R C A Review*, Vol. 17, pp. 469–502, 1956.
24. "1-Lb Camera Developed for Military Closed TV," *Electronic News*, Jan. 28, 1957.

Closed-Circuit Television Transmission

25. L. W. Morrison, "Television Transmission in Local Telephone Exchange Areas," *J. Soc. Motion Picture Television Engrs.*, Vol. 56, pp. 280–294, 1951.
26. F. A. Cowan, "Networks for Theatre Television," *J. Soc. Motion Picture Television Engrs.*, Vol. 62, pp. 306–312, 1954.
27. C. H. Elmendorf *et al.*, "The L3 Coaxial System," *Bell System Tech. J.*, Vol. 321, pp. 779–1005, 1953.

28. M. H. Kraus, "Developments in Closed-Circuit Television," *Elec. Eng.*, Vol. 74, pp. 974–979, 1955.
29. I. Kamen and R. H. Dorf, *TV Master Antenna Systems*, John F. Ryder, New York, 1951.
30. A. A. Roetken, K. D. Smith, and R. W. Friis, "The TD-2 Microwave Relay System," *Bell System Tech. J.*, Vol. 30, pp. 1041–1077, 1951.
31. "Army Television as Training Aid," *Electronics*, Vol. 24, pp. 148–150, 1951.
32. L. E. Flory, W. S. Pike, J. E. Dilley, and J. M. Morgan, "Developmental Portable Television Pickup Station," *R C A Rev.*, Vol. 13, pp. 58–70, 1952.
33. A. E. Ohler, "The 'Walkie Lookie,' A Miniaturized TV Camera Custom Built for Use by NBC at National Political Conventions," *Broadcast News*, Vol. 71, pp. 8–15, 1952.

Color and Stereo Television Equipment

34. G. H. Brown and D. G. C. Luck, "Principles and Development of Color Television Systems," *R C A Rev.*, Vol. 14, pp. 144–204, 1953.
35. "NTSC Signal Specifications," *Proc. I.R.E.*, Vol. 42, pp. 17–19, 1954.
36. P. C. Goldmark, J. W. Christensen, and J. J. Reeves, "Color Television—U.S.A. Standard," *Proc. I.R.E.*, Vol. 39, pp. 1288–1313, 1951.
37. L. T. Sachtleben, D. J. Parker, G. L. Allee, and E. Kornstein, "Image Orthicon Color Television Camera Optical System," *R C A Rev.*, Vol. 13, pp. 27–33, 1952.
38. J. D. Spradlin, "The RCA Color Television Camera Chain," *R C A Rev.*, Vol. 13, pp. 11–26, 1952.
39. H. R. Johnston, C. A. Hermanson, and H. L. Hull, "Stereo Television in Remote Control," *Elec. Eng.*, Vol. 69, pp. 1058–1062, 1950.
40. V. K. Zworykin, "Industrial Television and the Vidicon," *Elec. Eng.*, Vol. 69, pp. 624–627, 1950.

Television Microscope

41. V. K. Zworykin, "Electric Microscope," 1° Congresso Internazionale di Elettro-Radio-Biologia (Venice, Italy), Vol. 1, pp. 672–686, 1934.
42. J. Z. Young and F. Roberts, "A Flying-Spot Microscope," *Nature*, Vol. 167, p. 231, 1951.
43. F. Roberts and J. Z. Young, "The Flying-Spot Microscope," *Proc, Inst. Elec. Engrs.*, Vol. 99, Part III-A, pp. 747–757, 1952.
44. F. Roberts, J. Z. Young, and D. Causley, "Flying-Spot Microscope," *Electronics*, Vol. 26, pp. 137–139, July 1953.
45. V. K. Zworykin, L. E. Flory, and R. E. Shrader, "Television Microscopy in the Ultraviolet," *Electronics*, Vol. 24, pp. 150–152, 1952.
46. E. H. Land, E. R. Blout, D. S. Grey, M. S. Flower, H. Husek, R. C. Jones, C. H. Matz, and D. P. Merrill, "Color Translating Ultraviolet Microscope," *Science*, Vol. 109, pp. 371–374, 1949.
47. V. K. Zworykin and F. Hatke, "Ultraviolet Television Color-Translating Microscope," *Science*, Vol. 126, pp. 805–810, 1957.

Accessories

48. E. R. Thomas and W. L. Norvell, "Television for Monitoring Stack Emission," *Elec. Eng.*, Vol. 72, pp. 224–227, 1953.

chapter 4

Achievements of Closed-Circuit Television

In the preceding chapters we have tried to indicate the ways in which closed-circuit television might be employed to advantage, and we have examined the equipment which has been developed for such applications. In this chapter we shall attempt a survey of the uses to which it has been put. Of necessity, this survey is fragmentary. Numerous applications of closed-circuit television remain unpublished or have received mention only in trade journals which are not readily accessible. Others are shrouded by the secrecy requirements of government classification. Nevertheless, we hope that even an incomplete account of current applications will help in suggesting additional uses and in assaying the role which closed-circuit television can play in our civilization.

As before, it is convenient to employ the fields of industry, research, medicine, education, commerce, and the military as bases of classification. Subheadings will suggest themselves on the basis of the present distribution of closed-circuit television uses.

INDUSTRY

Special, low-cost types of television equipment were first developed to meet the needs of industry. This fact is reflected in the general acceptance of the term "industrial television" as a synonym for closed-circuit television. Within industry, the utilities were the first to recognize its usefulness. From them acceptance has spread to various branches of manufacturing, transportation, agriculture, etc.—in brief, to all the major divisions of industry.

Utilities. Closed-circuit television gained its entry into the utilities field as a means of water-level gage observation in power stations. In

Fig. 4.1. Picture of water level gage on monitor located on operator's control panel. (Courtesy of Diamond Power Specialty Corporation.)

modern installations the separation between the gage and the control point may be as much as 250 feet. Under such circumstances the image obtained with mirror systems giving a direct view of the gages is excessively small. Remote-indicating instruments do not have the requisite reliability, as attested by boiler explosions which occurred upon the failure of two parallel indicators.[1] Television installations provide a clear view of the gages without the need of costly duct work for a mirror system or of a separate "water tender" connected with the control room by an intercommunication system. Hence the television camera has become standard equipment for water gage observation in large power stations (Fig. 4.1).

Another use of the television camera in the utilities field which at the present time may well have outstripped water-gage observation is continuous flame monitoring of the power-station furnaces. Figure 4.2 shows a Utiliscope installation at the Port Jefferson Power Station of the

[1] See Wilson (reference 1).

Long Island Lighting Company.[2] The camera views the interior of the enormous pulverized-coal-burning furnace through an aircooled window in the top wall. Figure 4.3 shows the lighted ignition torches, the light oil burners for initiating the combustion, and, finally, the normal appearance of the pulverized-coal flames. An experienced operator can thus infer from the monitor screen whether fuel feed, air intake, etc., are satisfactory.

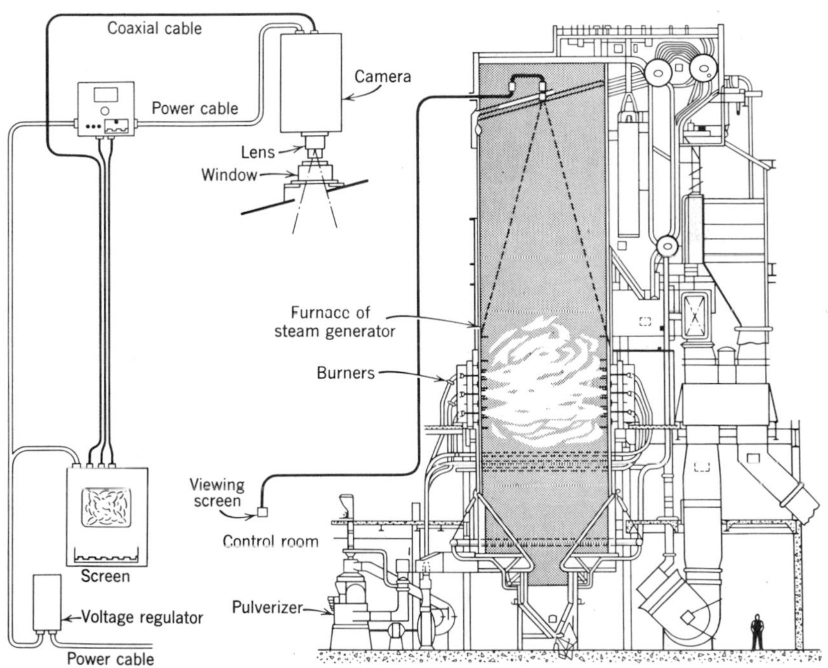

Fig. 4.2. Utiliscope installation for viewing furnace interior at Port Jefferson Station. (Courtesy of Diamond Power Specialty Corporation.)

The placement of the camera or cameras varies widely in different installations, depending on the disposition of the burners. Figure 4.4 shows the mounting of two water- and air-cooled camera windows in the sidewall of a gas-burning furnace of the Pacific Gas and Electric Company, together with the circulation system. In all such applications protection of the camera from the intense heat of the furnace interior is essential.

[2] See Exley (reference 2).

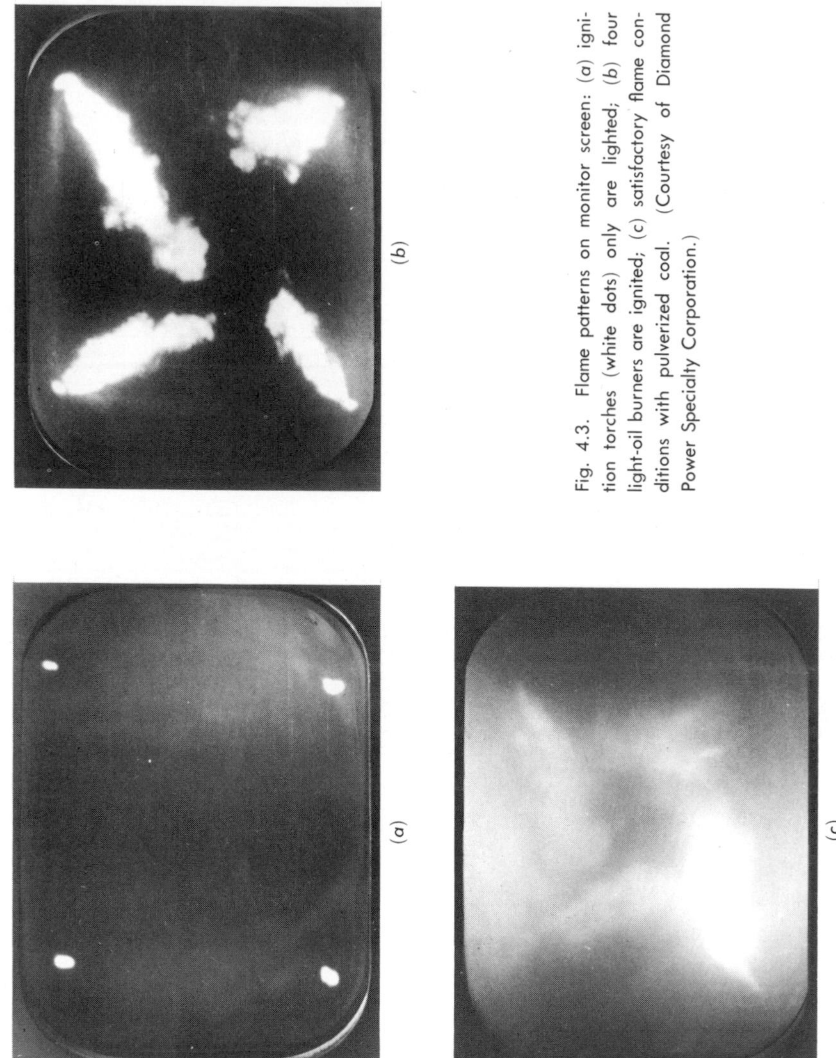

Fig. 4.3. Flame patterns on monitor screen: (*a*) ignition torches (white dots) only are lighted; (*b*) four light-oil burners are ignited; (c) satisfactory flame conditions with pulverized coal. (Courtesy of Diamond Power Specialty Corporation.)

Fig. 4.4. Mounting of water-cooled windows and cameras in side wall of furnace (installation for Pacific Gas & Electric Company). (Courtesy of RCA.)

Under certain circumstances the color of the flame, apart from its distribution, can give valuable information; in such instances it is advantageous to use camera tubes in which spectral sensitivity peaks in the red and the blue, or red and blue filters in combination with a tube with a response covering the entire visual range, such as the Vidicon.

The utility of flame observation in the furnaces can be enhanced by simultaneous smokestack observation from the same control point. This not only makes it possible to check on compliance with smoke-abatement ordinances, but permits a correlation between flame appearance and completeness of combustion. The camera for observing the smokestacks (Fig. 4.5) is commonly housed in a small shed, giving weather protection, at a distance south of the plant sufficient to cover the upper portions of the stacks and the sky above them in the viewing field.[3] An iris with an opening controlled automatically by the video signal from the camera or by a separate photocell is generally advantageous in this application, to compensate for the large variations in ambient illuminations.

Still another example of the use of closed-circuit television in power plants is the observation of distant turbines and other machinery from a central control point, as practiced in the large Reuter power plant in West Berlin.[4]

[3] See Thomas and Norvell (reference 3).

[4] See reference 4.

Fig. 4.5. Weatherproof housing for camera for smokestack observation. (Courtesy of Diamond Power Specialty Corporation.)

Manufacturing. In the manufacturing field the steel industry offers a wide range of applications for industrial television. The high temperatures required in steel processing and the risk of physical injury to personnel in proximity to various phases of the operations render remote handling and control particularly attractive. For example, in Fig. 4.6 a television camera is mounted in the rafters of a United States Steel plant at Gary, Ind., 48 feet above the bed of rollers conveying hot steel-strip from the finishing stand to the coilers, a distance of 395 feet. The operator can observe the passage of the strip on a monitor in the control booth and can take immediate corrective action to prevent cobbles and pile-ups. Figure 4.7 shows schematically another United States Steel installation at the Geneva Works in Geneva, Utah, in which the operator observes the passage of steel slabs in front of the reheating furnaces; the view on the monitor tells him the proper moment for inserting the slab into the furnace, without danger of damage to the furnace walls. At the Weirton Steel Company in Weirton, W. Va., ITV cameras in cooled housings check the proper placement of the slabs within the reheating furnaces and thus prevent "cold edges" which would result in improper rolling properties. Monitoring the pouring process for large castings is important for the prevention of air inclusions and the formation of spongy spots. Here also a television camera

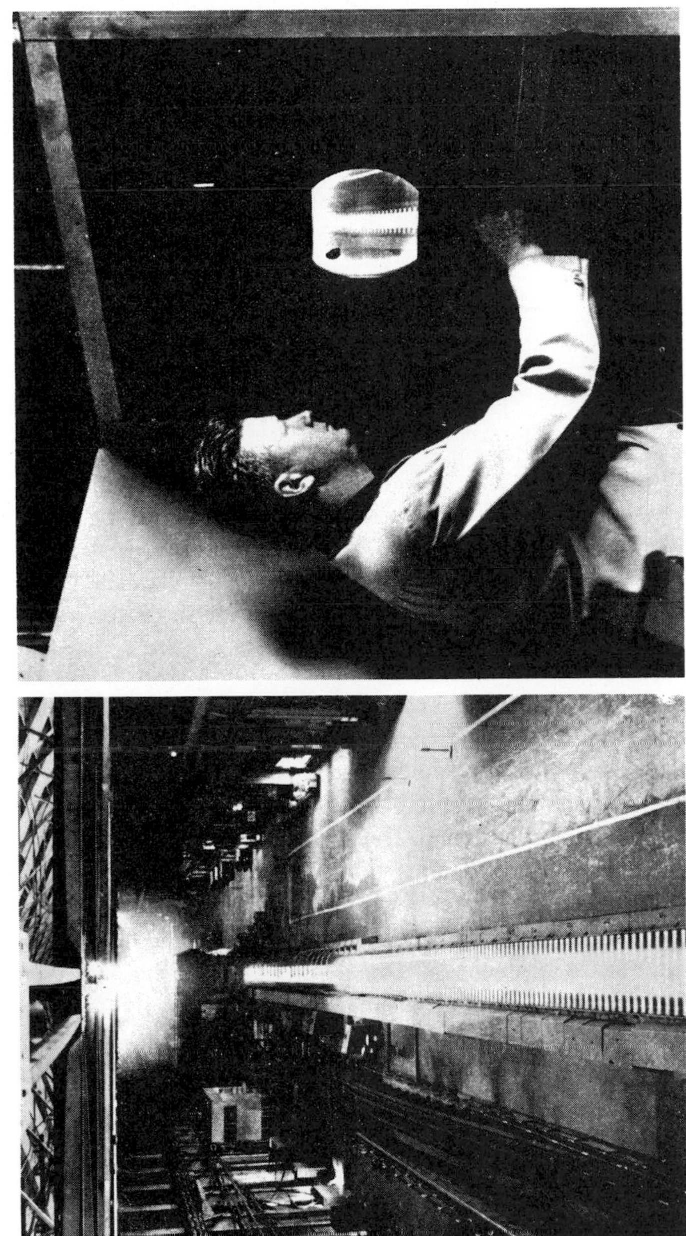

(a) (b)

Fig. 4.5. Closed-circuit television installation at United States Steel Plant, Gary, Ind.; (a) television camera mounted 48-feet high on rafters scans 395 feet of hot steel strip; (b) operator checks strip on passage from finishing stand to coilers on television monitor. (From Zworykin and Morton, *Television*, Wiley, New York, 1954.)

relieves the watcher of a hot and hazardous job and gives the operator of the pouring process a close-range view for his guidance. At a Timken Roller Bearing plant the proper stacking of steel tubing entering a furnace is checked continuously by television, and a separate watcher communicating with the operator by hand signals is rendered superfluous.

The role of closed-circuit television in fully automated plants is well illustrated by an alloy plate finishing plant of the Lukens Steel Company;

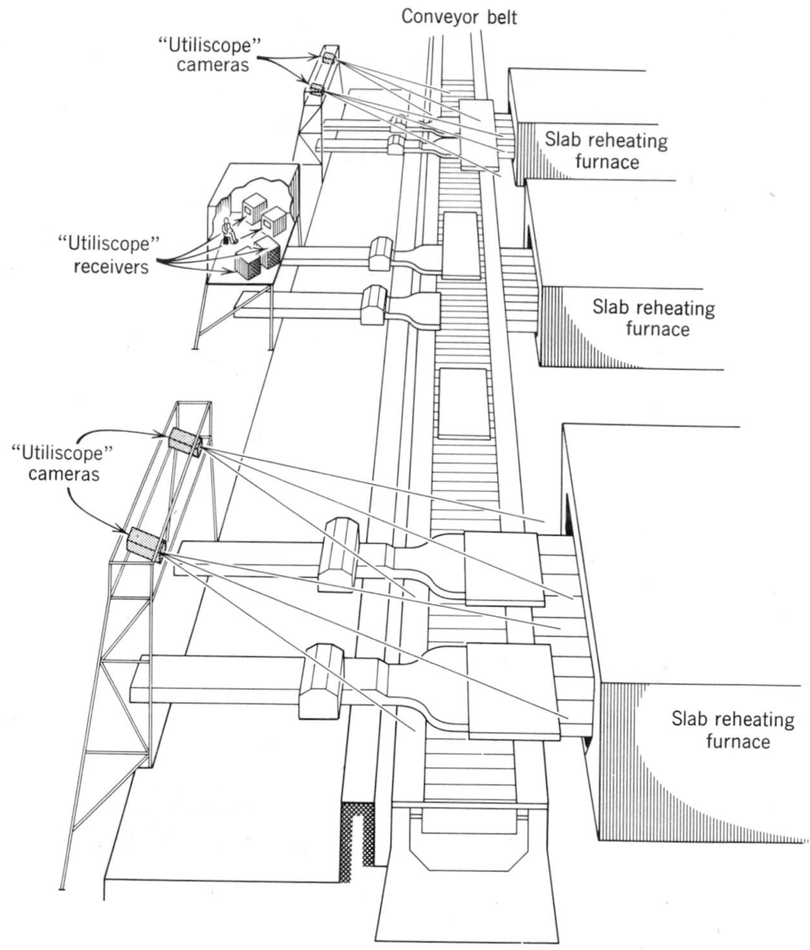

Fig. 4.7. Television system for the control of charging of slab-reheating furnaces at United States Steel plant at Geneva, Utah. (Courtesy of Diamond Power Specialty Corporation.)

Fig. 4.8. Employment of RCA TV Eye for optical alignment by Douglas Aircraft Company. (Courtesy of RCA.)

here sixteen men at control desks equipped with television monitors run the entire plant. Picture signals are supplied by nine RCA cameras placed at strategic points; six RCA TV Eye cameras enable operators to observe "blind spots" on the production line, and the remaining three heavy-duty ITV cameras aid in the control of the giant shears which trim the rough edges of finished alloy plate.

In the automotive industry, also, television serves to prevent hold-ups and to control the flow of materials. At the General Motors Fisher Body Works in Pittsburgh the baling machine operator employs this means to check on the conveyor moving scrap to the balers. Similarly, in the Ford Motor Company's stamping plant at Buffalo the baling operator uses television to observe the loading of freight cars with baled scrap; this enables him to shift freight cars so as to obtain optimum loading. Again, in the Cadillac Motor Car Division of General Motors television is employed for checking the loading of gondola cars with baling scrap.

In aircraft assembly plants optical techniques are widely employed for the alignment of parts. At a plant of the Douglas Aircraft Company the view of the optical target and the crosshairs provided by a micro-alignment telescope are observed on the 17-inch screen of a television monitor; this greatly eases the alignment procedure (Fig. 4.8).[5]

A similar simplification is achieved in the Cincinnati machine shop

[5] See Boucher (reference 5).

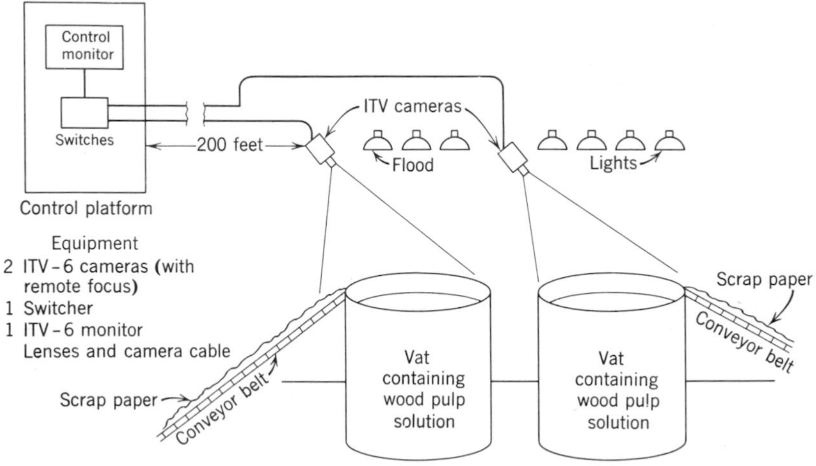

Fig. 4.9. Surveillance of batch processes in paper mills. (Courtesy of RCA.)

of the American Can Company, where the edges of chrome-plated scraper blades used in lithography coating machines are inspected for wear.[6] An image of the edge, as seen through a microscope equipped with an RCA TV Eye, is reproduced at a magnification of 288 on the monitor screen, on which the tolerance limits of the blade-width are marked.

At the Ford Parts and Equipment Division plant in Ypsilanti, Mich., readings from a battery of testing devices for automobile distributors are displayed pictorially on 17-inch monitors to speed up performance tests. The equipment is manufactured by the Airborne Instruments Laboratory in Mineola, N. Y.

At the plant of the Bulova Watch Company in Providence, R. I., RCA TV Eyes aid in intercommunication between the engineering and production departments to facilitate discussion of design changes and blueprint alterations.

The use of television to check on the smooth flow of materials—in this instance the loading of chips from conveyor belts into chip bins—also finds application in the pulp and paper industry.[7] The surveillance of batch processes by television, furthermore, leads to savings in manpower and increased efficiency of operation. Here (Fig. 4.9) the cameras are mounted above two vats which are approximately 15 feet in diameter and 6 feet high. Paper pulp in solid form is discharged into

[6] See reference 6.

[7] See reference 7.

the vats from a belt conveyor. Agitator blades located in the bottom of the vats whirl in a liquid solution in the vats. When the batch operation is completed, the liquid and pulp are drained off from the bottom of the vats and the processing is repeated. The discharge of the pulp into the vats, the proper filling and emptying of the vats, and the operation of the agitator blades can be observed by a single operator at the central control panel several hundred feet away. In a somewhat similar application, an RCA TV Eye system is employed in checking pulp-washing operations in the Spotswood, N. J., plant of Peter J. Schweitzer, a large producer of cigarette paper.[8]

In the food-processing industry, also, television simplifies operations. Thus, at the Ewa and Waialua sugar plantations in Hawaii the movement of cane from the cleaning plant to the grinding machinery over 250 feet of conveyor belts is observed continuously from the control station by means of television.[9] The camera is mounted high above the belt system and is protected by a glass window from spray and dirt. In this instance the savings from a single year of operation proved sufficient to cover the installation costs.

X-ray inspection, which has assumed an important role in many branches of industry, can be greatly aided by television. In heavy industry and machine-parts manufacture X-ray inspection is employed for the detection of flaws which might result in premature failure. In the manufacture of a variety of packaged goods it serves to check sealed containers for proper filling.

In principle, the pattern projected by an X-ray beam from a small source passing through the object to be examined could be viewed directly on a fluorescent X-ray screen. However, the image formed on the screen is generally so dim that detail can be distinguished only in a thoroughly darkened room. A considerable improvement is achieved by the employment of an image-intensifier tube, such as the Westinghouse WL-5997 (Fig. 4.10*a*). The X rays impinge here on a 5-inch fluorescent screen in intimate contact with a photocathode. The electron emission from the photocathode, the distribution of which corresponds to the light distribution in the X-ray picture, is then accelerated and imaged by an electrostatic lens system onto a small, aluminum-backed, fluorescent screen 1-inch in diameter.[10] This is viewed through a magnifier. With a total potential difference of 30 kilovolts applied between photocathode and viewing screen, the brightness of the final screen exceeds that of the X-ray screen by more than 200; a factor of 25 arises simply

[8] See reference 8.

[9] See reference 9.

[10] See Marshall (reference 10) and Morton and Flory (reference 11).

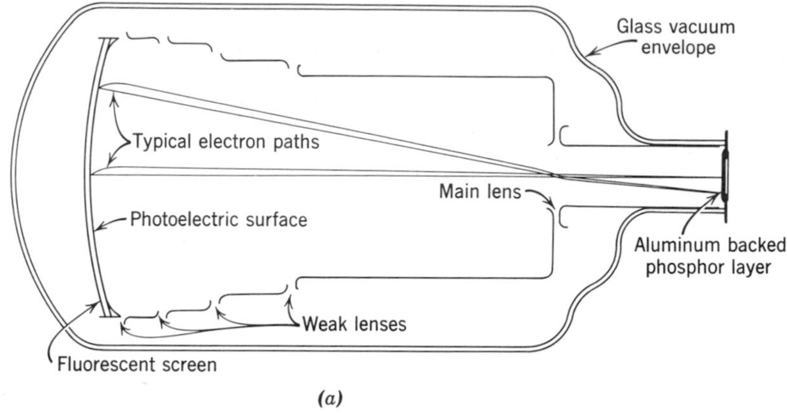

(a)

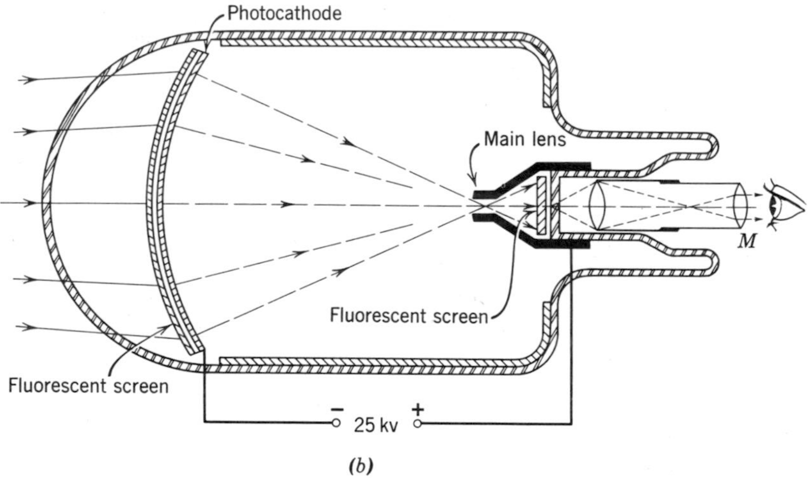

(b)

Fig. 4.10. Diagrams of (*a*) Westinghouse and (*b*) Philips image intensifier tubes.

from the size reduction of the picture and a further factor of more than 8 from a corresponding increase in the total light emission of the final viewing screen as compared to that of the X-ray screen. An image intensifier operating on similar principles, but with a larger size reduction factor (9) and increased brightness gain, is manufactured by Philips in Holland (Fig. 4.10*b*).[11]

In the image intensifier a simple light hood supplies sufficient protec-

[11] See Teves and Tol (reference 12).

tion from stray light for satisfactory X-ray viewing. On the other hand, observation through a high-power magnifier is tiring and is limited to a single person. If the picture formed on the final viewing screen of the image intensifier is imaged in turn onto the photosensitive target of a television camera tube, the picture can be viewed on a large monitor screen in a fully lighted room. Such a combination of an image-intensifier tube with a General Precision Laboratory iiTV system is employed by the North American Philips Company for the fluoroscopic study of metal flaws. The use of a television link in the observation of X-ray pictures has the added very important advantage of facilitating protection of the operating personnel from penetrating X-ray radiation.

If the object to be examined is very large, it becomes necessary to employ an ordinary large X-ray screen and to image it with a high-efficiency optical system[12] onto the target of the television camera or the photocathode of an image intensifier. In the Bendix "Lumicon" system, which is referred to once more in connection with medical fluoroscopy, a high-sensitivity RCA image orthicon is employed as a camera tube to make optimal use of the light emission of the X-ray screen without further electronic intensification.

With smaller objects, a camera tube with photoconductive target may be employed to transmit X-ray pictures; the X-ray photons absorbed in the photoconductive layer free large numbers of charge carriers which are transferred across the layer by the electric field within it. Noise measurements by Cope and Rose[13] on a Vidicon with a 1- to 2-mil selenium target showed that for every absorbed 75-kilovolt X-ray photon approximately 500 charges were transferred. The visibility of the X-ray noise in the transmitted picture indicated that the complete information carried by the absorbed X rays was available to the viewer. Figure 4.11 offers as an example the images of two potted junction transistors placed on the Vidicon face plate as observed on the monitor screen; the two vertical lines, which give some indication of the resolution of the system, are a 2-mil tungsten wire on the left and a 1-mil tungsten wire on the right. These pictures were transmitted at a rate of 30 per second with a 100-kilovolt, 5-milliampere, X-ray source placed at a distance of two feet from the object.

The two principal drawbacks of the direct use of the Vidicon camera tube for X-ray observation are its very small target area and the relatively small absorption (approximately 15 per cent for 70-kilovolt X rays) of the X rays in its thin photoconductive film. These are

[12]Such as the Eastman F/0.75 Fluor-Ektar lens.

[13]See Cope and Rose (reference 13).

remedied in a low-velocity photoconductive camera tube developed by the General Electric Company specifically for fluoroscopic use (Fig. 4.12).[14] This tube, with 30° electrostatic deflection, has a lead-oxide target 8½ inches in diameter and 8 mils in thickness. Its X-ray absorption is thus very much greater than that of the Vidicon target. The photoconductive layer transfers 12,000 electrons per 40-kilovolt X-ray quantum, so that no loss of information occurs within the television

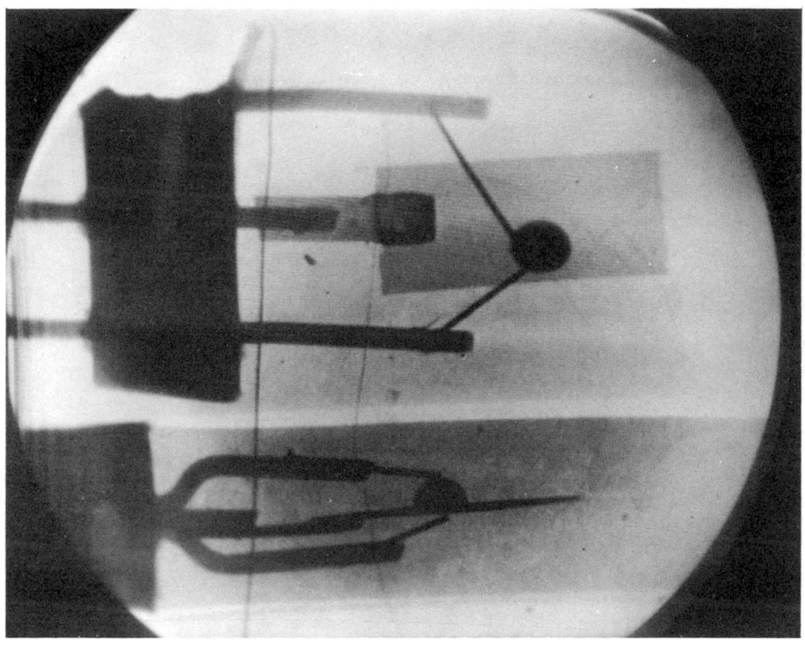

Fig. 4.11. X-ray pictures of potted junction transistors observed on monitor of Vidicon television chain (Cope and Rose, reference 13). (Courtesy of *Journal of Applied Physics.*)

system; except for a peak of sensitivity between 50 and 120 kilovolts (peak operating voltage of X-ray tube), the response of the tube is almost independent of photon energy out to 6 mev. The tube was originally designed for industrial applications; for medical applications the decay constant of the target, which was about one second, was too large. More recently the time constant has been greatly reduced, resulting in a tube well adapted for both industrial and medical work.

A very ingenious device for the fluoroscopy of objects of great density and thickness with internal moving parts has been developed at the

[14] See Jacobs and Berger (reference 14) and reference 15.

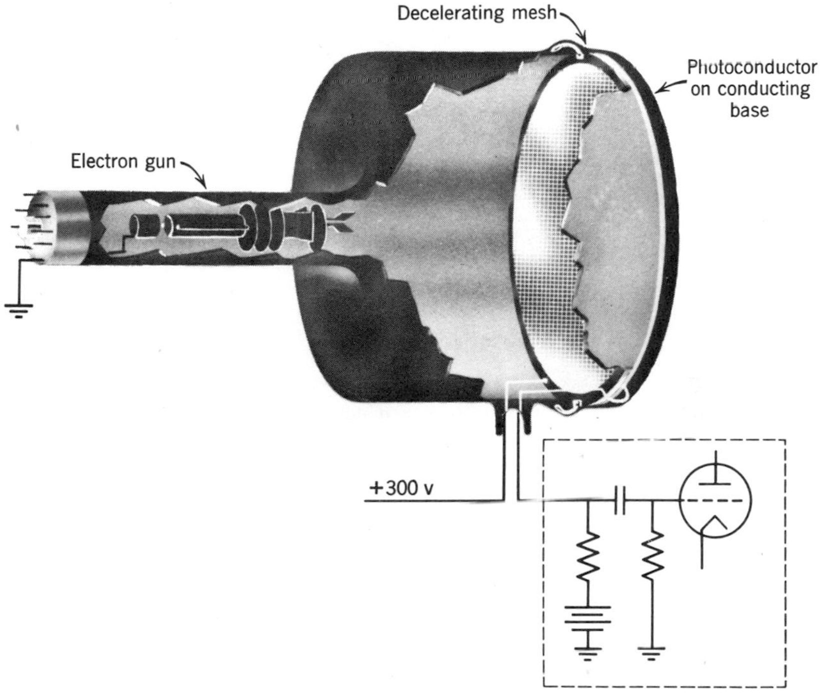

Fig. 4.12 Large-area photoconductive pickup tube for X-ray applications. (Courtesy of Dr. J. E. Jacobs, General Electric Company.)

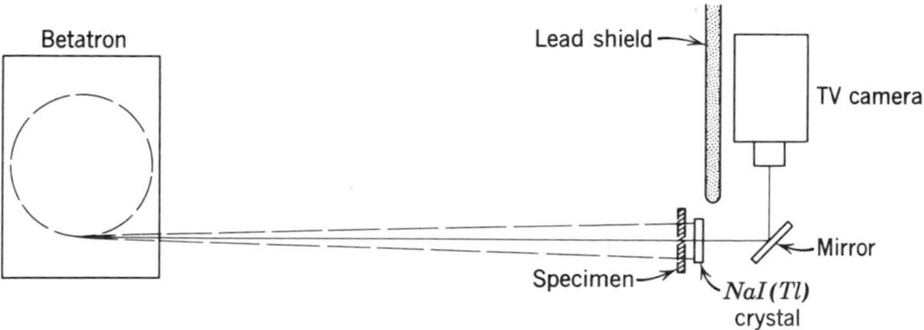

Fig. 4.13. System for penetrating-radiation fluoroscopy with thick scintillation crystal (Pruitt, reference 16).

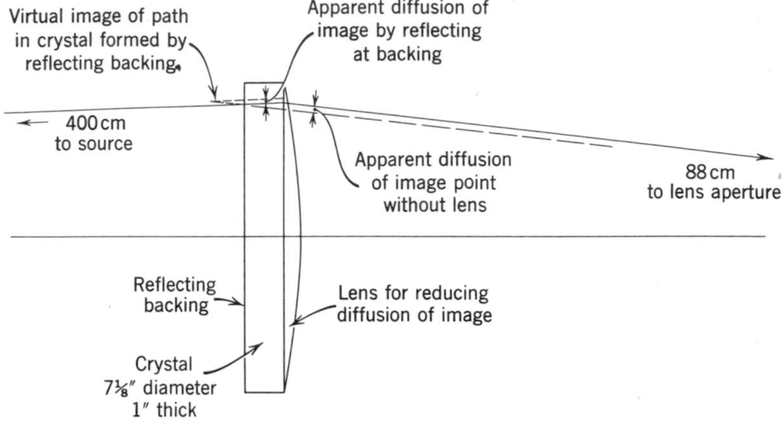

Fig. 4.14. Use of field lens for minimizing image diffusion by crystal thickness (Pruitt, reference 16).

National Bureau of Standards in Washington, D.C.[15] The 50 mev X rays from the NBS betatron pass through the object and impinge on a thallium-activated sodium iodide crystal 7⅛ inches in diameter and 1 inch in thickness (Fig. 4.13). The visible image formed within the crystal is imaged by a $f/0.75$ Eastman Fluor-Ektar lens with 110-mm focal length at a scale reduction of 7 : 1 on the cathode of an RCA 5820 image orthicon installed in a Dumont television chain operating on broadcast standards. A 45° mirror makes it possible to shield the camera from the penetrating radiation; furthermore, the optical system is enclosed in a blackened box to minimize contrast loss from light scattering.

For maximum sensitivity a mirror surface is placed on the crystal face remote from the camera. It is then possible to recognize some detail in the image at an irradiation of 5 ergs per square centimeter per second or 2000 X-ray photons per square centimeter per television frame.

The blurring in the image resulting from the thickness of the crystal can be greatly reduced by placing in contact with the crystal a plano-convex field lens (Fig. 4.14), whose focal length is chosen to image the X-ray source into the aperture plane of the objective. Any ray proceeding from the source through the object and the crystal is then viewed "end-on" by the lens. With this arrangement the apparent blurring of the image in the crystal does not exceed 0.015-inch. The

[15]See Pruitt (reference 16).

removal of the mirror surface at the far end of the crystal causes further improvement in resolution. The last effect is relatively small, since the distance between the source and the crystal (4 meters) is very much larger than the distance between the crystal and the lens (88 centimeters).

It may be noted that the sodium iodide crystal, which was supplied by the Harshaw Chemical Company, turns brown after an exposure of the order of 10^8 ergs per square centimeter. Bleaching in sunlight restores its transparency.

The piston motion in a small 1-cylinder engine has been employed to demonstrate the operation of the system.

Mining. Industrial television has been employed as an aid to coal mining by the Freebrook Corporation in Kittaning, Pa. Two ITV cameras are mounted on a coal-digging machine, one just behind the cutting tools in front of the machine and the second on the rear of the unit, facing back to observe a string of conveyor cars removing the freshly dug coal. The monitor screens are observed by the operator of the machine at a distance of about 500 feet. The front camera gives him a view of the digging operation, whereas the rear camera indicates whether the conveyors are properly aligned.

In another application television helps in the removal of 50 feet of overburden above the seam in strip mining.[16] The soil and rock are removed by a bucket wheel about 75 feet from the operator. Television cameras on either side of the wheel check on the bite taken by the bucket and enable the operator to adjust its position to take due account of ground nonuniformities. In a somewhat similar application the Hannah Coal Company has employed a camera mounted on a vertical crane boom to see that the 50 cubic-yard bucket is properly filled with each bite.

The mining industry offers many opportunities for the employment of television in checking conveyor belt operations. Figure 4.15 illustrates an installation at a large midwestern cement plant. Here belts convey limestone from a primary crusher to five raw-mill storage bins. Two cameras at the ends of the tripper, a 34-inch shuttle conveyer, show the operator when the bins are filled so that he can shift the tripper accordingly. Somewhat similar uses are the observation of conveyor belts which transport ore from crushers and of conveyor transfer points in concentrating plants for an immediate check on the clogging of equipment or of belt breakdowns. Still other applications are solely concerned with mine safety; thus a television camera has been installed to

[16] See Wilson (reference 17).

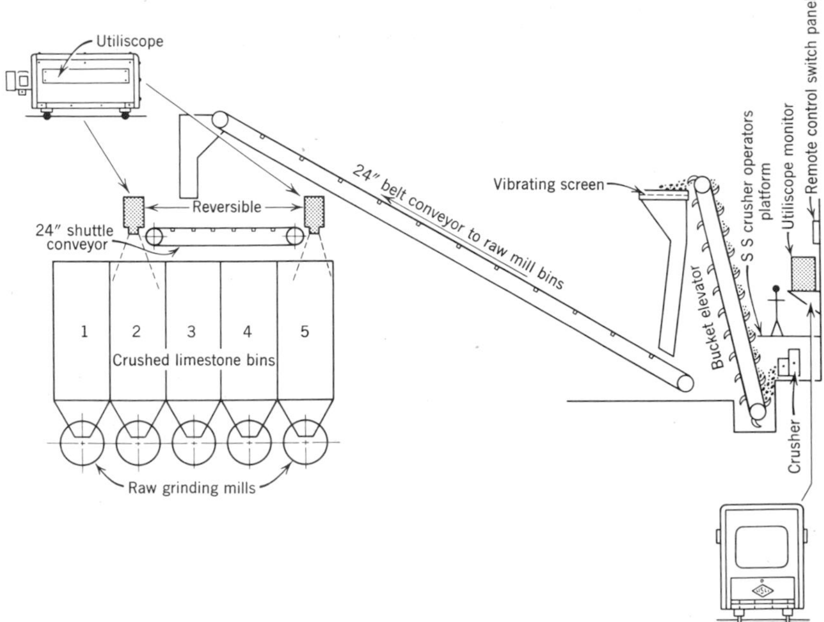

Fig. 4.15. System employing television for the remote control of the loading of limestone bins. (Courtesy Diamond Power Specialty Corporation.)

give the operator some 1500 feet away a view of the cables passing over a pair of sheave wheels in a mine shaft and to permit him to note immediately a disengagement of the cables.

Transportation. Industrial television finds extension use in railway yards.[17] At the Pennsylvania Railroad Pittsburgh terminal a television camera has been installed to observe freight-car and switcher movements on four spur tracks running into the post-office basement, the direct view of which is hidden from the Fort Pitt control tower by the passenger station; the transfer of approximately 100 mail cars in a day requires about 150 entries of the switching engine onto the main tracks. The installation of the television camera makes a separate control tower (the PH tower) superfluous.

In the 2-mile-long Taylor Yard of the Southern Pacific in Los Angeles plans call for day-and-night television surveillance by means of eight wide-angle cameras and five telephoto cameras. In a preliminary installation a remotely controlled camera is mounted at a height of 95 feet on

[17] See references 18 and 19.

a 110-foot tower with a 30-unit bank of 300-watt sealed beam lamps covering a 400-foot radius. Remote control permits the camera to be swung on a horizontal angle of 340°.

One of the most common uses of television in railroading is the checking of freight-car numbers as the cars enter a freight yard; the numbers, transmitted by cameras mounted next to the entrance tracks, are taken down by a clerk in the yardmaster's office (Fig. 4.16), thus making it unnecessary to station men at the tracks to telephone in the numbers. In larger yards with multiple entrance tracks, such as the Chattanooga Yard of the Southern Railroad, one camera is placed in a weatherproof housing next to every entrance track (Fig. 4.17). The video signals from the cameras are piped by way of their control units to a switching unit in the yardmaster's office, which distributes them to two viewing monitors and a 5-inch photographic monitor. The yardmaster can record the numbers directly from the viewing monitors or have them recorded by a camera on the 5-inch monitor; the camera takes one picture a second as long as the light beam falling on a photocell at the trackside is interrupted by a passing train. Thus one man can handle two trains coming in simultaneously or concern himself with other matters while

Fig. 4.16. Recording of freight-car numbers from monitor in yardmaster's office. (Potomac Railroad Yards). (Courtesy of Dage Television Division, Thompson Products, Inc.)

car numbers are recorded automatically. Cameras in other locations relative to the trains make it possible to check on proper loading and closures of the freight cars (Fig. 4.18) as well as on the condition of the undercarriage of the rolling stock. A quite different application tested on the Rock Island Lines utilized a microwave link to show train movements and passengers on the platforms at surburban Englewood, six miles away, to railway officials in downtown Chicago. Finally, television monitors have been provided in parlor cars of passenger trains

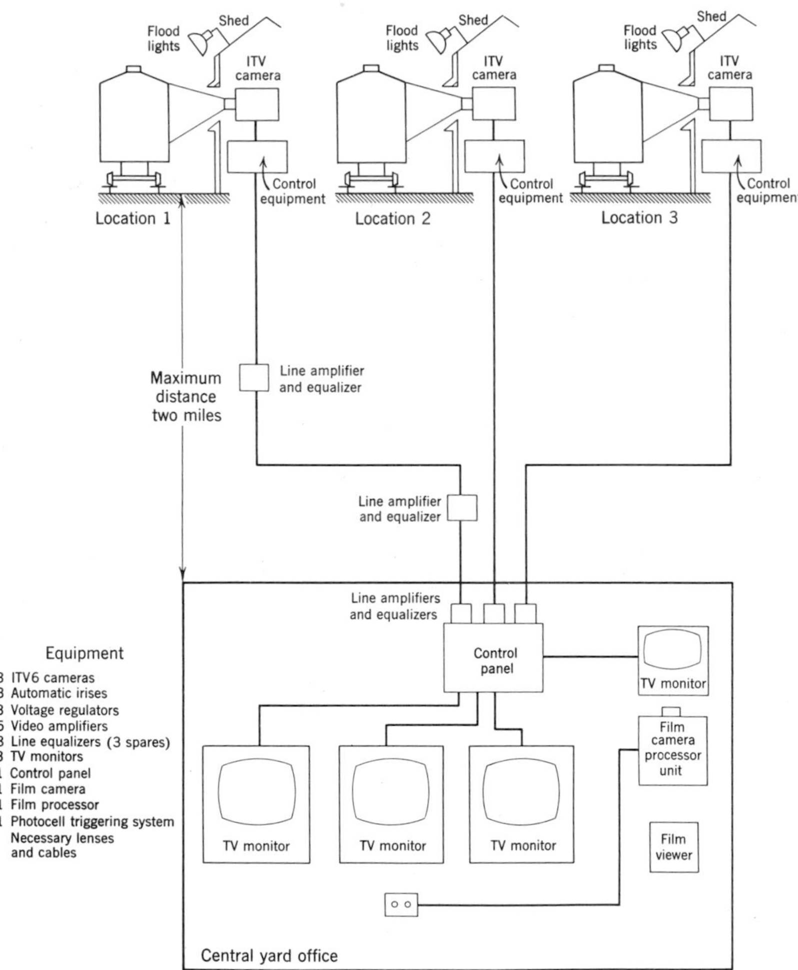

Fig. 4.17. System for recording freight-car numbers at Chattanooga Yard of Southern Railroad. (Courtesy of RCA.)

Fig. 4.18. Checking of freight-car closures by television (Southern Pacific Railway). (Courtesy of RCA.)

to give patrons an engineer's view of the right-of-way; the camera is mounted in the cab of the engine.[18]

Television has also proved helpful in the control of highway traffic.[19] In the ½-mile Memorial Tunnel near Charleston on the West Virginia Turnpike four cameras suspended above the roadway relay views of traffic to four monitors in a turnpike office at the end of the tunnel. If a car is stalled in the tunnel, stop lights can be switched on immediately at the ends of the tunnel to halt traffic until the disabled car can be started or removed. The New Hampshire Department of Public Works and Highways has installed a television camera on a bridge over a highway to transmit a view of traffic to the administration building by microwave link.[20]

In large cities, also, traffic control is aided by television. Thus in Detroit the Department of Streets and Traffic, with the assistance of the Michigan Bell Telephone Company, has installed cameras at critical points on the Edsel Ford and John C. Lodge Expressways, with relay links to the Veterans Memorial Building in Detroit's Civic Center.[21] Here traffic conditions are watched carefully during the rush hours, and ambulances, fire trucks, or expressway control cars are dispatched to meet emergencies as indicated on monitors. In the city of Hamburg,

[18] See reference 20.

[19] See reference 21.

[20] See reference 22.

[21] See Janicki (reference 23).

Fig. 4.19. Attendant at Downtown Merchants Parking Association parking lot in Oakland observes monitor while recording time on ticket. (Courtesy of RCA.)

Germany, television cameras have been installed at several intersections in the downtown business district.[22] The information provided by the monitors at a control center is utilized for the regulation of the flow of traffic by means of stop signals.

In New York City two cameras, each scanning a horizontal angle of 100°, have been employed to study the traffic pattern at Columbus Circle.[23] The cameras were mounted on a tower truck in the center island of the circle and could be raised to a height of 40 feet; the pictures were observed by traffic engineers in a trailer. The findings of the study were utilized in determining the best method for handling the increased traffic which has resulted from the opening of the Coliseum.

In large parking lots, such as that of the Downtown Merchants Parking Association in Oakland (Figs. 4.19 and 4.20), a birdseye view of the lot relayed from a camera to a monitor in a booth at the entrance per-

[22] See reference 24.

[23] See reference 25.

mits the attendant to assign vacancies to automobilists without leaving the booth. In the example shown an RCA TV Eye in a weatherproof housing on a pan-and-tilt mount atop a high pole automatically scans the parking area. The camera control unit is located in the tower formerly occupied by a second attendant required to spot vacancies.

A very large closed-circuit television installation is employed by the Pennsylvania Railroad Ticket Sales and Service Bureau at the Pennsylvania Station in New York for their telephone- and counter-reservation service. This dial-selective system installed by the Dage Television Division utilizes 100 cameras and 95 monitors. Its principle is illustrated by Fig. 4.20*a*. A dial is provided at every monitor position. Depending on the digits dialed, the closing of a particular relay in the video relay panel transfers the video signal from the corresponding camera to the monitor. After the "call" has been completed, a release key restores the "ready" position of the dialing circuit.

In the telephone reservation application the clerk dials a number corresponding to the number of days ahead for which a reservation is desired. This sends to the monitor a lay-out indicating the types of

Fig. 4.20. View of monitor screen in parking lot attendant's booth. (Courtesy of RCA.)

accommodation available on that date. If, after being informed of the availability of the desired accommodations, the customer requests a reservation, the clerk, by dialing another number, establishes connection between his Tel-Autograph transceiver and video monitor and the Tel-Autograph receiver and camera at the coupon file. He sends information regarding the reservation date, type of accommodation, destination, train required, and the customer's name and address to the "coupon shagger" by writing them down with the transceiver stylus. The coupon is then laid under the camera and the coupon number relayed by the clerk to the customer. Finally, coupon and Tel-Autograph record are filed together by the coupon shagger. In the counter application the procedure is essentially the same, with the exception that the customer has an opportunity to inspect the lay-out of available accommodations and has facsimile copies of the coupons delivered to him.

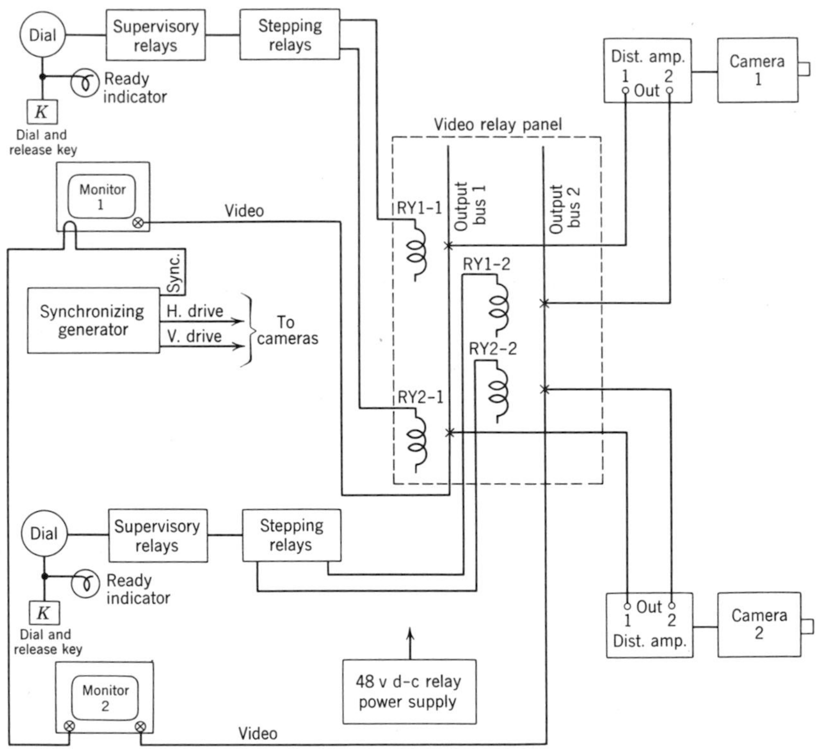

Fig. 4.20a. Principle of dial-selective television system. (Courtesy of Dage Television Division, Thompson Products, Inc.)

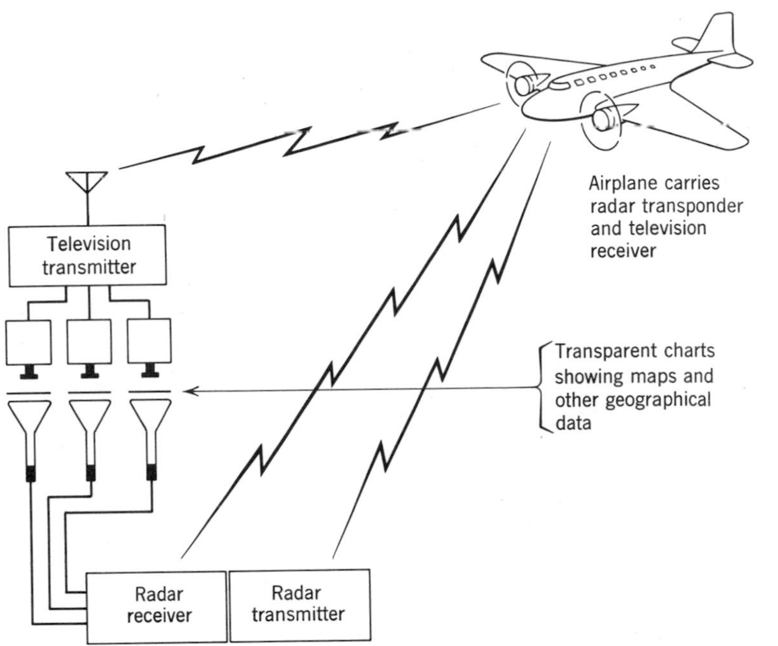

Fig. 4.21. Schematic diagram of ground station of TELERAN system.

At Portland Airport, in Oregon, United Air Lines is employing closed-circuit television for the dissemination of flight information.[24] The arrival and departure times posted on a large plexiglass panel in the dispatch office are transmitted by coaxial cable to four monitors in the terminal building (one in the terminal sales office, one in the ramp chief's office, and two in the lobby). The television method is faster than the transmission of the information by telephone and telemeter, previously used, and avoids possible errors in transmission. Similar "TV bulletin boards" have been installed by American Airlines at Chicago's Midway Airport.

An exceedingly interesting application of television techniques to air navigation and traffic control is realized in the TELERAN system, demonstrated shortly after the end of World War II.[25] The essential idea of TELERAN is the employment of ground radar to locate all the aircraft within a prescribed range of a TELERAN ground station and the retransmission by television of this information, superposed on a

[24] See reference 26.

[25] See Herbst, Wolff, Ewing, and Jones (reference 27), Ewing and Smith, reference 28, and Ewing, Schrader, and Smith (reference 29).

transparent map of the area, to the aircraft aloft (Fig. 4.21). Space is divided into some eight altitude zones, and a separate picture is transmitted to each zone. This picture contains the planes within the zone in question, along with geographical information of interest to planes at that altitude. Thus the pilot sees on his airborne receiver only the information of primary interest to him. Reduction of the picture-repetition rate to ten per second and time sharing of a frequency channel by some four separate video signals reduces the amount of radio spectrum space demanded by the system.

The TELERAN system incorporates many interesting refinements. In the transmitted picture planes are represented by radar pips. A signal-selection system controlled by the radar transponder on the plane causes a radial line to identify the pip representing the pilot's plane. A transparent disk indicating the heading of the plane is rotated by a gyro-controlled servo system in front of the viewing tube in the cockpit (Fig. 4.22). Weather maps are available to the pilot on a separate channel. In landing, as in flight, the pilot is guided by visual displays which minimize his dependence on voice information and circumvent the language barrier.

Natural Resources. Closed circuit television can be utilized in various ways in the preservation and exploitation of our natural resources. One of these is the prompt detection of forest fires. The Louisiana Forestry Commission has experimented with a television camera mounted atop a forest-fire tower; while rotating continuously in a plastic

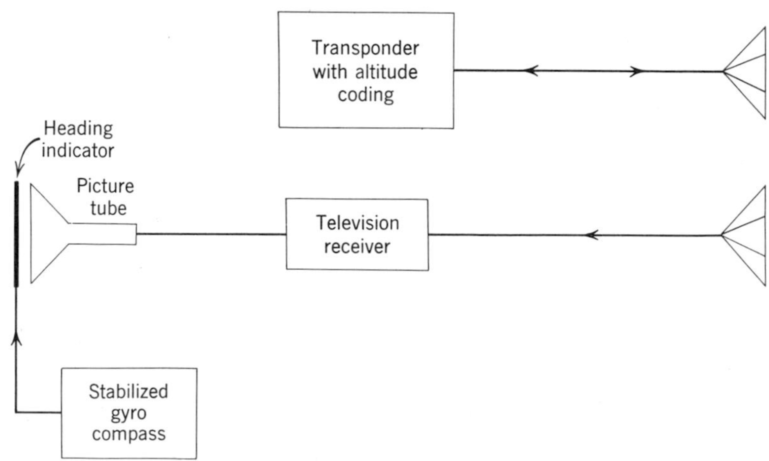

Fig. 4.22. Schematic diagram of airborne installation of TELERAN system.

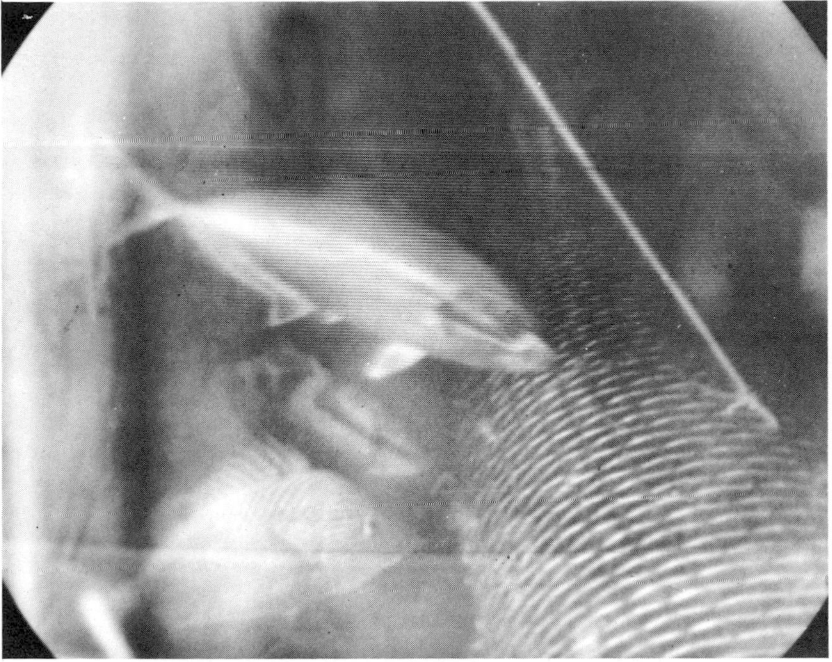

Fig. 4.23. View of fish transmitted by underwater camera for observing shrimp traps by U. S. Fish and Wildlife Service. (Courtesy of RCA.)

dome, it transmits a picture of surrounding forest lands by microwave link to a fire warden's station which may be some 25 miles away.[26] When the observer notes evidence of fire, he can stop the camera by remote control and exchange the long-focus lens employed for scanning for a short-focus lens which transmits a scale marked on the circumference of the dome; this indicates the azimuth of the fire relative to the fire tower. Two scale indications from two different fire-tower stations make it possible to determine the location of the fire.

Another study was carried out at Mt. Danaher, near Placerville, by the Hancock Electronics Corporation of Oakland for the California State Division of Forestry.[27] Here the camera, installed on an automatically or manually controlled tilt-and-pan mounting atop a 100-foot lookout tower, transmitted pictures to a fire dispatcher's office a few hundred yards away. An 8-inch focal-length lens was employed for scanning and a 20-inch lens for the examination of detail; a Wratten K2

[26] See references 30 and 31.

[27] See reference 32.

Fig. 4.24. Diving bell containing camera aboard U.S.S. *Pompano* (U.S. Fish and Wildlife Service). (Courtesy of RCA.)

filter gave the best picture detail. It was found that the detection on the monitor of fires, at times as much as 20 miles away, preceded the reception of fire messages from lookouts by 20 seconds to 5 minutes; the average was 2½ minutes.

Closed-circuit television has also been found valuable in the study of fishery methods and equipment.[28] The U.S. Fish and Wildlife Service of the Department of the Interior has conducted studies of nets and trawls at depths of more than 60 feet in the Gulf Stream off the east coast of Florida. In this "Operation Fisheye" a standard RCA ITV closed-circuit television system was employed with only natural sunlight as illumination. Satisfactory still and motion pictures could be obtained by photographing the monitor screen on the Service's research vessel, the U.S.S. *Pompano*. An example is shown in Fig. 4.23. In an-

[28] See reference 33.

other study of the operation of a new type of net an image-orthicon chain provided by the U.S. Navy Bureau of Ships[29] was used.

The external housing of the ITV equipment aboard the *Pompano*, with with the mechanism for 360° horizontal and 90° vertical displacement of the camera above the submersible, free-flooded, ball-type diving bell containing the camera, is shown in Fig. 4.24; the camera itself is contained in a watertight steel cylinder.

Marine Salvage. The use of underwater television for marine salvage was illustrated dramatically by the discovery in June 1951 of the wreck of the British submarine *Affray* at a depth of 280 feet in the English channel.[30] Figure 4.25 shows the name plate of the *Affray* as photographed on the monitor aboard the salvage vessel. The equipment employed in this operation utilized a Marconi image-orthicon camera and had been hastily assembled for locating the submarine in the three weeks following the sinking. Although tests with underwater television equipment had been carried out in the United States by the Cornell Aeronautical Laboratory and others at a considerably earlier date, the location of the *Affray* greatly stimulated interest in this technique, particularly in England. A second project which attracted a great deal of interest

Fig. 4.25. Name plate of submarine *Affray* transmitted from depth of 280 feet to monitor aboard salvage vessel (Courtesy of Marconi's Wireless Telegraph Co., Ltd.)

[29] See reference 34.

[30] See Stamp (reference 35).

was the search for fragments of the Comet aircraft which had crashed near Elba on Jan. 10, 1954, to aid in determining the cause of the tragedy. The equipment employed in the salvage consisted of two Pye underwater cameras and one Marconi-Siebe Gorman camera with a periscopic lens having a hemispherical field; approximately 60 per cent of the aircraft was recovered.[31]

Figure 4.26 shows the viewing dome and periscopic lens of the Marconi-Siebe Gorman underwater television camera as well as the floodlights attached to the camera housing.

Fig. 4.26. The viewing dome and periscopic lens of the Marconi-Siebe Gorman underwater television camera. (Courtesy of Marconi's Wireless Telegraph Co., Ltd.)

One of the Pye "Deep-Sea" underwater cameras is shown in Fig. 4.27. This camera can operate at depths down to 3000 feet. A 250-watt floodlight is attached to a fin which causes the camera to maintain a desired orientation when trawled. The 12-foot probe on the other side of the camera provides a size reference for objects viewed on the monitor screen.

The interior of a hand-held camera for use at shallower depths, which is identical with that of the "Deep-Sea" camera, is shown in Fig. 4.28. An image-orthicon camera tube is employed, since this permits the camera to operate at even lower light-levels than a diver.

In the normal use of the deep-sea camera for search purposes an ob-

[31] See Bathurst (reference 36) and reference 37.

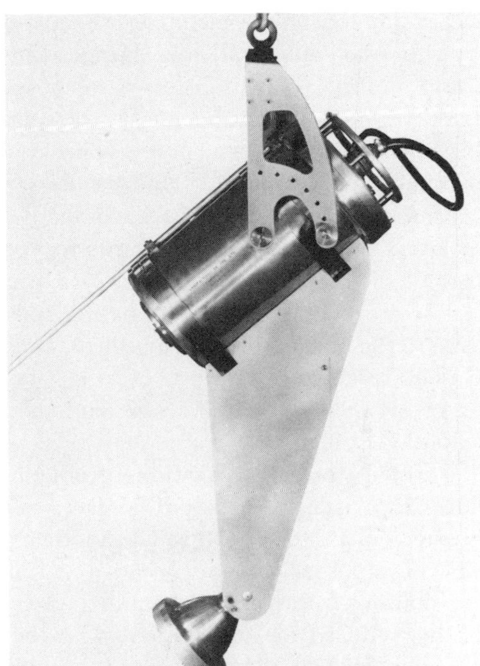

Fig. 4.27. Pye "Deep-Sea" Underwater Camera. (Courtesy of Pye Ltd.)

Fig. 4.28. Interior of Pye Underwater Camera. (Courtesy of Pye Ltd.)

ject is first located by echo-sounding apparatus and then identified by trawling the camera at slow shipspeed over the area in which the echo was obtained. For all deep-sea work one or several illuminating units must be attached to the camera; these may be tungsten-light sources or high-pressure discharge lamps. The lamp size, for given wattage, can be made smaller than for land use in view of the cooling action of the seawater. The camera itself, instead of being suspended, may be mounted on a tripod which comes to rest on the floor of the sea, or it may be slid down a rope supporting a grappling hook. In turbid waters it is wise to attach the illuminating units to a long extension arm or close to the bottom of the tripod legs so as to reduce background illumination caused by scattering. At times the interposition of a bag of clear water between the camera lens and the object to be examined proves helpful.

Turbidity presents a serious problem. In British coastal waters it limits the visibility to about 15 feet; in the clearest waters the range is extended to about 150 feet. Another problem is the limited field of view of the usual camera objective. If a flat window seals off the camera housing from the surrounding water, the angular field of view is further reduced by a factor equal to the reciprocal index of refraction of water, or 3/4. This effect can be nullified or even overcompensated by the addition of lens attachments. Special periscopic lenses, such as that referred to in connection with the Marconi-Siebe Gorman camera, are of particular value in search work. Figure 4.29 shows a view obtained with this equipment of a diver at work in a test tank. The Bureau of Ships has developed for free-swimming divers a small hand-held camera with a lens with a 100° field.[32] Here illumination is supplied by a superpressure gaseous discharge lamp attached to the front of the housing.

Other problems encountered in the design of underwater cameras concern the mechanical strength, corrosion resistance, and nonporosity of the housing. Most underwater camera housings employ stainless-steel and aluminum-alloy components to minimize corrosion difficulties. In the Pye cameras a "dampometer," consisting essentially of a circuit measuring the resistance of a piece of blotting paper between two electrodes, gives warning of the leakage of seawater into the housing.

Most of the earlier underwater cameras were extremely ponderous affairs; now compact lightweight units have also become available. The Kay Lab Vidicon cameras for shallow-depth and deep-sea work (down to 1000 feet) shown in Fig. 4.30 are examples. The weight of the heavier unit, which is marketed by Underwater Surveys of San Diego,

[32] See reference 38.

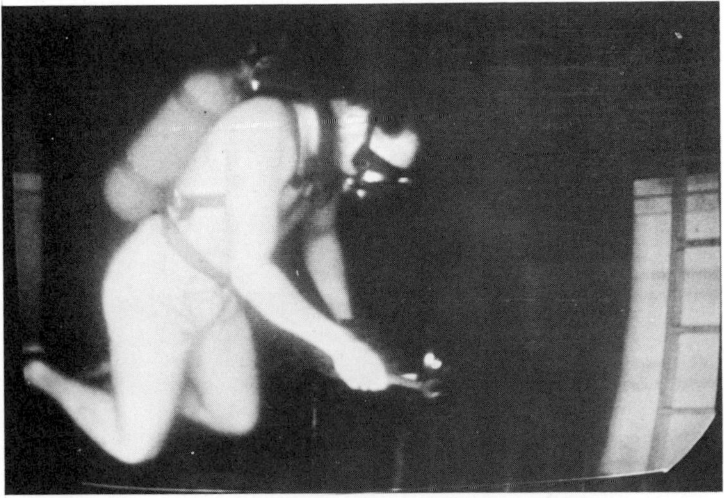

Fig. 4.29. View of diver at work in test tank transmitted by Marconi-Siebe Gorman underwater camera. (Courtesy of Marconi's Wireless Telegraph Co., Ltd.)

Calif., is only about 50 pounds. The housing is of plastic-impregnated aluminum alloy.

At the opposite end of the range of complexity is the underwater television equipment AN/SXQ XN-1, tested by the Bureau of Ships, which permits complete surface control of the movement of the camera unit.[33] The camera can be made to hover and cruise six inches above the ocean bottom without disturbing the mud and silt which would reduce visibility. Two monitors, as well as meters indicating cable length, cable tension, depth, hours of service of lamps, etc., are provided on the control console.

The advantages of the television camera in underwater work are manifold. First of all, it can be made to operate at greater depths than the human diver, whose range is approximately 350 feet. Furthermore, it can be made to descend and ascend rapidly, without pauses for gradual compression and decompression. Finally, it conveys visual information to those on board the salvage ship who are best able to judge its significance.

In most salvage operations the camera locates the object of search and the picture on the monitor instructs the diver with respect to his work before his descent. As the work progresses, supplementary instructions can be given based on the picture of the operations conveyed by the

[33] See Montgomery (reference 39).

(*a*)

(*b*)

Fig. 4.30. Shallow-depth (*a*) and deep-sea (*b*) Vidicon camera housings. (Courtesy of Kay Lab.)

camera. The camera may also be used for the inspection of harbor installations and the sides and bottoms of ships. However, the murkiness of harbor waters frequently places a limit on this use.

Ordnance. The utility of closed-circuit television in the handling of explosive materials is obvious. Accordingly, it has found wide application in ordnance depots, particularly in the disassembly of shells and other explosive items. Figure 4.31 shows an operator at Aberdeen Proving Ground, protected by an explosion-proof wall, running a drill by remote control and observing his work on a television monitor. This is only one of the many operations whose performance without hazard of injury to personnel is made possible by closed circuit television.

Plant Surveillance. The surveillance of plant entrances by television cameras transfers the checkpoint to the central office. Here gates can be opened by remote control and directions given to new arrivals by an intercommunication system. Figure 4.32 shows a typical camera installation for the identification of trucks entering the grounds at the Westgate-California Tuna Packing Company plant. A monitor station at the Louisiana Power and Light Company is shown in Fig. 4.33. Television cameras are also conveniently set up for the identification of security badges of employees at entrances to restricted areas.

At a plant of the Emerson Radio and Phonograph Corporation closed-circuit television chains which transmit views of the assembly lines to the executive offices permit the management to familiarize themselves with conditions in the plant without leaving their desks. A less routine application was the installation of a television camera by the Los Angeles police in a concealed position above the shipping platform of a

Fig. 4.31. Drilling a shell by remote control with the aid of television (Aberdeen Proving Ground). (Courtesy of RCA.)

Fig. 4.32. Television camera for identifying entering trucks at Westgate-California Tuna Packing plant. (Courtesy of Kay Lab.)

firm which had reported repeated losses of merchandise. With the aid of the camera the police were able to identify the thieves and to prevent further losses.

Fig. 4.33. View of plant entrance on monitor (Louisiana Power and Light Company). (Courtesy of RCA.)

Public Institutions. Closed-circuit television can also perform important functions in various public institutions. In the city jail in Houston, Tex., eight RCA industrial television chains are in use for the supervision of cell corridors and work and recreation areas. Figure 4.34 shows some of the equipment—in particular a line-up of control monitors on the left—in a guard office. Television not only reduces the number of guards required, but also greatly lessens the possibility of hostages being taken by rebellious prisoners, often the first step in a prison riot.

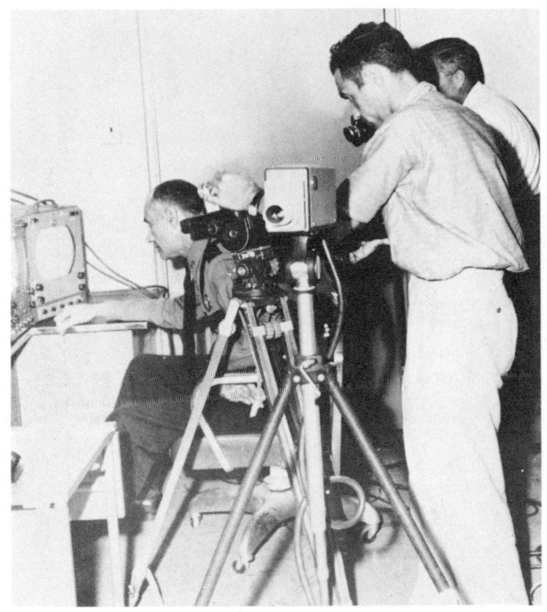

Fig. 4.34. Television in use at Houston city jail. (Courtesy of RCA.)

Another use of television by public-safety agencies has been demonstrated by the New York Police Department in cooperation with the Radio Corporation of America. In order to perform their task most effectively, detectives are required to view periodically "line-ups" of persons arrested for felonies or major misdemeanors in the city area. By establishing microwave links between the several police stations and transmitting television pictures of the "line-ups" to all of the stations, a great deal of travel time can be saved. The same system can be employed effectively for transmitting pictures of missing or

Fig. 4.35. Demonstration of television for transmitting "line-ups" at Manhattan Police Headquarters. (Courtesy of RCA.)

wanted persons or other pictorial information of value in the performance of police duties. Figure 4.35 shows a demonstration of the system before Mayor Wagner and Police Commissioner Adams of New York, at the Manhattan police headquarters, in which detectives posed as "suspects." Another group viewed the pictures as received at the Brooklyn headquarters about seven miles away.

Closed-circuit television also finds an important application in hospitals and institutions for the mentally ill. Continuous observation from the desk of the floor nurse or attendant of seriously ill patients makes possible adequate care with the limited personnel normally available. Wards with provision for television observation of patients have been established at the Walter Reed Army Hospital in Washington, D.C.

A quite different application is realized at Morristown Memorial Hospital (N.J.) where patients can visit by television with friends and relatives—in particular children—who are not admitted to the wards. Still another use, namely entertainment and occupational therapy, is the objective of a closed-circuit installation at the Benjamin Franklin Turberculosis Hospital in Columbus, Ohio.

Motion Pictures. Ever since the end of World War II efforts have been made, both in the United States and in Great Britain, to adapt television techniques to motion-picture production.[34] The practice of kinescope or tape television recording, universally employed in television studios to permit rebroadcasting of programs, represents the ultimate in this direction: television cameras only are trained on the set. The production director successively channels the signal output from one or the other camera to the transmitter and the recording kinescope. Wipes and dissolves are employed to effect smooth transitions. The film camera views only the completed program, as sent out on the air, on the kinescope of the recording unit.

This procedure is clearly appropriate both for rebroadcasting and for providing a permanent record of programs which have been transmitted, but it has certain shortcomings for general film production. First, the kinescope or tape record is not equal in quality to good 35-mm film obtained with a film camera. Second, although the television recording process is highly economical of film, it lacks the flexibility of the conventional process. If, in the conventional process, the final film is prepared from a number of films shot simultaneously by several differently placed cameras, imperfections can be edited out and the performance of the actors shown to the greatest advantage.

However, television techniques can be of great value to motion-picture production even when the advantages of the direct recording of the action on 35-mm film and of subsequent editing are fully retained. At the present time these techniques are widely employed in the preparation of films for television use. Television enters both in the original exposure of the film on location and in its later editing.

In the exposure of the original negative film television camera chains linked to the motion-picture cameras serve essentially as electronic viewfinders. In the Video-Film Camera produced by A. Simon[35] and employed by him for the filming of numerous high-ranking television shows in Hollywood a beam splitter between the lens turret and the film gate of a conventional film camera projects a duplicate image on a Vidicon target. The video signal generated by the Vidicon tube controls the picture both on a viewfinder kinescope mounted on the camera and on remote monitors viewed by the production director. Since these monitors, one for each video-film camera, show the director precisely what each camera records, he can judge immediately, without waiting for film development, whether a retake is required. This results in a saving

[34] See Abramson (reference 40).

[35] See Simon (reference 41).

Fig. 4.36. DuMont Electronicam-35 Camera. (Courtesy of Allen B. DuMont Laboratories, Inc.)

in the time of the director, the actors, and the supporting personnel as well as in film.

One of the compound cameras employed in the Dumont Electronicam TV-film system is shown in Fig. 4.36.[36] Since the Electronicam system is designed for simultaneous television broadcasting and film recording, the television component is an image-orthicon studio camera. In the television broadcast the several Electronicam cameras are employed like ordinary studio cameras; the program director switches one or the other to the transmitter and "take-air monitor" as desired. The transmitted program is also recorded in a kinescope recording unit. The film thus

[36] See Caddigan and Goldsmith (reference 42).

obtained serves as editing master for preparing the final film of the production. It is run synchronously with the developed film from the several cameras and with the sound record through an electronic film editor and serves as a convenient guide for the cutting and splicing of the film to form the final negative master.

Electronicam cameras are available for 35-mm and 16-mm film recording. In both the film is exposed directly behind the objective lens turret, and the image on the camera-tube photocathode is formed by a system of relay lenses, prisms, and mirrors. In one type of 16-mm camera which is not employed for direct television broadcasting a mirror sector disk is inserted between objective lens and film gate. This cuts off the illumination on the film and directs it toward the television camera during the pull-down intervals when film illumination is not desired at any rate. Hence the illumination requirements are the same as those for a simple 16-mm film camera. In other Electronicam units the light from the objective is split 50:50 by an optical cube directing half the light to the film and half to the television camera relay-lens system.

The Electronicam TV-film system is generally employed in live transmissions and in the preparation of rebroadcast film at the Dumont New York studios.

In the process of film editing the employment of television techniques has the important advantage of rendering unnecessary the preparation of positive films from the original negative films; electronically, a negative image can be converted into a positive image by the simple device of adding a stage of amplification. Figure 4.37 shows in greater detail a television film editor of the type employed at the Disney studios. The negative films obtained from the several cameras are passed through synchronously operating Vidicon film cameras in which the outputs are applied to individual monitors showing the pictures taken by the cameras in positive polarity. The operator employs a tape memory-control to record which of the outputs is to be employed in the final film. His choice is recorded on magnetic tape synchronized with the film cameras. Upon playback the tape switches the outputs of the Vidicon film cameras to a composite picture monitor which shows the complete production. If it is satisfactory, the tape record may be employed as a guide for cutting the negative film as required for the final master. If unsatisfactory, the tape record may be corrected and the composite picture observed once more on the monitor.

The preparation of high-quality feature films by employing television cameras only and using kinescope recording for forming the final film is also under serious consideration. The firm High Definition Films Ltd.

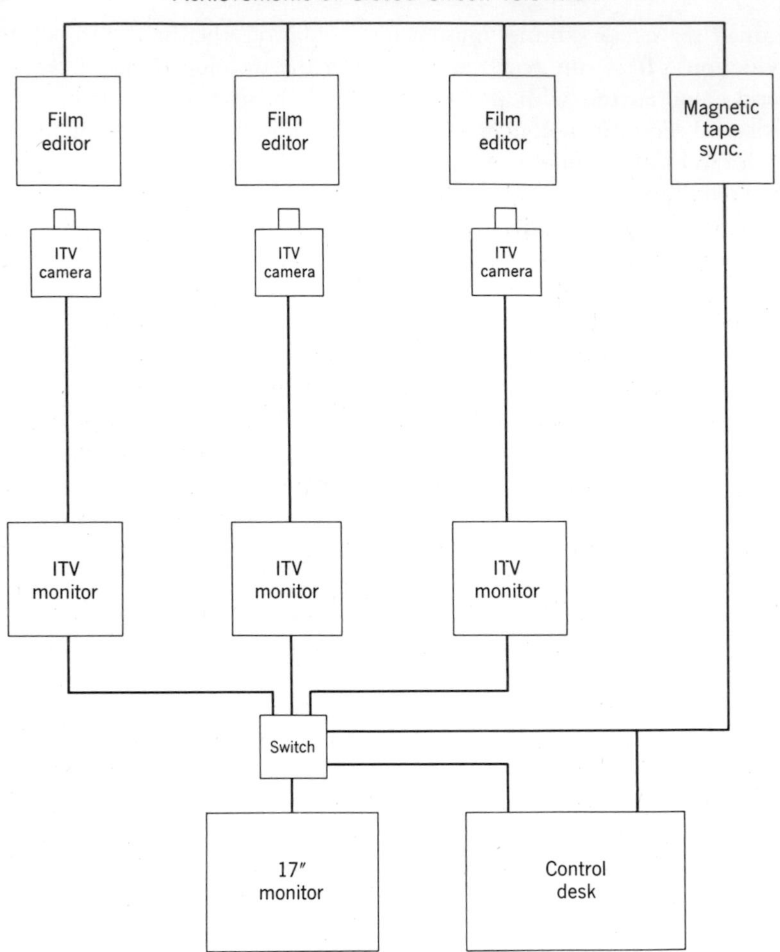

Fig. 4.37. ITV equipment used in electronic film editor (Disney studios). (Courtesy of RCA.)

has been formed in England for this express purpose.[37] The required high picture quality is attained with an increased number of picture lines (e.g., 625 or 834) with sequential scanning and an increased transmission band (e.g., 12 megacycles) as well as a number of other refinements which are inadmissible in broadcast practice but perfectly feasible in closed-television circuits. At an earlier date (1952), the National Broadcasting Company prepared a film for a television program by transmitting video signals from several cameras located at San Juan Capistrano over two microwave links to the Hollywood studios, 60 miles

[37] See Collins and Macnamara (reference 43).

away, and recording them there on 35-mm film. The scenes were shot in several sequences and the material edited, cut, and assembled to form a single, smooth-running film.

Closed-circuit television plays a role not only in the production of motion-picture film, but also in providing additional programs for motion-picture theatres. Theatre television has been employed in the past primarily for special sports events; thus the Marciano-Charles heavyweight prizefight of September 1954 was shown simultaneously in 71 theatres. An event of a somewhat different type was the opening-night performance in New York of the Metropolitan Opera Association which was transmitted on closed-circuit television coast-to-coast two months later. Transmission occurs over the video cable and microwave facilities of the Bell Telephone System. The organization of the telecasts and the theatre projection equipment are provided in large part by companies such as Theatre Network Television, Inc., for which local servicing is supplied by the RCA Service Company.[38]

PHYSICAL AND ENGINEERING RESEARCH

The ability to withstand conditions unsuited to human comfort or even human existence makes the television camera a useful substitute observer in many research applications. In others the great intrinsic sensitivity of certain camera tubes, their response to ultraviolet and infrared radiations invisible to the eye, the possibility of electronic contrast enhancement, and the independence of the final picture brightness with respect to the light-level of the original scene make television a useful research tool.

Astronomy. A Pye television camera has been used by Peter Fellgett at the Cambridge University Observatory to convert a 12-inch solar telescope and a 25-inch refractor into electronic astronomical telescopes.[39] Pictures formed by ultraviolet and infrared radiation of the sun selected by a spectrograph revealed details which had not been observed before. The refractor was employed for studies of the moon, Jupiter, and Saturn. It was found that the electronic method of recording the images was less affected by atmospheric tremor than the conventional direct photographic method.

The Lumicon system marketed by Bendix[40] employs a special RCA image orthicon with wide-spaced target[41] and a special wide-band, low-

[38] See Halpern (reference 44).

[39] See reference 45.

[40] See reference 46.

[41] See Rotow (reference 47).

noise amplifier. It operates with 1029 scanning lines, a frame-period of $^1/_{30}$ second, and an amplifier passband of 15 megacycles. It is estimated that a 200-inch telescope equipped with a television imaging system of this type could penetrate as far into space as a 1200-inch telescope; in other words, the sensitivity of the television recording system is approximately 36 times as large as that of a conventional photographic recording system.

Aeronautics. Extensive tests of the application of closed-circuit television in aeronautical research have been carried out at the Lewis Flight Propulsion Laboratory of the National Advisory Committee on Aeronautics in Cleveland.[42] In one of these a Vidicon camera was placed in a small supersonic wind tunnel to observe Schlieren patterns in the air flow about supersonic probes placed in the tunnel. It was found that the resolution in the reproduced picture was ample to indicate the desired detail; furthermore, a sound-level of 100 decibels prevailing in the wind tunnel had no effect on the picture. More recently (1955) three RCA ITV systems and four 24-inch monitors were placed into service for observing tests in a new 10 x 10-foot tunnel specifically designed with closed-circuit television in mind (Figs 4.38 and 4.39).

A Vidicon camera was also tested for rocket-flame observation. Here the variations in scene brightness are very large, so that difficulties from blooming or reduced resolution in regions of high light-level may be expected. But, in fact, no objectionable blooming was observed with the Vidicon camera. In one test, however, with the noise-level at 140 decibels, noise striations were observed in the picture.

With an image dissector camera employed for flame observation no blooming whatever was observed, as might be expected from the operation of the image dissector. Furthermore, at a noise-level of 110 decibels the picture was unaffected by noise. On the other hand, with a non-storage camera tube, such as the image dissector, stroboscopic effects arise in the observation of moving objects. Specifically, pulsations and rotations at multiples of the frame frequency are "stopped" in the reproduced picture, and periodic motions with slightly higher or lower frequencies are reproduced as slow forward and reversed motions. In the observation of rocket flames these spurious effects were not disturbing.

Image-orthicon cameras did not prove suitable for flame observation because of blooming and microphonics.

Color television should be particularly valuable in the combustion processes, since much information regarding combustion conditions is conveyed by the color distribution in the flame. Hence a field-sequential color camera, which was available at the time of the tests, was employed

[42] See Friswold (reference 48).

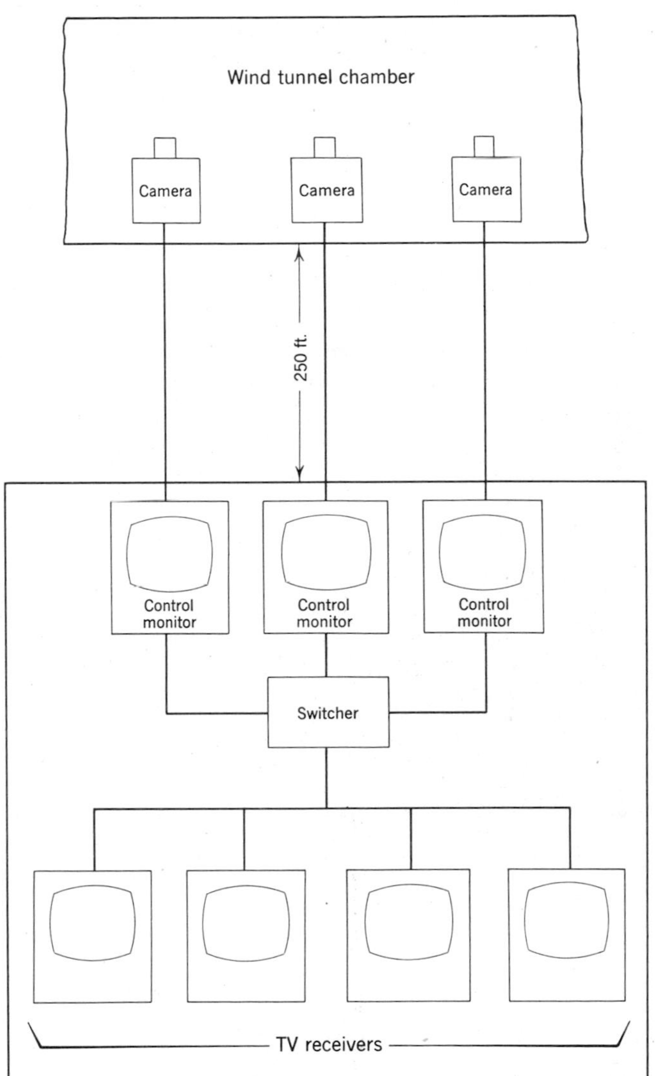

Fig. 4.38. Schematic of television installation for wind-tunnel studies at Lewis Flight Propulsion Laboratory. (Courtesy of RCA.)

for observing the tail cone of a jet-engine afterburner (Fig. 4.40). The Dumont color television chain operated with 525 lines and 180 frames per second and had a passband of 18 megacycles. The principal drawback of the system was excessive color break-up in the viewing of the high-velocity flame. This difficulty should be overcome by the substitution of standard compatible color television cameras.

For the safety of the operating personnel, experimental rocket and jet engines are generally operated by remote control. The television camera is mounted nearby in a protective housing on skids. It was found that the television equipment quickly amortized itself through savings in scarce experimental propellants and by minimizing damage to experimental installations. With continuous television observation fuel valves could be shut off as soon as flaws developed or an ignition failure took place.

Television cameras have also been mounted on aircraft in flight, in particular to study icing conditions on various parts of the structure and to observe the proper operation of the landing-gear equipment. Thus, in the United States, an industrial television system has been installed on a nonrigid airship to determine the all-weather flying capacity of

Fig. 4.39. Schlieren pattern observed in wind-tunnel tests at Lewis Flight Propulsion Laboratory. (Courtesy of RCA.)

Fig. 4.40. Field-sequential color camera observing tail cone of a jet engine afterburner. (Courtesy of Allen B. DuMont Laboratories, Inc.)

such ships. The camera itself is mounted on a remotely controlled pan and tilt unit in a weatherproof housing on top of the envelope; this permits observation of the control surfaces of the airship, as well as of the envelope itself. The camera is joined to the control unit in the car by a 300-foot cable around the body of the ship. To meet the special conditions of operation, additional heaters at the front of the camera housing are installed to aid defrosting.

In Great Britain, to accelerate airworthiness tests on a turbopropeller engine, a Pye television camera was mounted in the port engine nacelle of a Proteus Ambassador flying boat;[43] the camera was focused on the entry guide vanes and the picture relayed to a 14-inch monitor inside the aircraft. Since the objective of the test was a study of the performance of the engine under acute icing conditions, water was sprayed by a grid of 37 nozzles supported by a light, tubular structure in front of the port engine and fed by a 135-gallon tank in the rear of the craft. Tests were performed at 10,000 to 30,000 feet altitude and at temperatures down to −44° C. These tests, which, without television, would have

[43] See reference 49.

required 200 hours of flying time, were completed in 20 hours of flying time.

Closed-circuit television has also been found useful for the observation of human reactions under simulated flight conditions. To observe the effects on personnel of the high accelerations encountered in aircraft operations, the test subject is placed in the gondola of a centrifuge, and an industrial television camera is mounted on the same gondola. The signal from the camera is relayed to a stationary monitor through a sliding contact. Continuous viewing of the subject by television provides medical personnel with more immediate information than that obtainable by motion-picture recording. A centrifuge installation employed for this purpose by the French Air Force permits the attainment of a reactive force of 15 g, or 15 times the force of gravity, within one second.[44] The Vidicon camera chain was provided for this purpose by La Radio Industrie. The Naval Air Development Center at Johnsville, Pa., has employed an image-orthicon camera for similar purposes.[45]

Automotive Engineering. Closed-circuit television is applied by the General Motors Corporation to a variety of engineering problems. One of these, which illustrates the versatility of television, is the study of the action of automobile suspensions in road tests. The camera, in this instance, is attached to the undercarriage with a direct view of the suspension.

Nuclear Research. Protection from radiation damage in the handling of radioactive materials presents great opportunities for service to closed-circuit television. In a research program carried out by the Remote Control Engineering Division of the Argonne National Laboratory emphasis was placed on developing manipulation and viewing techniques which would enable the operator to perform his tasks as nearly as possible in the same manner as he would without the protective remote-control linkage.[46] This was achieved by the development of ingenious mechanical master-slave manipulators employed in conjunction with large windows of nondarkening glass which give the operator a direct binocular view of the work. It was recognized, however, that this was only a limited solution. With operations performed at higher radiation levels and at greater distances from the operator the mechanical manipulators would have to be replaced by robots with slave hands controlled by force-reflecting servos and the direct-view windows by binocular television units. Figure 4.41 shows a scientist at the Argonne National Laboratory performing a pouring operation with a mechanical

[44] See reference 50.

[45] See reference 51.

[46] See Hull (reference 52).

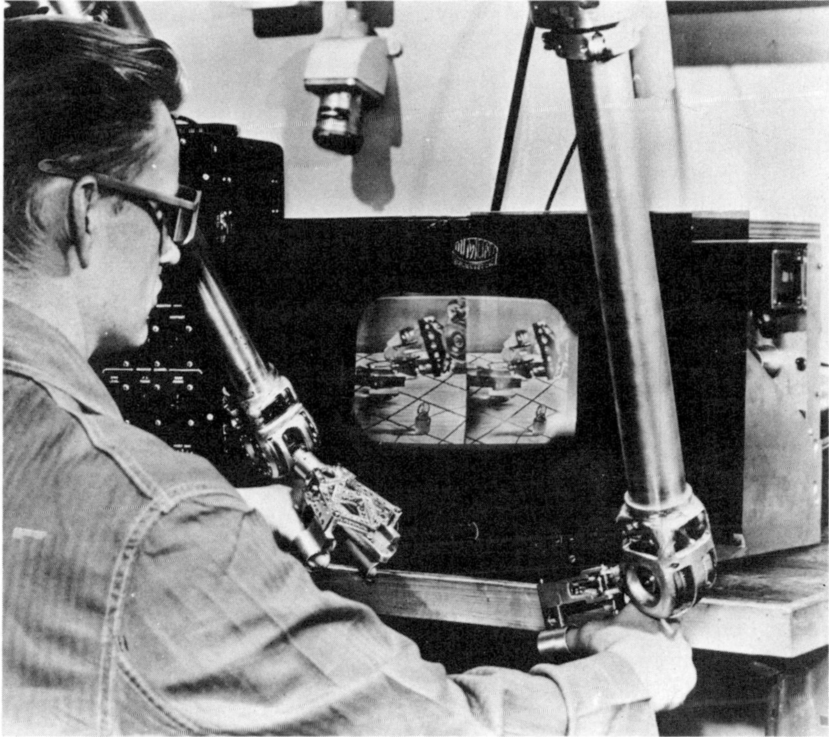

Fig. 4.41. Observation of a pouring operation with a mechanical manipulator by means of stereo television. (Courtesy of Allen B. DuMont Laboratories, Inc.)

manipulator and watching the progress through stereo spectacles on a split-screen stereo monitor.

In a more recent installation at the Atomic Energy Commission's Hanford, Wash., plutonium plant, which is operated by the General Electric Company, a field-sequential color television chain serves a similar monitoring purpose.[47] Two color monitors installed in the cab of a crane handling highly radioactive materials replace a mirror system previously employed for observing the hooks of the crane. Color television is advantageous here, since color-coded objects are involved in the remote manipulations. A somewhat different use is the checking of integrating gamma-ray detectors with Cobalt 60 slugs in a concrete tunnel at the Naval Air Development Center in Johnsville, Pa.[48]

[47] See reference 53.
[48] See reference 51.

During the calibration a 15-inch concrete shield is interposed between the meter and the monitor to afford protection to the operating personnel.

The ruggedness of television as an observing medium is well illustrated by another application. At the Calder Hall reactors in England provision is made for inserting a special television camera, developed by Pye Ltd., into the reactor when it is shut down in order to observe processes taking place in its interior.[49] The camera, modified from a regular industrial television unit, fits into a stainless steel tube 3½ inches in diameter and is connected to the control equipment by a 75-foot cable. A battery of lights is grouped around the lens to provide illumination. Furthermore, a rotatable mirror system makes it possible to obtain side views from the camera. Since the temperature of the interior of the reactor is 150 to 200° C, carbon dioxide is pumped around the camera into the reactor, maintaining the camera temperature at approximately 50° C.

Oceanography. The television techniques developed for marine salvage are equally applicable to underwater research. The research vessel of the British Institute of Oceanography, the *Discovery II*, has carried out extensive examination of the ocean floor and of marine fauna and flora with the aid of Pye underwater television cameras.[50] Image-orthicon cameras with stereo attachments and split-field monitors provide three-dimensional views, permitting more accurate interpretation. A three-dimensional television installation by the Fenjohn Photo and Equipment Company is used by the Maryland Fisheries Commission for the examination of oyster beds.[51] Also, for telemetering applications from great depths, i.e., the remote reading of instruments, the transmission of a picture of the meter face by television often represents the simplest and most flexible technique.

MEDICINE AND BIOLOGY

Closed-circuit television techniques may be applied in numerous ways to advance the life sciences and medicine, in research and practice as well as in education. In addition to contributing to our fundamental knowledge in the biological field, they facilitate a number of important diagnostic methods.

Microscopy. The advantages in research of television microscopy over direct microscopy are threefold. Television microscopy permits the

[49] See reference 54.

[50] See reference 55 and Allanson(reference 56).

[51] See reference 57.

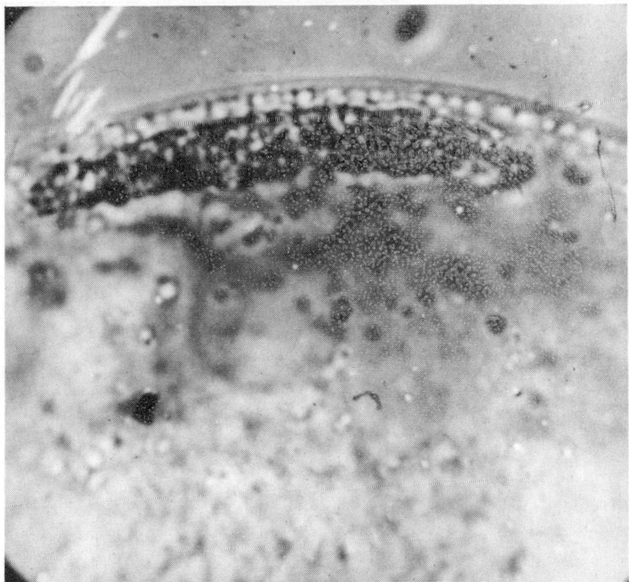

Fig. 4.42. Segment of a centrifuged egg of the sea urchin *Arbacia punctulata* photographed with a television microscope. The cortical granules appear as bright particles directly beneath the outer membrane. (Courtesy of Dr. A. K. Parpart.)

observation of specimens with illumination to which the eye is insensitive; it makes it possible to emphasize detail of particular importance by electronic contrast enhancement; and it greatly increases the ease of following motion in specimens even at very high magnifications of the order of 4000.

The last circumstance enabled Dr. A. K. Parpart of Princeton University to follow the Brownian and translational motions of granules 0.2 to 0.4 micron in diameter within the cytoplasm of red blood corpuscles of a certain class of fishes.[52] He could deduce from these motions that the shapes of these corpuscles and the changes of shape resulting in dissolution with liberation of hemoglobin must be a consequence of surface conditions on the cells rather than of any organized internal structure.

In similar fashion, the television microscope enabled Dr. Parpart to follow with precision the motion of echinochrome particles in sea-urchin eggs and to take motion pictures of other flow phenomena within living cells. He found the electronic contrast enhancement obtained with a Vidicon sensitive in the range 3600 to 4500 A equal to or better than

[52]See Parpart (reference 58).

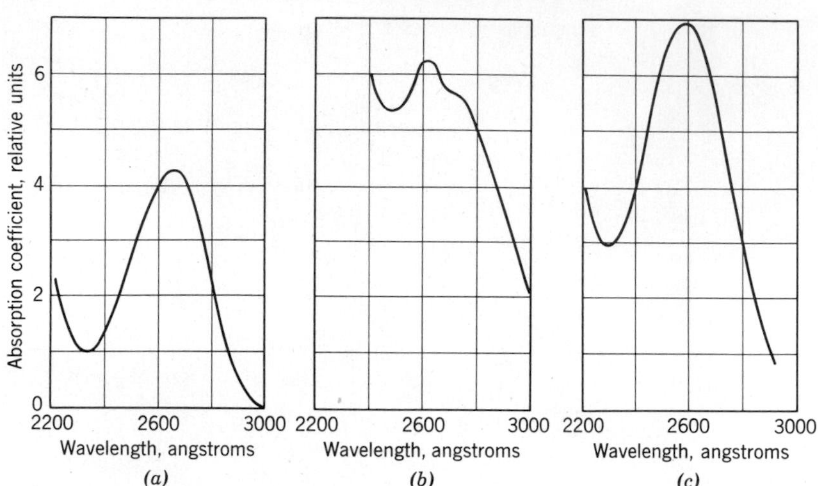

Fig. 4.43. Ultraviolet absorption curves for thymine (*a*), liver cytoplasm (*b*), and yeast nucleic acid (*c*). (After J. F. Scott and R. L. Sinsheimer, "Microabsorption Spectroscopy" in O. Glasser, *Medical Physics,* Vol. 2, Interscience, Yearbook Publishers, N.Y., 1950.)

that obtainable by phase-contrast microscopy; best results were obtained, of course, by a combination of the two techniques.[53]

In still another investigation with the television microscope Dr. Parpart was able to demonstrate the existence of structure in a layer of protoplasm directly beneath the outer cell membrane of a sea-urchin egg, which had been centrifuged with forces several thousand times gravity (Fig. 4.42); the lighter and heavier particles within the cell were thus moved to opposite ends of the cell, outside of the field of view.[54] It has been shown that the cortical granules, which become evident only with very careful focusing, play a critical role in the development of the egg.

Dr. P. O'B. Montgomery[55] of the University of Texas Southwestern Medical School employs a television microscope for the oil immersion phase microscopy of living cells. Microsurgery performed on the cells with a micromanipulator can be readily followed on the monitor screen, which may also be photographed for permanent record with a Bolex movie camera. Finally, with an ultraviolet-sensitive Vidicon in the television microscope, direct photometry of the monitor image permits estimates of the relative ultraviolet absorption of different parts of the specimen.

[53] See Parpart (reference 59).

[54] See Heilbrunn (reference 60), p. 34.

[55] See Montgomery (reference 61).

The possibility of continuous high-magnification viewing of specimens illuminated by ultraviolet radiations is a particularly important advantage of television microscopy. Although most of the components of a living cell are transparent in the visible range of the spectrum, they exhibit strong characteristic absorptions in the ultraviolet, particularly in the range between 2,200 and 3,000 A. Examples of absorption curves for this range are shown in Fig. 4.43. A comparative study of cell preparations illuminated by different narrow spectral bands of ultraviolet radiation may be helpful in locating concentrations of specific cell constituents. This is brought out clearly by the micrographs of an identical unstained kidney tissue section, illuminated by 4000-A and 2537-A radiation, respectively, which are shown in Fig. 4.44. In the picture on the right the strong absorption of the short-wave ultraviolet radiation by nucleic acid indicates the location of the cell nuclei; these are practically indistinguishable in the micrograph on the left.

The two pictures in Fig. 4.44 were obtained by photographing the picture transmitted by the ultraviolet television microscope shown in Fig. 3.87 on the monitor screen. The spectral response of the ultraviolet-sensitive Vidicon, which has a selenium photoconductive layer, is shown in Fig. 3.13. The quantum efficiency of a photoconductive layer of this type is fairly constant over the indicated range and is of the order of unity.

The absence of distinctive absorptions of cell constituents in the visible has led to the adoption, in conventional microscopy, of staining and fixing techniques to bring out details in cell structure. These processes kill the cells and may be expected to bring about certain morphological changes. With direct observation of the specimens in ultra-violet illumination by means of the television microscope it becomes possible, in principle, to study the structure of and processes within unmodified living cells.

However, this possibility exists only to a limited degree. The very absorption processes which lead to differentiation of detail within the cell result, in part, in chemical changes which lead to the death of the cell. Luckiesh[56] finds that a Bacterium coli culture has a survival ratio of $1/e = 0.37$ for an exposure to 0.002 joules per square centimeter (or $2.6 \cdot 10^{15}$ photons/cm^2) of 2537-A radiation. Figure 4.45 shows the decrease in germicidal action with increasing wavelength.

The study of living materials with ultraviolet illumination thus makes it desirable that the intensity of the illumination required to yield a satisfactory picture be as small as possible, or at any rate small compared to a lethal dose. The Appendix provides a detailed comparison,

[56] See Luckiesh (reference 62).

in this respect, of two types of television microscopes which have been described briefly in Chapter 3: a television microscope with a storage-type camera tube, such as the Vidicon, and the flying-spot microscope. The basic arrangement of both is shown once more schematically in Fig. 4.46.

The analysis given in the Appendix leads to the following conclusions:

1. For observation of objects with detail resolution close to the limiting resolution of an optical microscope, the Vidicon television microscope requires two to three times the average illumination of the object needed by the flying-spot microscope.

2. Flying-spot tube phosphors now available cannot provide sufficient illumination in the ultraviolet spectral range of greatest interest (e.g., near 2600 A) to give the desired high resolution at standard scanning rates. In the Vidicon microscope the provision of adequate illumination presents no serious problem.

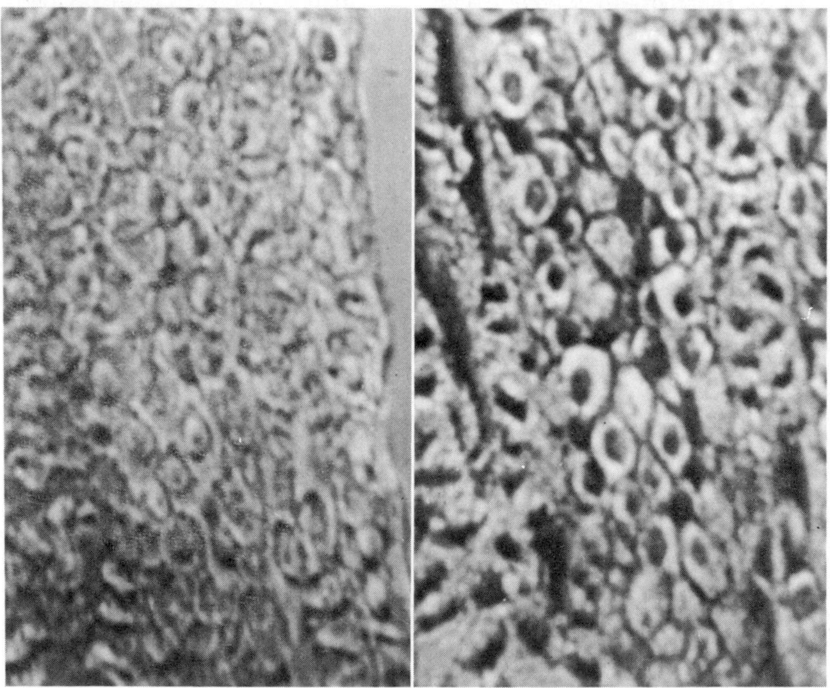

Fig. 4.44. Photographs of identical sections of unstained kidney tissue illuminated at 4000 A and 2537 A obtained from monitor screen of television microscope. (From Zworykin and Morton, *Television*, Wiley, New York, 1954.)

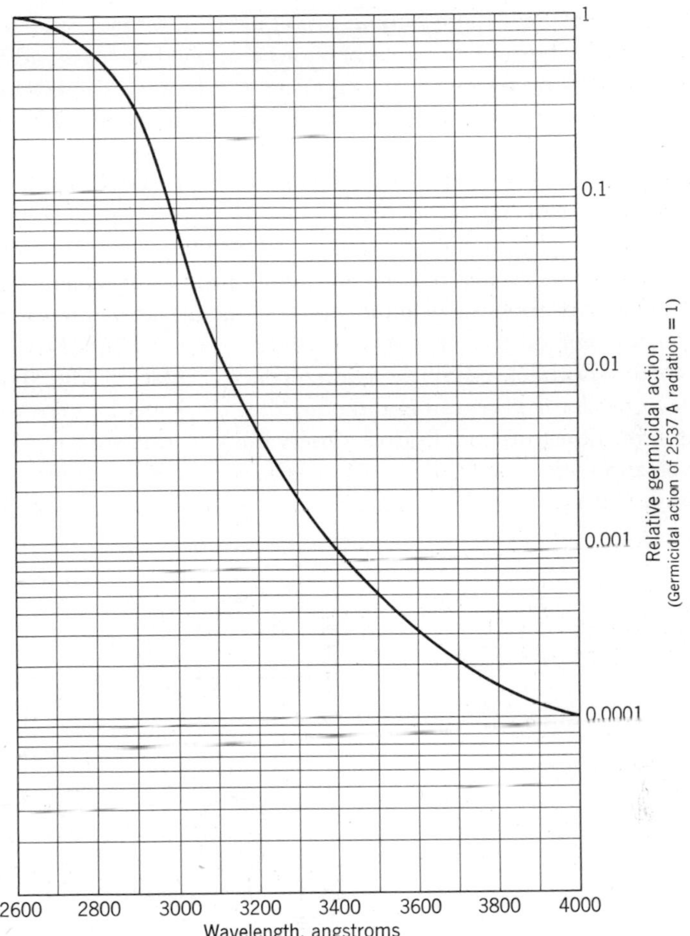

Fig. 4.45. Variation of germicidal action with wavelength (after Luckiesh, reference 62).

Thus the Vidicon television microscope[57] alone permits the study of specimens in the farther ultraviolet at top resolution and standard scanning rates. In particular, the flying-spot microscope appears unpromising in applications such as high-magnification color translation microscopy (see p. 135), in which narrow wavelength ranges must be selected from the total illumination.

[57] Or, more generally, the television microscope with a storage-type camera tube; an image orthicon with ultraviolet-transmissive face plate could, in principle, be substituted for the Vidicon.

On the other hand, there remain broad areas in biology and medicine in which the flying-spot microscope can be applied to great advantage. In particular, if quantitative information is to be extracted from the video signal, its strict proportionality of signal to light intensity and the absence of stored-signal carry-over from frame to frame are decided advantages. To some extent these may be offset by the spreading of the scanning spot resulting from flying-spot-tube phosphor persistence. It may also be noted that the graininess of the flying-spot tube screen injects some noise in the signal and that nonuniformity of screen deposition in the flying-spot tube has similar effects as nonuniform photosensitivity of a camera-tube target. For low scanning speeds and coarser line patterns these drawbacks may be overcome by replacing the flying-spot tube by a mechanical scanning disk.

The transition from qualitative observation to quantitative measurement of absorption or light emission is particularly straightforward in television microscopy. The visual information is in the form of electrical

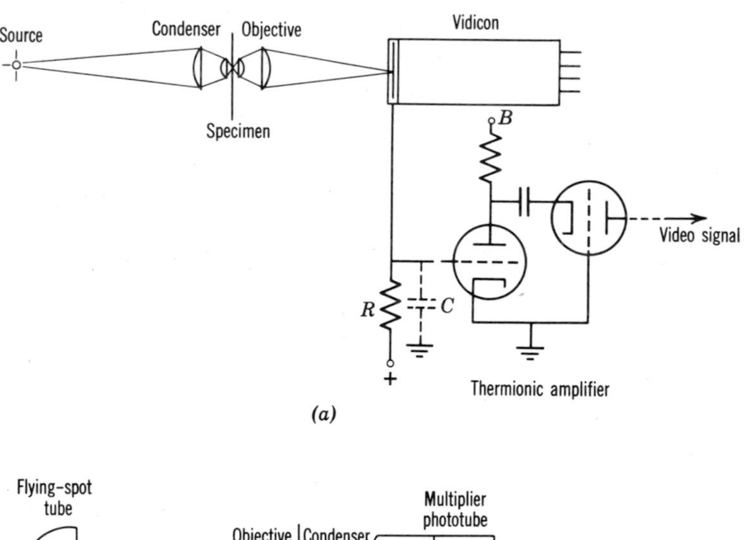

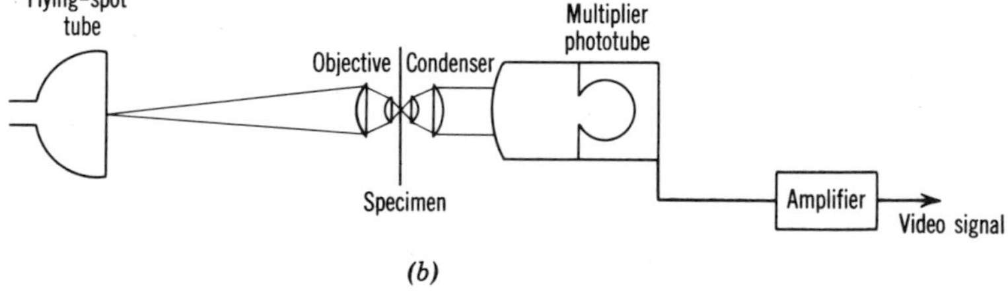

Fig. 4.46. Schematic diagram of Vidicon television microscope (*a*) and flying-spot television microscope (*b*).

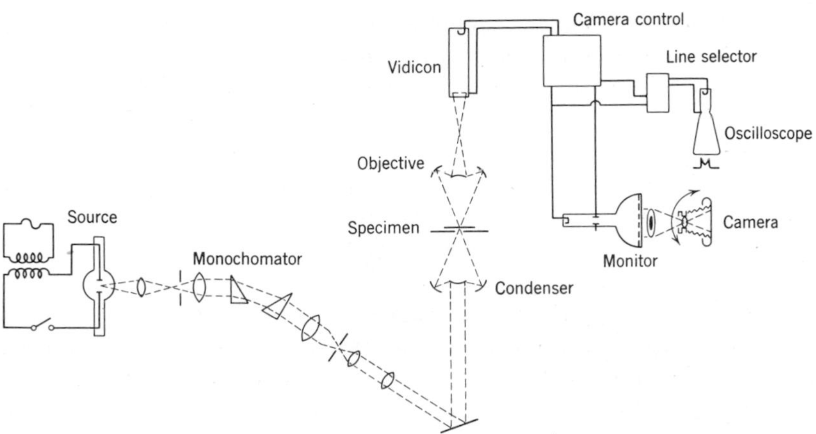

Fig. 4.47. Apparatus for studying U-V absorption in cells (G. Z. Williams, reference 65).

signals which may be applied to a variety of measuring instruments. For example, to obtain a representation of the brightness distribution along a particular television line, the video signal is applied through a gating circuit, which selects the time intervals corresponding to the line in question, to the vertical deflection of a cathode-ray oscilloscope;[58] the horizontal deflection of the oscilloscope is synchronized with the horizontal deflection of the television display.

The technique just described has been applied by George Z. Williams[59] of the National Institutes of Health to the study of reactions within living cells. Dr. Williams' equipment is shown schematically in Fig. 4.47. Radiation from a medium-pressure mercury arc (a General Electric C3-H85 lamp), which emits strongly throughout the ultraviolet spectrum from 2500 A up, is dispersed by a large-aperture Farrand quartz prism monochromator. The monochromator, fitted with a quartz condenser lens, serves as illuminator for a microscope with Bausch & Lomb Grey Type V reflective condenser and objective and with the cell preparation placed on the mechanical stage between them. The objective projects a magnified image of the specimen on the target of an RCA-ITV-5 Vidicon camera (replaced since by a more up-to-date RCA TK-21A), which supplies video signals to the control monitor and to a line-indicating Tektronix Model 524D television oscilloscope. The camera is so mounted that it can be aimed in turn at the monitor and at the oscilloscope; it records the oscilloscope tracing directly below the

[58]See Fisher (reference 63), and Buyer (reference 64).

[59]See Williams (reference 65).

monitor picture. With due consideration of the contrast factors introduced by the several elements in the television and oscilloscope chain, a satisfactory correlation could be obtained between the oscilloscope amplitudes and the corresponding absorptions measured by ultraviolet densitometry. The television monitor was also employed for rapid and accurate focusing in ultraviolet photomicrography. In this instance a prefocused photomicrographic camera was mounted on the same stand with a television camera, permitting rapid interchange.

The above equipment was employed in particular in a study of metabolic processes in normal and cancer cells. Dilute (0.001 molar) tetrazolium solution introduced into the surroundings of the living cell reacted with various constituents to form characteristic insoluble ultraviolet-absorbing "formazans." The spectral absorption of these formazans varies with the nature of the cell reagent, so that tetrazolium serves as an effective indicator, nontoxic in the concentrations here employed. A characteristic cell picture obtained from the monitor, together with the corresponding oscilloscope record, is shown in Fig. 4.48.

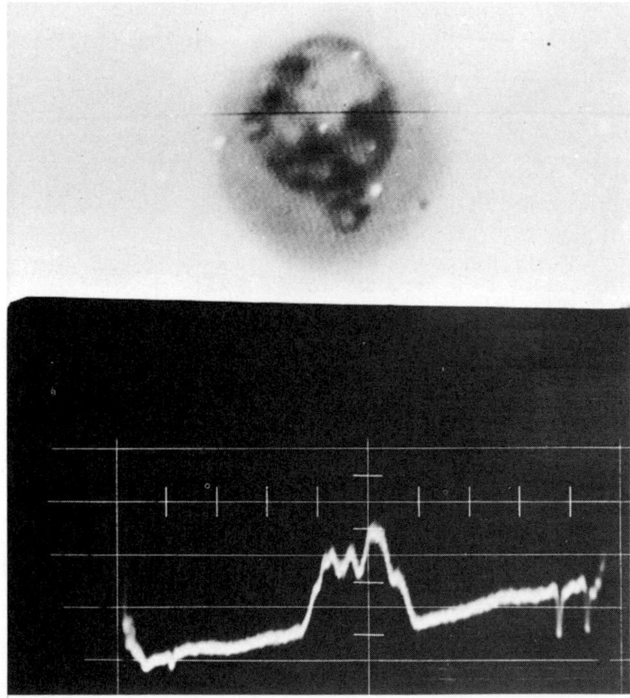

Fig. 4.48. U-V photomicrograph of cancer cell with oscillograph trace of absorption along selected scanning line. (Courtesy of Dr. G. Z. Williams, National Institutes of Health.)

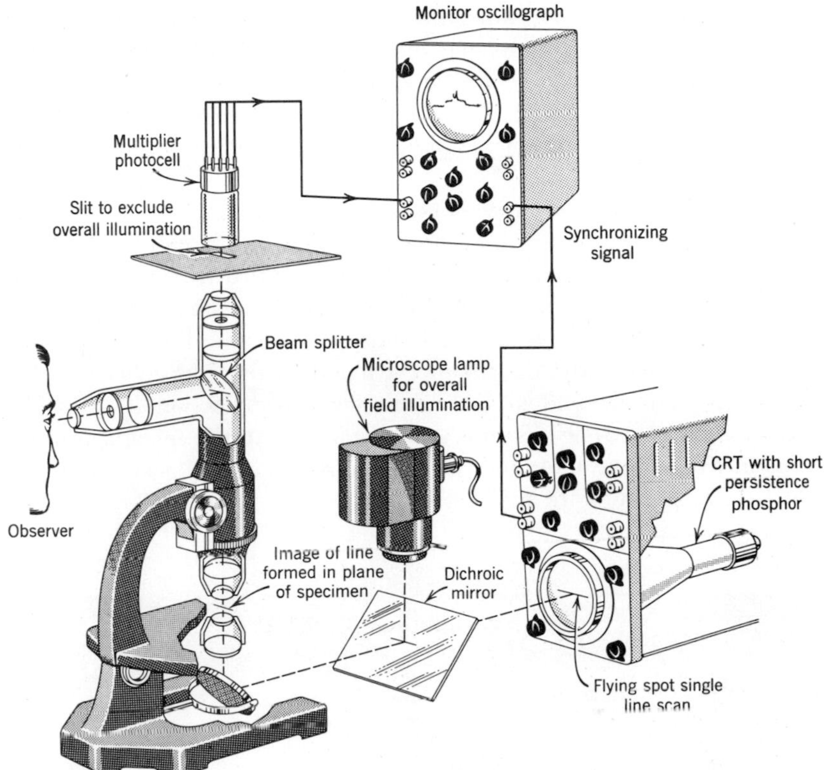

Fig. 4.49. Flying-spot apparatus for studying absorption in living tissues (Loeser and Berkley, reference 66). (Courtesy of *Science*.)

Extensive studies by television techniques in quantitative measurements on living material were carried out also by Loeser and Berkley[60] of the Western Reserve University Medical School and the Allen B. DuMont Laboratories. Nontoxic nuclear stains (acriflavine) were employed to cause nuclear material to give off a yellow fluorescence under excitation by near-ultraviolet or blue light. The fluorescence is accompanied by enhanced absorption of the exciting radiation. In practice it was much easier to obtain an oscillograph record of this enhanced absorption than of the fluorescence.

Both image orthicon and Vidicon chains were employed to study specific organs in live frogs with quartz-rod illumination, tissues suspended over the microscope condenser (at a magnification of 440), and

[60] See Loeser and Berkley (reference 66).

cancer-cell smears. A DuMont Type 280 oscillograph showing the intensity variation along a selected line was so interconnected with the television monitor that the same line appeared as a white line on the monitor picture. Although the Vidicon camera proved less sensitive than the image orthicon camera at low light levels, it was found adequate for most studies.

Experiments were also carried out with the use of a scanning disk and with a flying-spot tube for line selection. The set-up employed in the second instance is shown in Fig. 4.49. The entire field was observed with faint background illumination. A single blue line was projected by the flying-spot tube on the specimen, and the blue light transmitted by the specimen (or the fluorescence excited by it) was collected by a multiplier phototube and applied to the vertical deflection of an oscilloscope in which the time base was synchronized with the flying-spot tube. A slit in front of the multiplier phototube reduces the background illumination collected by the multiplier.

Fig. 4.50. Experimental 3V medical color camera transmitting picture of stained tissue slide to color receiver.

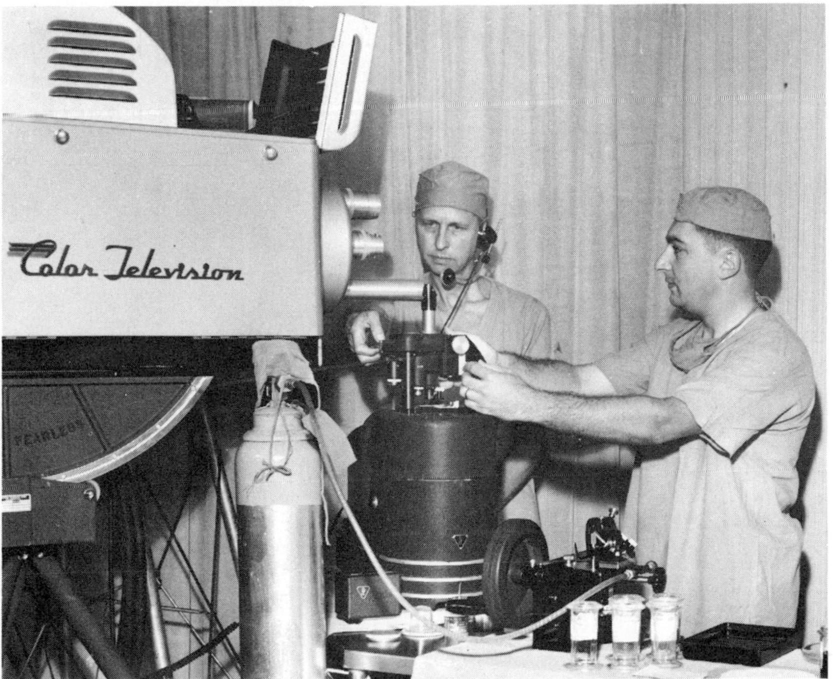

Fig. 4.51. Transmission of microslide with studio color camera at Annual Congress of American and Canadian Surgeons, Philadelphia, 1955. (Courtesy of RCA.)

In numerous applications of television microscopy the addition of color is a material advantage. Figure 4.50 shows a three-Vidicon medical color camera transmitting the picture of a stained tissue slide to a color receiver. Standard studio color cameras have been used in a demonstration sponsored by the Armed Forces Institute of Pathology and by the Radio Corporation of America to show the practicality of diagnosis of biopsies at a distance; in this instance the view of the specimen was transmitted on a closed circuit from Philadelphia to Baltimore and Washington. Figure 4.51 shows the set-up at a slightly later demonstration before the Annual Congress of the International College of Surgeons.[61] Provision for similar uses of color television has been made in an extensive installation at the Walter Reed Army Medical Center.[62]

A study of color-image processing, as part of a broader project on electronic-image processing, is also being carried out at the National

[61] See Griffith (reference 67).

[62] See reference 68.

Institutes of Health in Bethesda, Md.[63] Here motion pictures of the circulation in the frog mesentery and liver were obtained from the monitor of a field-sequential color-television system, produced by the Columbia Broadcasting System, which permitted reduced illumination as compared with direct cinematography. The effect of color substitutions and "crispening" techniques for increasing contrast was investigated.

Particle Counting and Identification. The problem of particle counting plays a role in many fields outside medicine and biology. The average particle size, or the number of particles in unit mass, is an important factor in the effectiveness of pigments and catalysts. Dust-particle counts and pollen counts are of concern to public health authorities. Counts of a similar character are useful in assaying the performance of ore mills. With this in view, universal instruments, such as the DuMont *Iconumerator* which counts particles of coin dimensions as well as of microscopic size, have been developed.

Other instruments have been designed for more specific purposes, such as red-blood-cell counts. They can, in general, be readily adapted for the counting of white blood cells and other microscopic particles. Since the blood count is accepted as one of the important tests of the state of human health, it has become a standard feature of thorough physical examinations. In particular, periodic blood counts are mandatory for persons engaged in work in which they may be exposed to penetrating radiation.

Red blood cells are round disk-shaped bodies which are 0.0001 to 0.0005 inch in diameter and have a maximum thickness of the order of 0.0001 inch. On the average, about 5 million of them are contained in a cubic millimeter of blood. The white corpuscles, about twice the size, are fewer in number and are commonly disregarded in making the red-blood-cell count; there may be only one white blood cell to a thousand red blood cells. If a white-cell count is to be made, the red cells are first dissolved.

To make a blood count a drop of blood diluted in a prescribed ratio is placed on a counting chamber. This is a microscope slide on which a precisely ground depressed area traps an accurately known amount of solution between the bottom of the chamber and the cover glass. The technician then places the counting chamber on the stage of a microscope and counts the number of particles within an area outlined on the chamber. This counting is a tiring, time-consuming task, subject to human error. Hence numerous methods of performing the count mechanically have been proposed and tried out in practice.

Some of these methods are quite indirect and seek to infer the number

[63] See Brown (reference 69).

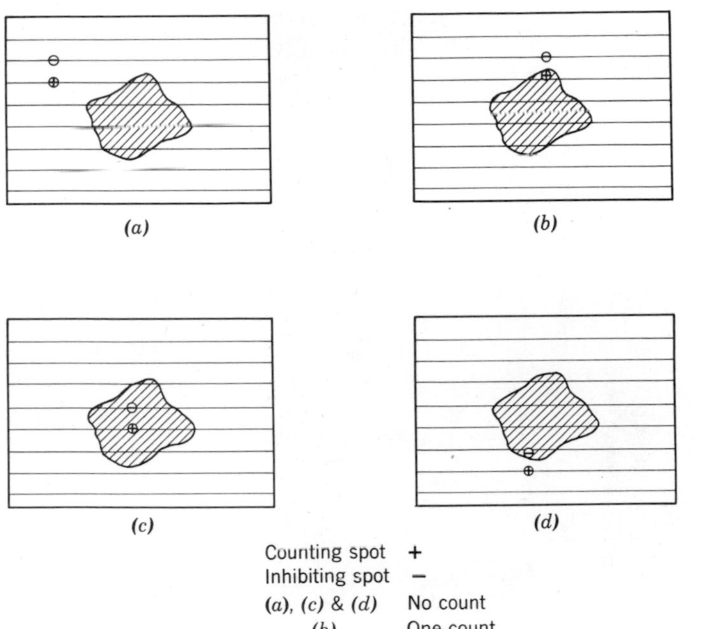

Fig. 4.52. Counting of particles with double-spot technique. (Courtesy of Dr. F. Roberts.)

of particles from the turbidity or absorption of the sample. Others seek to measure the relative volume occupied by the corpuscles and the suspending solution by measuring the relative amount of time a corpuscle is in the field of the microscope objective as the slide is displaced.[64] Neither procedure yields an actual cell count.

True particle counts are provided by the aforementioned Iconumerator. Here a flying-spot tube scanning pattern is projected on the specimen. The direct video signal and the video signal delayed by one line period are applied to an anticoincidence circuit; this circuit transmits signal pulses resulting from the incidence of the flying-spot on an opaque particle only when no similar pulse occurred in approximately the same location on the preceding line. Thus regularly shaped particles are counted only once, irrespective of size.

In a system proposed by Roberts, Young, and Causley[65] an optical technique achieves the same result as the delay line in the Iconumerator. The light from the flying-spot tube passes through a doubly refracting prism, so that the specimen is scanned by two line patterns, plane

[64] See Frommer (reference 70).

[65] See Roberts, Young, and Causley (reference 71).

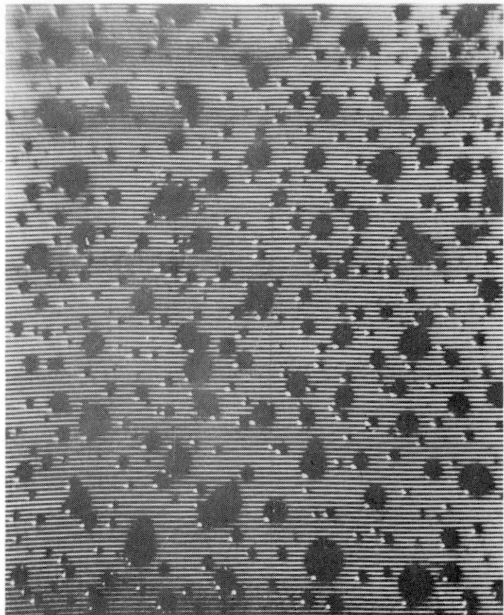

Fig. 4.53. Steel dust dispersion with counting dots, as viewed on monitor of flying-spot microscope. (Courtesy of Dr. F. Roberts.)

polarized at right angles to each other and displaced by a distance of the order of a scanning line. A polarizing cube separates the two components of the transmitted light and directs them toward two multiplier phototubes, the output of which is applied to an anticoincidence circuit similar to that employed in the Iconumerator.

Both systems give an accurate count of an assembly of nonoverlapping particles without re-entrant contours (Fig. 4.52). Two particles overlapping in a vertical direction are counted as a single particle. On the other hand, particles with re-entrant contours may be counted as several particles. With particles of regular shape, such as red blood cells, only overlapping leads to error. Its effect can be reduced by the employment of relatively dilute solutions. Figure 4.53 shows a dispersion of steel dust particles (1 to 30 microns in diameter) counted with a flying-spot microscope using a 2-mm oil-immersion objective. The white dots indicate counted particles. A different approach to particle-counting is used in the *Sanguinometer* of Flory and Pike.[66] Here the total number of transits of the scanning line through particles are counted. This becomes a measure of the total number of particles only if the number of transits per particle—or the average particle diameter—also is known. The average particle diameter is measured by com-

[66] See Flory and Pike (reference 72).

paring the transit times through a particle with the time delay provided by an adjustable delay line. The delay line adjustment is interconnected with a shunt on the count-rate meter in such fashion that the meter gives a direct reading for the total number of particles in the field, irrespective of average size, when a magic-eye indicator tube shows that the delay line matches the mean transit time through a particle.

The complete Sanguinometer is shown in Fig. 4.54. Dark-field illumination is employed to minimize background noise; a picture of a counting-chamber field as seen on the monitor screen is shown in Fig. 4.55. In the count-rate meter the incoming pulses are converted into pulses of uniform amplitude and width by a pair of cascaded regenerative clippers; they are integrated by a capacitance which discharges through the count-rate meter.

In order to measure the pulse length the individual pulses are clipped and differentiated after passage through a wide-band amplifier. The signal pips caused by the leading edges of the pulses are inverted, passed through the adjustable delay line, and applied to the suppressor grid of a 6AS6 coincidence tube; the pips caused by the trailing edges are ap-

Fig. 4.54. The RCA Sanguinometer.

plied to the control grid of the same tube. Hence, if the adjustable delay line is of such length that the arrival of the pips at the coincidence tube coincides, plate current flows in the tube. The flow of plate current is indicated on an electric eye mounted on the front panel of the meter in newer models of the particle-counter. The delay-line adjustment, which is ganged with the meter shunt, is visible at the bottom of the meter case in Fig. 4.54. It permits a time-delay adjustment between 0.15 and 0.6 microsecond with 0.025 microsecond intervals.

The system was first tested with simulated particle fields consisting of punched-hole patterns projected on a screen and reimaged on the Vidicon target of the camera. It was found that for particle diameters varying by a factor of 2 and counts ranging from 75 to 300 the error of the counter scarcely ever exceeded 5 per cent. Subsequent tests were made, with the cooperation of Dr. Leon Hellman of the Sloan-Kettering Institute, on samples of real blood. The results of these tests are shown in Fig. 4.56. The straight line drawn through the points may be regarded as an empirical calibration curve of the instrument for specimens of this type. The zero intercept of the curve must be ascribed to spurious noise counts. Eventual drifts of the instrument could be checked with the aid of a specially prepared fixed blood slide.

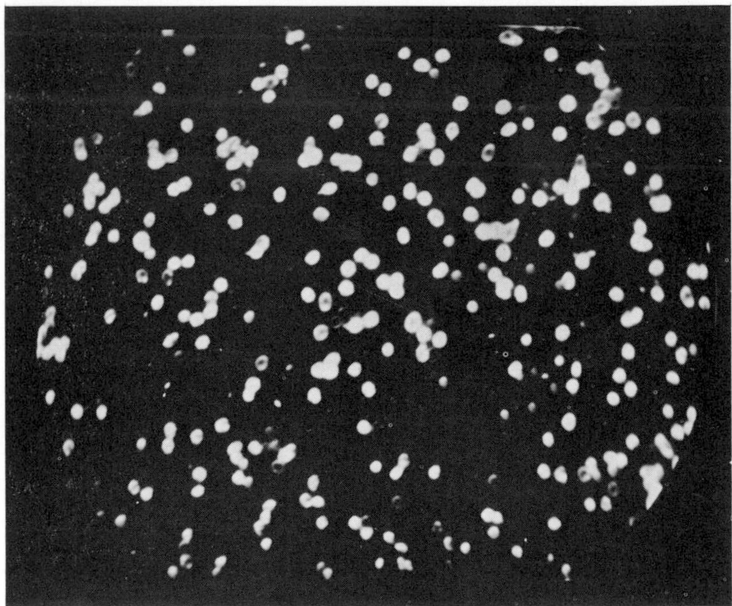

Fig. 4.55. Blood sample in counting chamber, as seen on monitor screen of RCA Sanguinometer.

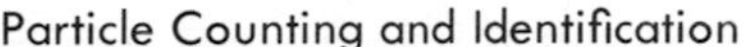

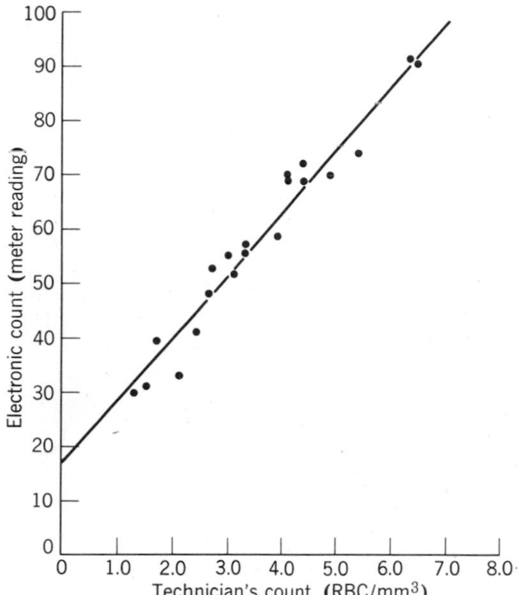

Fig. 4.56. Comparison of Sanguinometer count with manual count.

Another particle identification and counting problem of great importance was first attacked by Mellors and Silver of the Sloan-Kettering Institute.[67] Further development of the instrumentation has been undertaken by Walter Tolles of the Airborne Instruments Laboratory. The problem in question is the early diagnosis of cancer by the recognition of isolated cancer cells in smears. The diagnosis proposed by Mellors and Silver relies on the fact that the nuclei of cancer cells stained with certain basic fluorescent dyes, or fluorochromes, fluoresce more intensely than those of normal cells associated with them. In their apparatus the specimen slide, with its stained cell suspension, is scanned by a flying spot of long-wave ultraviolet radiation (Fig. 4.57). The spot size is of the same order in diameter as a cell nucleus, namely, 10 microns. It is formed by imaging, on a reduced scale, a Nipkow scanning disk with 20 apertures on the specimen. Since the disk rotates at 30 revolutions per second and the scanning pattern consisting of 20 overlapping lines is 0.1-mm high and 0.25-mm wide, the scanning time for a single nucleus is about 67 microseconds. The mechanical stage is displaced automatically from one scanning area to the next so that, in due time, the entire field is explored.

[67] See Mellors and Silver (reference 73).

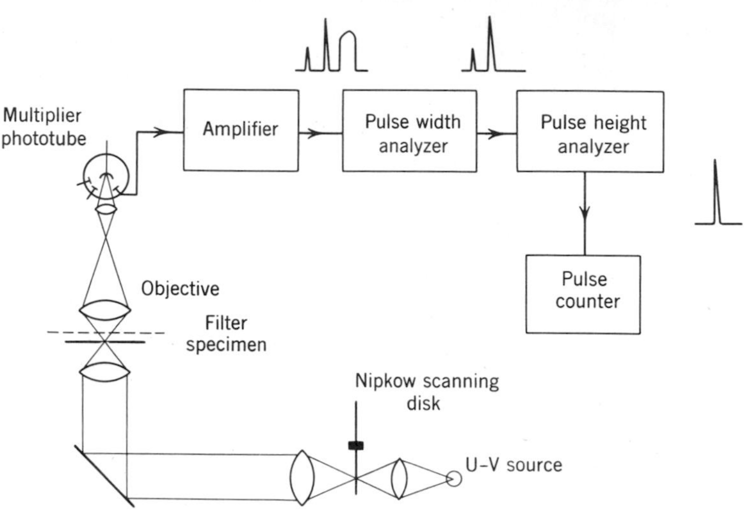

Fig. 4.57. Flying-spot scanner for cancer cell detection (Mellors and Silver, reference 73).

The scanning is made sufficiently slow so that the signals produced by the fluorescent light from the cell nuclei, directed onto the photocathode of a multiplier phototube, are not affected greatly by shot noise or amplifier noise. Electronic discriminators reject both excessively wide pulses originating in cell clusters and the lower pulses generated by the nuclei of normal cells. The residual high and narrow pulses, such as are produced by cancer cell nuclei, are counted by an electronic counter.

In the *Cytoanalyzer* developed by Walter Tolles and his associates[68] cells in a Papanicolaou smear are measured with respect to the size (cord dimension) and optical density of the nucleus. Every accepted measurement appears as a dot on an oscilloscope screen on which vertical deflection is proportional to absorption, horizontal deflection to chord length. The dots are photographed by an open-shutter camera, so that a complete distribution pattern is obtained for every smear. If an appreciable number of dots falls into a range of size and density which corresponds to abnormal or questionable cells, the smear is examined by a trained cytologist. Since the great majority of smears will yield primarily normal distributions, the labor of the cytologist is greatly reduced by preliminary automatic scanning.

To minimize the number of spurious abnormal cell records, counts arising from particles other than cells, as well as those from cell clusters

[68] See Tolles (references 74 to 76).

and folded cells, must be eliminated. This is accomplished by gating circuits controlled by the absolute and relative absorption of the cytoplasm on either side of the nucleus. Unless the cytoplasm absorption falls between two prescribed limits and the ratio of the nuclear absorption to the cytoplasm absorption exceeds a certain value, the count is eliminated automatically.

In the scanner of the Cytoanalyzer (Fig. 4.58) an image of the continuously displaced specimen is projected into the plane of a scanning disk with 30 apertures at a common radius of 75 millimeters, rotating at 30 rps. The disk apertures are so dimensioned that light from a specimen-area 5 microns in diameter reaches the multiplier phototube. The scanning lines are 250 microns in length and the rastèr height equals the width of the smear; as one side of the smear is reached, the specimen is displaced by 250 microns in the direction of the scanning lines, and the specimen motion perpendicular to the lines is reversed in direction. Thus a complete smear area of 1 x 2 centimeters is scanned automatically in approximately 4 seconds.

Area Displays of Skin Potentials. Television systems of a very rudimentary character are employed in demonstrating the variations in skin potentials accompanying heart and brain activity. The conventional multichannel electroencephalograph or electrocardiograph provides one-dimensional representations of the time-variation of these potentials at selected points. The analyst must correlate these variations in some manner in order to obtain an idea of the space variation of the potentials and to obtain indications of localized abnormalities. In area displays, first suggested by Dr. Douglas Goldman for the localization of brain tumors, the sweep of potential waves across the body surface, along with their variation in time, can be made immediately evident.

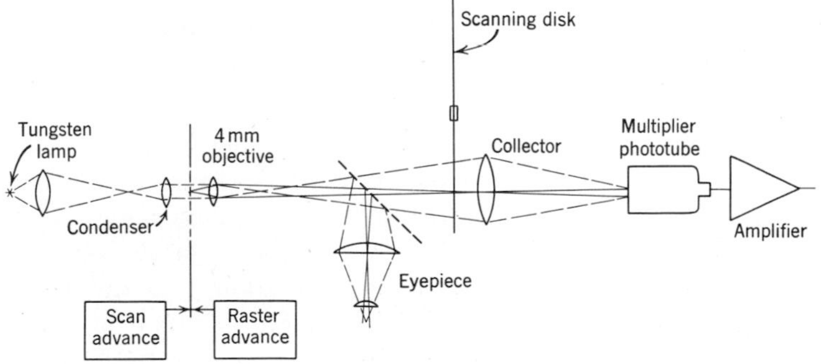

Fig. 4.58. Schematic diagram of cytoanalyzer scanner (Tolles and Bostrom, reference 75).

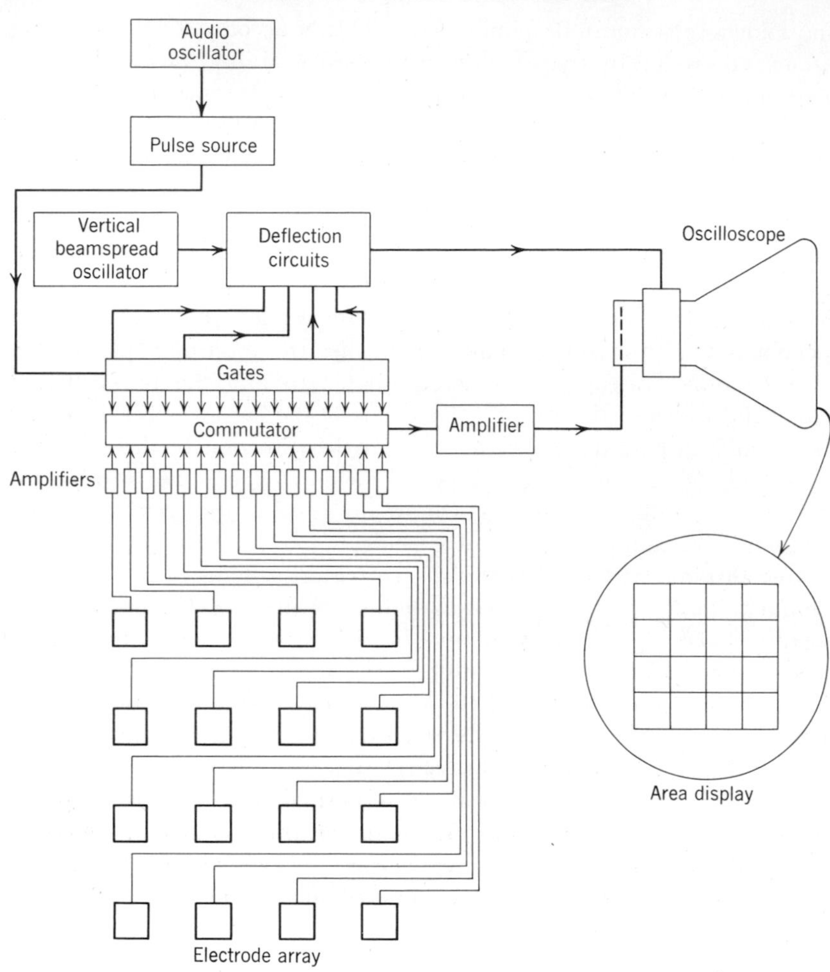

Fig. 4.59. Sequential area display of skin potentials (Goldman *et al.*, reference 78).

Two different techniques have been employed to generate the area display. In the system devised by Stanford Goldman and his associates[69] at the Massachusetts Institute of Technology (Fig. 4.59) the amplified signals from an array of 16 electrodes on the chest of the patient are applied by an electronic commutator to the grid of a cathode-ray tube. The pattern generated on the tube face may be observed directly or photographed with a motion-picture camera for

[69] See Goldman (references 77 and 78).

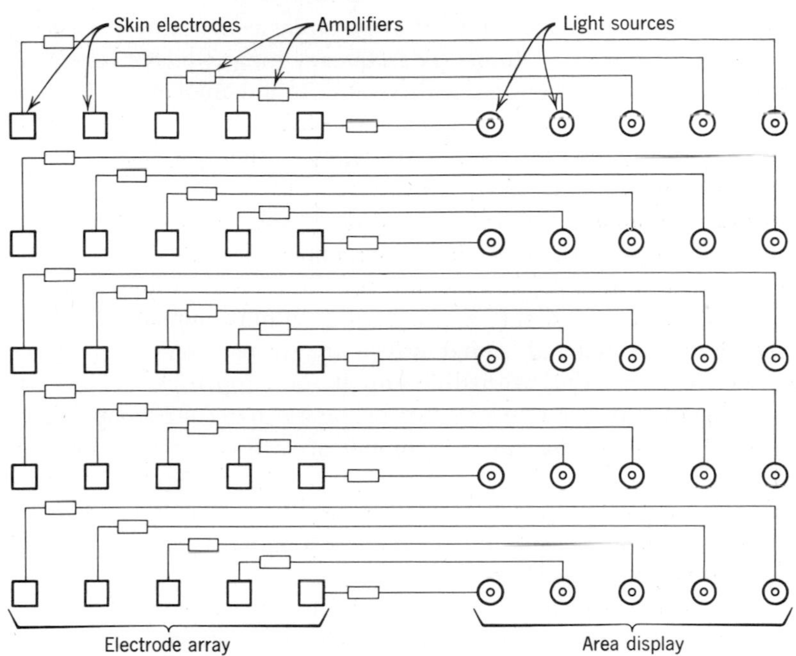

Fig. 4.60. Simultaneous area display of potentials (Lilly, reference 79).

reprojection. John C. Lilly,[70] at the Johnson Foundation of the University of Pennsylvania, and the National Institutes of Health, Bethesda, Md., employs a simultaneous representation (Fig. 4.60): 25 skin-contact electrodes arranged in a regular array continuously control the intensity or spot size of circular light sources arranged in a geometrically similar array. The system of light sources is photographed by a motion-picture camera at a high speed—64 or 128 pictures per second—and is reprojected at the lower speed of 16 pictures per second. The progression of the potential waves across the exposed cortex of experimental animals shows up very strikingly at the lower speed and exhibits consistent correlations with brain activity. A system combining the simultaneous and sequential approach, which increases both time and space resolution by employing an array of 256 electrodes and a picture repetition rate of 1000 per second, has been devised, at Lilly's suggestion, by Carl Barus.[71]

[70] See Lilly (reference 79).
[71] See Barus (reference 80).

The very low signal level of the skin potentials—they rarely exceed 50 microvolts in amplitude—limits the frequency range which can be transmitted and requires amplifiers with very little low-frequency ("flicker") noise injection. A display system for the indication of brain activity, which resembles Lilly's in several particulars, is the *Toposcope*, developed by Harold Shipton at the Burden Institute in England.[72]

Ultrasonic Ranging. A technique even further removed from standard television practice than the aforementioned area displays is the utilization of ultrasonic ranging for the location of tumors. Unlike X rays, which simply reveal variations in the atomic number and density of the absorbing material, sound waves are strongly reflected by interfaces between materials with different elastic properties. Hence they may be employed to reveal changes in the mechanical properties of tissues with a substantially uniform content of carbon, oxygen, hydrogen, and nitrogen.

The technique of ultrasonic ranging has been explored particularly with a view to its possible use for cancer diagnosis. Thus Wild and Reid[73] of St. Barnabas Hospital in Minneapolis have developed apparatus for exploring any part of the human body in which malignant tumors are of relatively frequent occurrence. Different methods of scanning—B-scan, sector scan, or PPI scan, to borrow the terminology of Radar—are employed, depending on the region studied. However, the technique is essentially the same in all cases.

One-microsecond pulses of 15-megacycle sound waves are transmitted into the tissues by a quartz-crystal transducer at a repetition rate of 1000 second^{-1}. The crystal is coupled to the tissues by a water column which must be as long as the depth to which the tissues are explored. A receiver connected across the crystal parallel to the transmitter detects the echoes reflected at various depths within the tissues. At the same time the crystal is displaced slowly along a line parallel to the tissue surface (e.g., in B-scan). On the oscilloscope screen each vertical excursion of the beam is triggered by the pulse emission and is proportional to the time which has elapsed since the emission; the beam intensity is proportional to the amplitude of the echo. Horizontal deflection is synchronized with the displacement of the crystal.

The display on the oscilloscope is thus essentially a picture of a section of the tissues traversed by the sound beam. The requirement of a water column equal in length to the depth to be explored derives from the fact that echoes from a greater depth tend to be masked by secondary echoes from the tissue surface, i.e., echoes which have been

[72] See Walter (reference 81).

[73] See Wild and Reid (reference 82).

reflected by the crystal and have then been reflected by tissues a second time.

Ways of improving the depth and azimuthal resolution of ultrasonic ranging as well as ways of avoiding misinterpretations resulting from multiple reflections ("spooks") have been studied in detail by Douglass H. Howry of the University of Colorado School of Medicine.[74] A special difficulty in ultrasonic ranging is the great sensitivity of the amplitude of the received echo pulse to the inclination of the reflecting surface. Dr. Howry has developed a technique for stereo representation of objects by preparing ultrasonic projections, using combined azimuthal and vertical scan, for different positions of the transmitter. The various projections not only permit a three-dimensional reconstruction of the object, but eliminate errors resulting from spooks and the practical invisibility of flat surfaces inclined by an appreciable angle to the direction of scan.

The future of ultrasonic ranging in diagnosis is still in doubt. However, it provides a promising new approach to an important problem.

Radiology. By contrast, the practice of X-ray examination for diagnostic purposes and of X-ray and radioactive cancer therapy is quite generally accepted. Here television techniques can contribute in various ways.

The most important application of television is in fluoroscopy, i.e., the direct observation of X-ray shadowgraphs of the patient formed on a fluorescent screen. It has all the advantages cited in connection with industrial fluoroscopy, with the added very important one that it provides a way of reducing the X-ray dosage of the patient. In conventional techniques the exposure of the patient in a fluoroscopic abdominal examination may approach the established maximum tolerance dosage.

Even so, the picture observed on the fluoroscopic screen is far inferior to that which may be recorded on an X-ray plate. The latter may reveal contrast differences of the order of 1 or 2 per cent and can come close to conveying the entire information carried by the incident X-ray beam. The fluoroscopic picture, on the other hand, may permit the recognition of intensity differences no smaller than 20 or 40 per cent and reveals only relatively coarse detail.

As W. E. Chamberlain[75] has shown in a classical paper, this is a result of the inefficient utilization by the human eye of the light emission of the fluorescent screen, rather than of any defect of the screen itself. At the low light levels of the fluoroscopic screen (0.0001 to 0.01 millilambert), cone vision in the fovea centralis of the retina, which is

[74] See Howry (reference 83).

[75] See Chamberlain (reference 84).

Fig. 4.61. The employment of an RCA-ITV camera with a Philips image amplifier for fluoroscopy at Temple University (Stauffer, Oppenheimer, Stewart, and Lynch, reference 87). (Courtesy of Dr. H. M. Stauffer.)

responsible for high-resolution vision at normal light-levels, does not exist. Vision is entirely by means of the rods, in the peripheral portions of the retina. Adequate use of rod vision also has the drawback of requiring very long dark-adaptation times, which may be of the order of an hour. Chamberlain pointed out that if the brightness of the fluoroscopic screen could be amplified by a factor of 100 or 1000, the viewer could utilize his normal cone vision, and the picture observed would be comparable in detail and contrast resolution to that recorded on X-ray film.

The principal means by which the desired increase in brightness may be obtained have already been indicated. The brightness intensifier by itself has made the motion-picture recording of physiological processes practicable by reducing the required X-ray dosage below the accepted tolerance limits. Thus the recording with the Westinghouse Fluorex intensifier of the movement of the soft palate during speech was demonstrated to doctors in Baltimore in 1955.[76] Excellent results have also been obtained with the General Electric Company's photoconductive X-ray camera tube, the X-icon, in a simple industrial television chain.[77] At Temple University in Philadelphia the combination of a Philips intensifier and an RCA Vidicon camera chain, realizing even greater sensitivity, has been tested for its usefulness in direct fluoroscopy[78] (Fig.

[76] See Steinweg (reference 85).

[77] See Jacobs and Berger (refrence 14).

[78] See Stauffer, Oppenheimer, Stewart, Blackstone and Lynch (references 86 and 87).

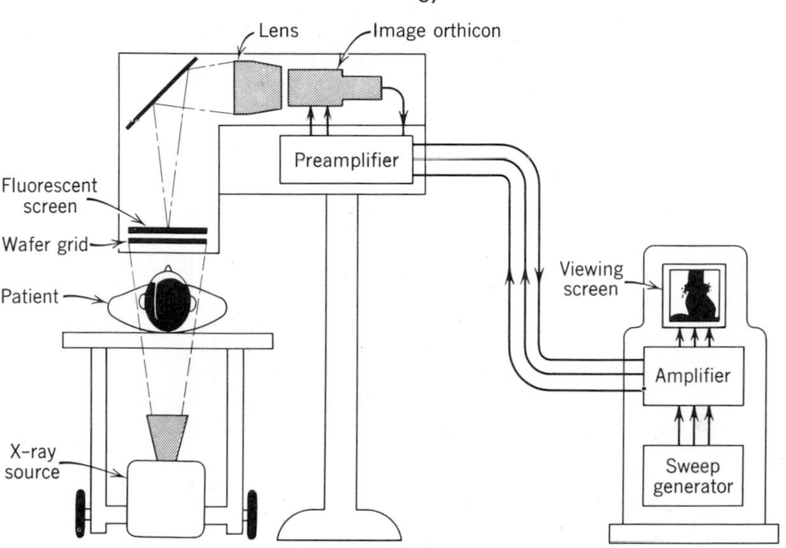

Fig. 4.62. Television system for observing X-ray screen (Morgan, reference 89). (Courtesy of *American Journal of Roentgenology.*)

4.61). Here the television link permits simultaneous observation by several people, gives the observer freedom of movement, facilitates his protection from stray radiation, and provides the possibility of electronic contrast adjustment. Similar equipment, employing a Dage television chain, has been installed in the Cleveland Clinic Heart Catheterization Laboratory for examining the heart and detecting structural defects requiring surgery.

The advantages indicated above are combined with that of permitting the examination of arbitrarily large portions of the human body if a conventional fluoroscope screen is viewed with the help of a high-sensitivity television camera and a highly efficient optical system. The Bendix Lumicon system, based on earlier fluoroscopic studies of Drs. R. H. Morgan and R. E. Sturm[79] at Johns Hopkins University, is an example. Its application is illustrated in Fig. 4.62. The pickup tube is an image orthicon with wide-spaced target to extend the operation to lower light-levels. It is capable of transmitting recognizable pictures if the screen has a brightness comparable to an outdoor scene in medium moonlight, a condition under which only rod vision is effective. The kinescope screen may be as much as 50,000 times brighter than the fluorescent screen; hence viewing is permitted under conditions close to

[79] See Morgan and Sturm (reference 88).

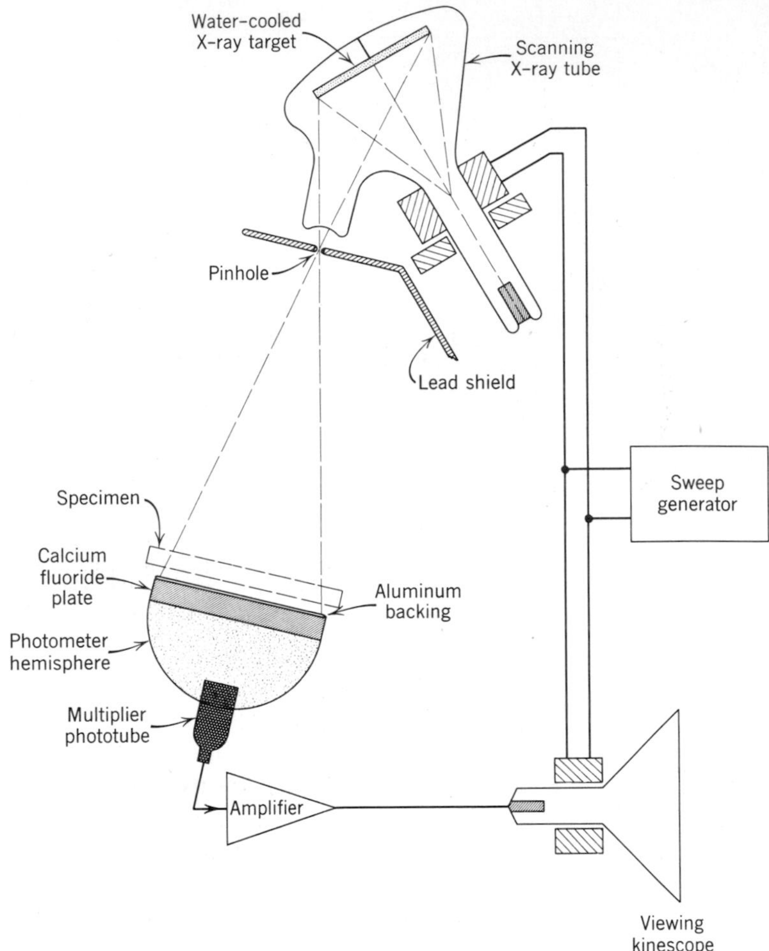

Fig. 4.63. Flying-spot system for X-ray fluoroscopy (Moon, reference 90).

maximum visual acuity.[80] A 1029-line scanning pattern and a broad (15-megacycle) transmission channel provide sufficient detail to allow utilization of this high cone-vision acuity. The system thus meets the requirements laid down by Chamberlain for an effective screen intensification system.

It is of interest to note that the flying-spot principle, which is intrinsically favorable from the point of view of minimizing the exposure of the patient or object required for a record of a given quality, has also been

[80] See Morgan (reference 89).

applied to the problem of fluoroscopy. The arrangement devised by R. J. Moon[81] of the Institute of Radiobiology and Biophysics of the University of Chicago is shown schematically in Fig. 4.63. In the X-ray tube a water-cooled tungsten target is scanned in a standard pattern by a sharply focused electron beam. A small fraction of the X rays produced upon impact pass out of the tube through a pinhole, so that a pinhole image of the pattern is projected on the patient or object to be observed. The transmitted X rays generate fluorescence in a large, clear, aluminum-backed calcium fluoride plate in which emission is concentrated as much as possible on the photocathode of a multiplier phototube. The output of the phototube controls the screen brightness of a kinescope in which deflection is synchronized with the deflection in the X-ray tube.

The chief difficulty with this system is the attainment of adequate X-ray intensity at the object. While in conventional fluoroscopy the useful X-ray intensity arriving at the object is obtained from a spot on the anticathode which may be millimeters or even centimeters in dimension, in a flying-spot system the radiation from only one picture element, a small fraction of a millimeter in size, can be utilized at a time. This is achieved with the aid of the small pinhole, typically 0.001 square centimeter in area. The flying-spot technique has not achieved practical utilization in fluoroscopy.

Closed-circuit television has also found application in nuclear therapy. Figure 4.64 shows a Kay Lab camera, combined with a Fluorex image intensifier, used at the Cedars of Lebanon Hospital in California for locating the beam from a radioactive cobalt bomb in cancer therapy. Remote control guidance by television minimizes exposure hazards for the operating personnel.[82]

In principle, television techniques are also applicable for the mapping of concentrations of radioactive materials in tissues. An example is the determination of the extent and activity of a thyroid gland by studying the distribution of radioactive iodine in the thyroid area after oral administration. The concentration is measured with the aid of a scintillation counter. The intensity of the radioactive emissions is generally so small that only very slow, mechanical scanning (about 20 inches per minute) can be employed.[83] At the end of each scanning line a transverse displacement by a line width is effected, and the scanning motion reverses direction. Every scintillation pulse is recorded as a black dot

[81]See Moon (reference 90).

[82]See Morgan, Sturm, Miller, and Torrance (reference 91).

[83]See Cassen, Curtis, Reed, and Libby (reference 92), Curtis and Cassen (reference 93), and Sopp, Geyer, and Lehman (reference 94).

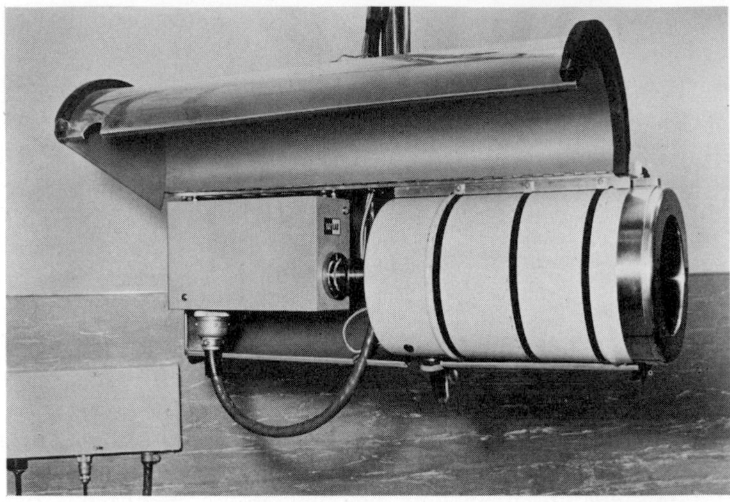

Fig. 4.64. Industrial television camera with image intensifier for positioning rays from cobalt bomb for cancer treatment at Cedars of Lebanon Hospital. (Courtesy of Kay Lab.)

through carbon paper by a stylus mounted on the scintillation-counter carriage. The relative concentration of radioactive material is inferred from the density of black dots on the record.

Psychotherapy. An interesting experiment in psychotherapy for mental patients by means of closed-circuit television is being carried out at Agnew State Hospital in California under the auspices of the Department of Psychology of San Jose State College. It is hoped that the impression of personal contact, which would enable a single trained therapist to reach a large number of patients at a time, can be conveyed adequately in this manner.

EDUCATION

There is probably no service to man in which television can make a greater contribution than in education. This may be true even if we leave out of account the educational aspects of ordinary broadcast television and restrict our attention to education in the formal sense. In the public school, at the college level, in professional instruction, and in job training television has an important job to do. Dean Pollock of New York University summarizes his estimate of the role of television in the statement: "It now seems clear that television offers the greatest opportunity for the advancement of education since the introduction of printing by movable type."[84]

More specifically, Dean Pollock believes that television can fulfill the following functions:

1. It can improve the quality of instruction by bringing the teacher psychologically closer to more students than is now possible in the ordinary classroom.
2. It can bring the material of instruction, i.e., written matter, demonstrations, etc., closer to the average student than is possible without it.
3. It can meet the growing teacher shortage without down-grading the quality of instruction by increasing the number of students reached by one good teacher.
4. It can improve the economic status of teachers by utilizing technological progress to increase their professional efficiency.

These considerations render a careful investigation of the best uses of television in education of great value.

Views expressed by Milton Eisenhower when President of the Pennsylvania State University and by a special faculty committee of Dartmouth College closely parallel Dean Pollock's statement. Thus, even though this enthusiasm has not been uniformly shared by all educational administrators and teachers, there has been a widespread readiness to experiment with the new medium, especially at the college level. Financial support for such experimentation has been provided by state governments, a number of concerns in the television industry, and, in particular, by the Ford Foundation's Fund for the Advancement of Education.[85]

Public Schools. Experiments with closed-circuit television have been carried out in public schools in Montclair, N. J., Pontiac, Mich., Columbus, Ohio, Phoenix, Ariz., and Denver, Colo. However, the first complete school-system closed-circuit installation was placed in service at Pocatello, Idaho, in February 1956. Altogether, eleven schools are connected by a community distribution system to a television studio at Idaho State College. Separate rooms with 21-inch receivers are set aside for television teaching. Special teachers, who once traveled from school to school, are now able to reach the entire student body from one location. Duplication of equipment for showing educational films, as well as interschool film transport and excessive film wear, is eliminated. The television system also serves to present student-originated programs,

[84]See Pollock (reference 95).

[85]See Zorbaugh (reference 96).

such as plays, discussions, and musical events. Since the community antenna system reaches the homes of the area, parents as well as children detained at home can share in the programs.

A more extensive plan for public-school closed-circuit television was launched on June 26, 1956 by the Washington County Board of Education at Hagerstown, Md.[86] This plan, supported by the Ford Foundation's Fund for the Advancement of Education, the Radio-Electronics-Television Manufacturers' Association, and several other groups, contemplates a five-year program which began by linking eight Hagerstown city schools in September 1956 and eventually expects to cover 47 schools throughout the county.

It is highly unlikely that a similar pattern will be followed in large cities; here the transmission of school programs over broadcast channels provided by educational television stations or by contract with commercial stations becomes the more economical approach. However, large schools can be expected to have their own closed-circuit systems. A start in this direction was made in the fall of 1956 by Evanston Township High School. Furthermore, building plans for the George Westinghouse Vocational High School in Brooklyn call for the construction of a television studio for broadcasting lectures and other educational programs over closed circuits within the school system and for teaching students in television techniques.[87]

Colleges and Universities. In 1956 some 100 institutions of higher education in the United States used closed-circuit television-teaching techniques, generally on an experimental basis. In many, such as Northwestern University, Indiana University, Kansas State College, and Boston University, the training of students in the television arts was the primary objective. Courses at other institutions, however, have included nearly every subject on the curriculum. The nature of the television installation and the manner in which television is utilized also vary widely from place to place, ranging all the way from individual television chains employed as an aid to classroom teaching to the 50-classroom, closed-circuit system of Stephens College in Columbia, Mo., and the new Electrical Engineering Building at the Case Institute of Technology in Cleveland, which has 40 lecture rooms equipped for closed-circuit reception and transmission.

Three instructional television research projects sponsored by the Ford Foundation's Fund for the Advancement of Education are of special interest. These have been carried on at New York University, where 500 students have taken television courses in creative composition and

[86]See Brugger (reference 97).

[87]See reference 98.

Fig. 4.65 Originating room for lecture transmission at Stephens College. (Courtesy of RCA.)

English literature; at Stephens College, where a freshman orientation course entitled "Ideas and Living Today" employs television to reach 850 students in 50 small discussion groups; and at Pennsylvania State University, where altogether 2500 students are enrolled in 10 courses taught with the aid of television; this program was inaugurated after a preliminary study (in 1954-1955) in which 600 students (830 including "controls") took courses in general chemistry, general psychology, and psychology of marriage.

In the Stephens College experiment television provides a group of nearly 1000 students with an opportunity for intimate guided group discussions on themes presented by an outstanding authority. A visiting lecturer or "master teacher" lectures for 20 minutes on television to 50 groups scattered about the campus (Fig. 4.65). For the remaining 40 minutes the teachers, acting as discussion leaders, take up the subject with active student participation.

The equipment employed consists of RCA-ITV-6 Vidicon cameras and monitor control-units and auxiliary monitors (Fig. 4.66). Ninety per cent of the television production work is carried out by Stephens

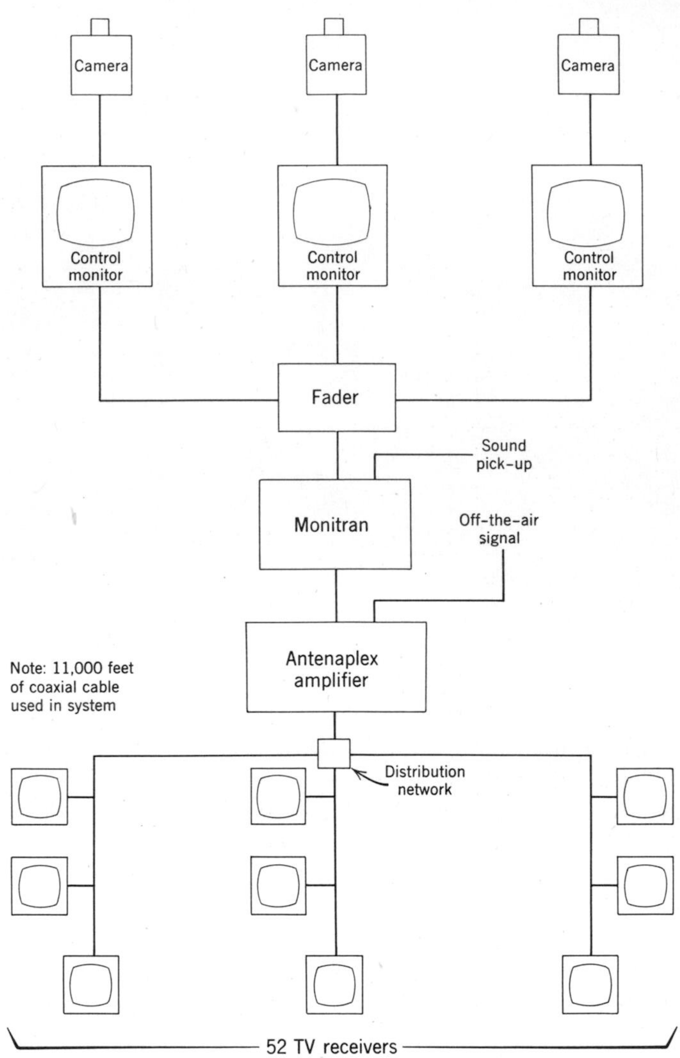

Fig. 4.66. Closed-circuit television system at Stephens College, Columbia, Mo. (Courtesy of RCA.)

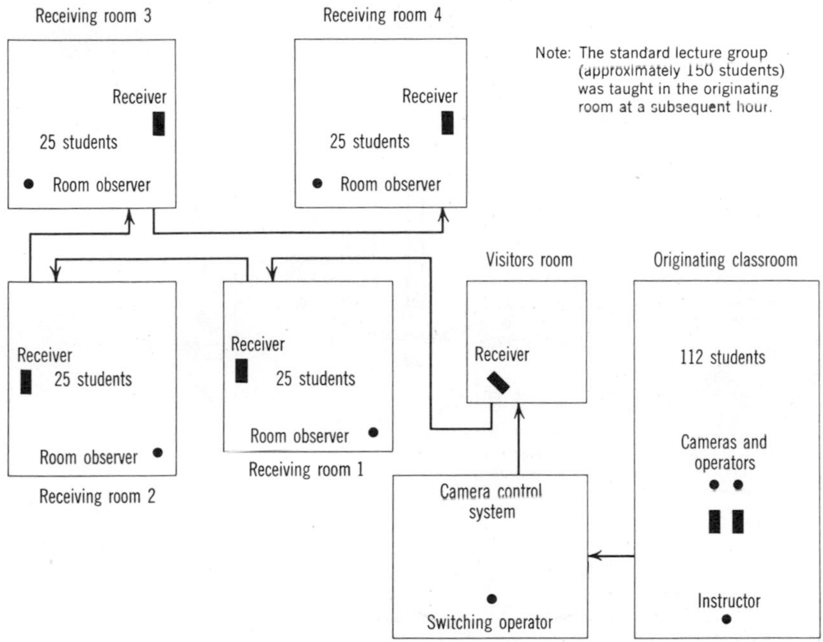

Fig. 4.67 Classroom arrangement for chemistry course at Pennsylvania State University (Carpenter and Greenhill, reference 99).

students of radio and television, who have developed original techniques for the optimum utilization of the equipment.

The most extensive and most fully reported project is that carried on at Pennsylvania State University with the support of the Fund for the Advancement of Education.[88] Since the Fund was primarily concerned with the potentialities of closed-circuit television for meeting the impending teacher shortage, the 1954-1955 study dealt with standard courses taught as usual for an entire semester over closed-circuit television. The performance of students taught in a standard classroom, in the originating classroom, and in reception rooms provided with monitors was compared and the reactions of administrative officers, teachers, and students recorded.

The courses covered were general chemistry, general psychology, and psychology of marriage. The two closed-circuit installations, at Osmond laboratory and in Sparks Building, are shown schematically in Figs. 4.67

[88] See Carpenter and Greenhill (references 99 and 100).

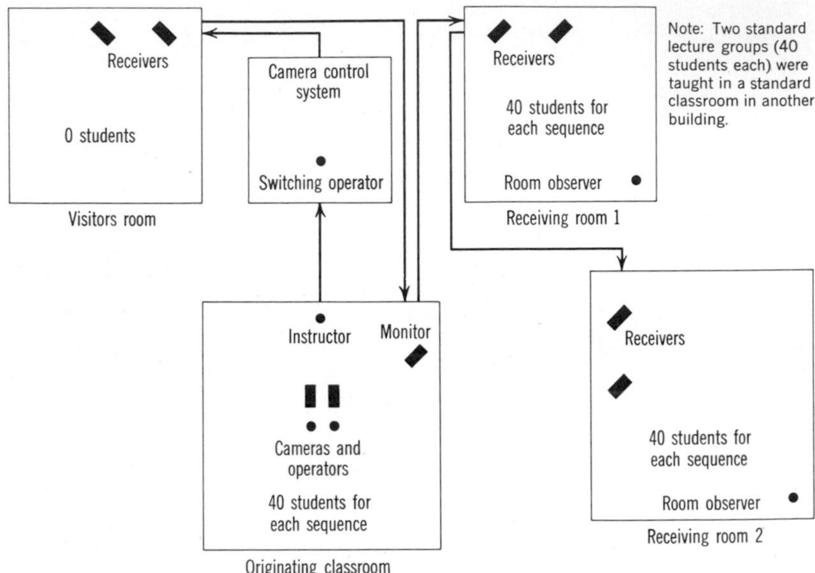

Fig. 4.68. Classroom arrangement for psychology course at Pennsylvania State University (Carpenter and Greenhill, reference 99).

and 4.68. The equipment consisted of moderate-cost, "Professional" Dage Vidicon equipment (Fig. 4.69), with 24-inch monitors supplemented by 8-inch speakers installed in the classrooms (Fig. 4.70).

Because the courses were unmodified for television presentation, it was not to be expected that the students would do better in the television classes than in the standard classes. As a matter of fact, the difference in performance did not prove statistically significant. Although students preferred small classes conventionally taught to television classes of similar size, they appeared to prefer the television classes to large standard lecture classes. Improved seeing and hearing, particularly for students otherwise on the back rows of the lecture room, proved a major attraction of television. The reduced interaction between student and teacher, the absence of color, and the limited area covered by the camera were most frequently cited as drawbacks by students.

Instructors, though uniformly accepting television on an experimental basis, varied from enthusiastic to somewhat negative in their reactions. The obvious advantage of fewer, smaller classes proved to be partly balanced by the more careful preparation which television classes de-

Fig. 4.69. Originating classroom for chemistry course (Carpenter and Greenhill, reference 99). (Courtesy of L. P. Greenhill.)

Fig. 4.70. Receiving classroom for psychology course (Carpenter and Greenhill, reference 99). (Courtesy of L. P. Greenhill.)

Fig. 4.71. Television as an aid to teaching in a Cornell University physics class. (Courtesy of RCA.)

manded. Lack of student-teacher rapport, the bright lights, the absence of color, and limited blackboard space were regarded as objectionable by several. Television was welcomed most by teachers who had to handle excessively large classes. Administrators, similarly, were impressed by the ability of closed-circuit television to deal with the problem of increasing enrollments.

In 1955-1956 television teaching was employed at Penn State in courses in general chemistry, general psychology, psychology of marriage, speech, business law, economics, air science, education, and music appreciation. Techniques were varied to arrive at conclusions regarding its most effective use.

Television becomes an unquestioned gain for both student and teacher when it simply serves to give more students a better view of demonstrations and lecture materials. Vidicon cameras and auxiliary monitors have been employed for this purpose in physics lectures at Cornell University since 1951[89] (Fig. 4.71). A great variety of demonstrations, such as the Millikan oil-drop experiment, Brownian movements, ion tracks in cloud chambers, and the diffraction of light by small objects, are made clearly visible on monitors strategically placed in the lecture room. Students in biology at Princeton have benefited in similar man-

[89] See reference 101.

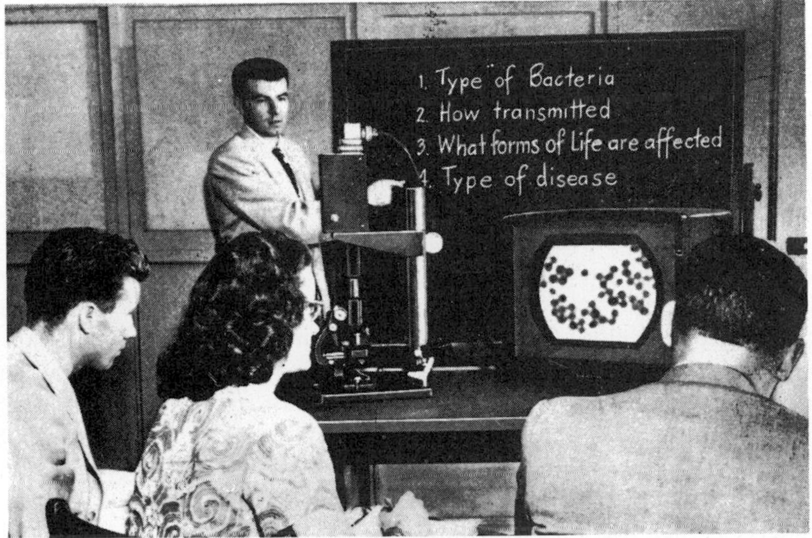

Fig. 4.72. The TV microscope in a bacteriology course. (From Zworykin and Morton, *Television*, Wiley, New York, 1954.)

ner by the use of the television microscope (Fig. 4.72). Louisiana State University, in its laboratory course on chemical microscopy, has found the same technique immensely effective in giving all of the students an opportunity to see just what was going on under the microscope.[90]

Medical and Dental Schools. The value of television in the teaching of surgery has become increasingly evident since the first closed-circuit transmissions at Johns Hopkins University Hospital in 1947, followed by a demonstration before a meeting of physicians in New York. This demonstration utilized standard black-and-white studio equipment. Two years later, at an American Medical Association convention in Atlantic City, Smith, Kline, and French exhibited a field-sequential color television chain supplied by the Columbia Broadcasting System. Numerous demonstrations followed. Perhaps the most impressive were the "Telecolor Clinics" held by the American Cancer Society in conjunction with the Columbia Broadcasting System in the period from October 1953 to June 1954.[91] These programs, originating in the Columbia Presbyterian Medical Center and the Memorial Center in New York, were transmitted to specific receiving sites in eight cities ranging from New York to Dearborn, Mich., over leased cable and

[90] See Carpenter and Greenhill (reference 100).

[91] See Holleb and Buch (reference 103).

microwave channels. The audiences were made up of practicing physicians who wished to keep abreast of the latest findings in the field of cancer research.

More recently, Smith, Kline, and French have shifted from field-sequential to RCA compatible color-television equipment in their educational service to the medical profession, which has embraced 1138 clinics in the period from 1949 to 1956.[92] The new equipment, which comprises two TK-41 color-television studio cameras, one TK-45 surgical color camera (Fig. 3.76), two Telemural color-television projectors (Fig. 3.75), and all of the necessary control equipment and cable, is transported in a color-television mobile unit and set up on arrival at the demonstration hospital. A four-man production staff and an eight-man technical staff attached to the unit make certain that the presentation is not only on a high level technically, but employs the best methods of stimulating and maintaining audience interest. Commonly, the demonstration hospital and the auditorium are a considerable distance apart. Under such conditions a microwave or video-cable link is established between them; in addition, two-way telephone lines permit the audience to direct questions to the surgeons and to receive direct answers from them. The conversion to compatible equipment has had the obvious advantages of facilitating expansion of the equipment and the utilization of existing intercity video loops and of making the services of local broadcasters available when needed. In addition, the new color projectors have been found to deliver a brighter and larger picture and to demand much smaller power consumption.

Compatible color television equipment has been employed also in color-television transmissions sponsored by the Armed Forces Institute of Pathology and other organizations (see p. 217). Figure 4.73 shows an RCA Medical 3V Color Camera, suitable for transmissions of this type, installed above the operating table at the Walter Reed Army Hospital in Washington, D. C.

Apart from these special efforts, television is used for the routine training of students in a number of medical and dental schools. Owing in part to the foresighted action of the State of Kansas in providing funds for the evaluation of television in medical education in 1949, the University of Kansas Medical Center became a pioneer in this field.[93] In the same year a Remington Rand Vericon chain was installed and daily 50-minute television instruction periods in surgical techniques were instituted for third-year medical students. Although the chain was designed for nonstandard operation (350 lines, 60 fields per second),

[92] See Greenmeyer and Schmidt (reference 104).

[93] See Schafer (reference 105).

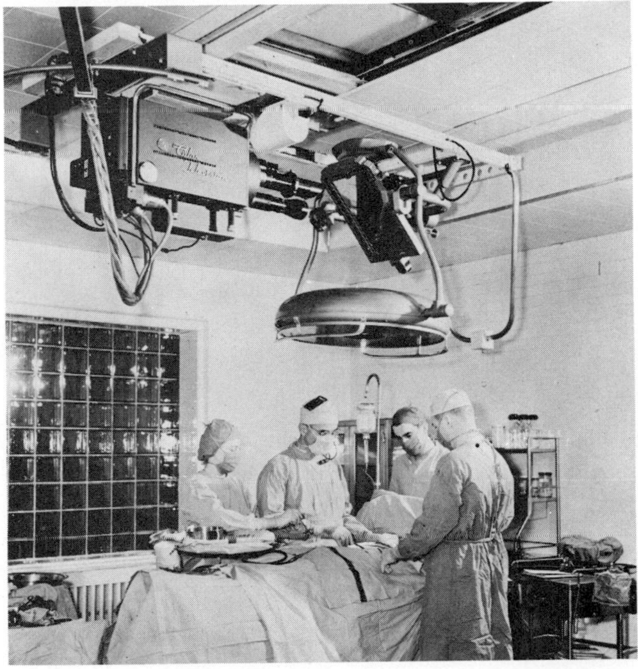

Fig. 4.73. RCA 3V Medical Color Camera transmitting surgical operation at Walter Reed Army Hospital, Washington, D.C. (Courtesy of RCA.)

auxiliary equipment was acquired to permit operation on broadcast standards, in accordance with the expressed hope that most significant developments in monochrome and color transmission would be compatible with or adaptable to equipment designed for commercial monochrome use.

It was soon found that the lack of color constituted a serious drawback in television presentations. Consequently, the monochrome chain was replaced by a color-television chain as soon as it became available; the only type offered at the time (1951) was again incompatible, namely a field-sequential CBS-Remington Rand Vericolor chain.

Considerable experience was gathered with this equipment. In particular, it was found that, to hold the student's interest, it was important to provide carefully planned and executed programs. Furthermore, the technical problems raised by the optimum utilization of the equipment demanded skills beyond those of the ordinary technician. Thus, an electronics engineer, a program director, and two technicians were selected to form an appropriate staff for a single color-television chain

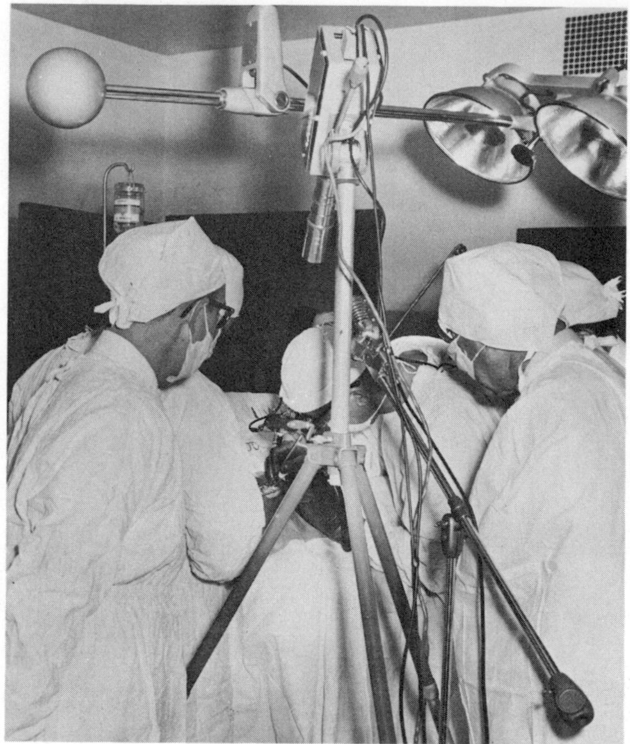

Fig. 4.74. RCA TV Eye camera transmitting ear fenestration operation at Pittsburgh Eye and Ear Hospital. (Courtesy of RCA.)

with several auxiliary monitors. It was found also that television could be used to advantage in various phases of medical teaching outside of surgery. Plans have been formulated to extend the television system at the Kansas University Medical Center and to link it by microwave with other institutions in the area.

An extensive color-television installation, largely devoted to the teaching of surgery and other medical, dental, and veterinary techniques, was made in 1956 at the Walter Reed Army Medical Center in Washington, D. C.[94] The equipment includes four regular RCA studio color-television cameras, three 3V medical color cameras, a 3V color film camera, and 30 color-television receivers. There are color-television origination centers in the Armed Forces Institute of Pathology, the Walter Reed Army Hospital, and the Army Medical Service Graduate

[94]See reference 68.

School. These are linked, so that any of the receivers can tune in on any of the studios. Provision is also made for relaying the signals to an auditorium equipped with a color-television projector. Another color-television installation, comprising an image-orthicon color camera, a Vidicon surgical color camera, and a Vidicon color film camera is scheduled at the University of Michigan.

The installations which have just been described are relatively costly and elaborate in character. It has been demonstrated, however, that much simpler equipment can be highly useful in medical and dental instruction. Figure 4.74 shows a simple RCA TV Eye camera with a long-focus lens transmitting a delicate ear fenestration operation, in which a passage is bored through sound-blocking bone formation. In spite of the small dimensions of the operating field, visiting surgeons at the Pittsburgh Eye and Ear Hospital could readily follow the action of the surgeon's tools on the monitor screens (Fig. 4.75).

TV Eye cameras have also been employed with great success at the University of Kansas City School of Dentistry and Temple University School of Dentistry in Philadelphia. Figure 4.76 shows the camera in use; Fig. 4.77, the picture viewed on the receiver. At the School of Dentistry of the University of Texas all lecture material in certain laboratory courses is presented by television. In Chicago the School of Dentistry of Loyola University utilizes a Dage television system in twelve

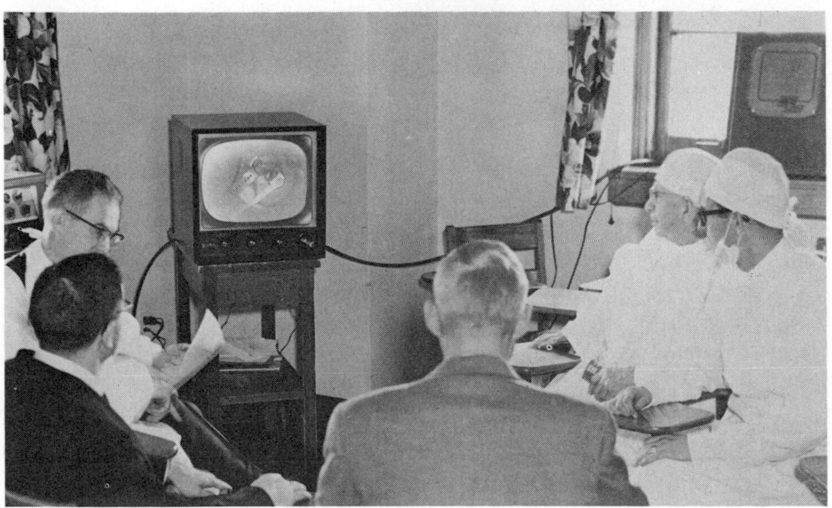

Fig. 4.75. Group of visiting physicians watching ear fenestration operation on monitor. (Courtesy of RCA.)

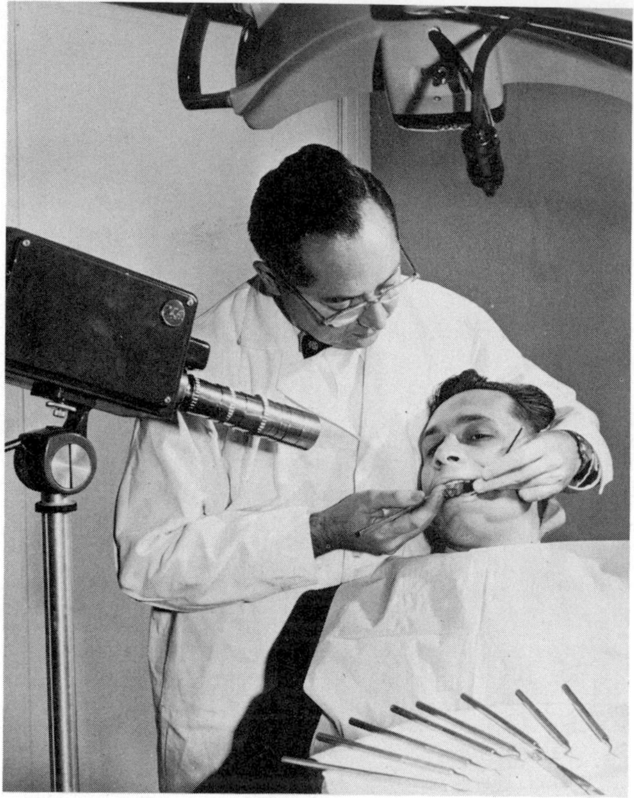

Fig. 4.76. Television camera in Temple University School of Dentistry. (Courtesy of RCA.)

courses. All the classrooms, as well as three laboratories and two amphitheatres, are wired for television reception of programs originating in surgery or in the school's television studio. By giving the entire class a close-up view of delicate manipulations, television spares instructors tiring and time-consuming "repeat performances."

At the Nebraska Psychiatric Institute in Omaha television aids in the training of psychiatrists.[95] The treatment rooms are provided with camera ports and microphones concealed in the ceiling. Three General Precision Laboratory Vidicon cameras permit simultaneous coverage of three rooms; at the control room the most significant treatment is selected for transmission to the auditorium, where large groups of students can watch the scene projected on a large viewing screen. Thus

[95] See reference 106.

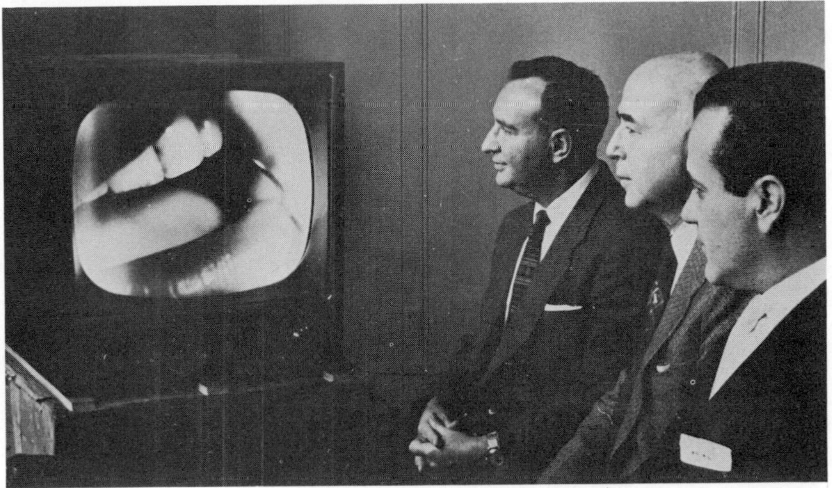

Fig. 4.77. View of patient's teeth on monitor. (Courtesy of RCA.)

advanced students can watch the actual treatment of patients by experts without intruding in any way on the process.

Job Training. An interesting example of the use of television to minimize training time is provided by the experience of the Radio Corporation of America with the assembling of special equipment needed at ten theatres to meet opening-date deadlines for Cinemascope showings. With the aid of a TV Eye camera and a microphone an expert assembler guided six workers watching his operations on individual monitors and listening to his explanations over a public address system (Fig. 4.78).[96]

Television finds many uses as well in technical training of a less transitory nature. The National College of Rubber Technology in London is completely wired for closed-circuit television, and the operation of rubber-processing machinery in the shops can be watched on a 27-inch monitor by students in a lecture room, unimpeded by close quarters and noise. The television installation was provided by Pye Ltd.

COMMERCE

Closed-circuit television finds numerous applications in commerce. Department stores, banks, and corporations use it to reach selected audiences, to provide protection against fraud and theft, and as a convenient means for exchanging visual data.

[96] See reference 107.

(b)

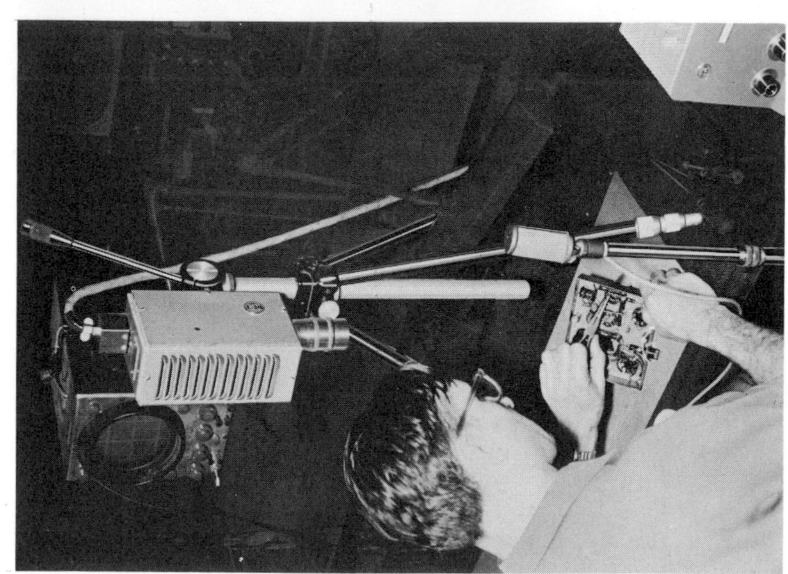

(a)

Fig. 4.78. Guidance of workers performing assembly operations by TV Eye. (Courtesy of RCA.)

Department Stores. The principal role of closed-circuit television in department stores has been the prevention of pilferage and shop lifting. Bamberger's in Newark, N. J., employs four Dage cameras for this purpose, two camouflaged and two in plain sight[97] They are monitored in a security room; detectives are dispatched by transistor radio when suspicious actions are observed. The cameras which are open to view are designed to discourage attempts at theft. In similar manner, in a West Coast market three TV Eye cameras survey 22,000 square feet of floor area, and three monitors are under surveillance in a control room.[98] The RCA TV Eye also discourages shop lifting in the W. T. Grant Department Store in Norfolk, Va. Filene's uses remotely controlled cameras at its Needham, Mass., warehouse to check shipping and receiving docks[99] in the merchandise storage area. Observation of the monitors and control of the cameras is exercised by a security guard stationed over 1500 feet away.

Television can also arouse the interest of passers-by. Thus DuPont employed the RCA TV Eye to show promenaders on the Atlantic City Boardwalk what was going on in its exhibit. L. W. Ayres in Indianapolis presents fashion and style shows on television to bring customers into the store. The Allied Stores System employs a considerably more elaborate system; this comprises two RCA image-orthicon color cameras, which are sent from city to city to present scheduled style shows and merchandise demonstrations at its numerous department stores. Finally, the novelty of seeing themselves on the television monitor is exploited again and again to draw the attention of people to a particular advertising message.

Banking. In a bank television gives the teller immediate access to the required records, which may be located at some distance from the teller's window. It also permits the bank to use lower-rental space for its bookkeeping and records department and makes possible maximum utilization of limited space for customer service. In large institutions it gives all tellers equal access to the records. Thus an alphabetical distribution of customers' accounts along the row of teller's windows becomes unnecessary and customers can be served more efficiently.

This improvement has been realized in the Provident Institution for Savings in Boston[100] which has installed seventeen receivers, one at every teller's window, and ten cameras. When the teller wishes to verify a signature and bank balance, she telephones her request to the records

[97] See Mackin (reference 108).

[98] See reference 109.

[99] See reference 110.

[100] See reference 111.

Fig. 4.79. Camera location in records department of Provident Institution for Savings in the Town of Boston. (Courtesy of RCA.)

Fig. 4.80. Receiver at teller's window at the Provident Institution. (Courtesy of RCA.)

Fig. 4.81. Desk-installed television monitor at Riggs National Bank in Washington, D.C. (Courtesy of RCA.)

department, which places the signature card or balance record over a camera port for her inspection on the receiver (Figs. 4.79 and 4.80). At the New York Savings Bank in New York a branch relies entirely on television for the verification of signatures at the central records office.[101] A somewhat similar problem is solved in drive-in banks, exemplified by a branch of the Delaware County National Bank in Chester, Pa.[102] Here monitors in the drive-in teller's booths are connected with a TV Eye camera in the records room in the bank building across the street.

It may be noted that the signature verification on a check may be left up to the teller, a conventional practice, or up to the records department; in the second instance the television camera is located at the teller's window and a view of the submitted check is transmitted to the records room. Both methods are currently employed in banks.

At the Riggs National Bank in Washington, D.C., television serves to provide a link between the bank's headquarters and the bookkeeping department, located several blocks away. Figure 4.81 shows a monitor

[101] See references 112, 113, and 114.

[102] See reference 115.

installed inconspicuously in a bank-officer's desk. In London Glyn Mills and Company, a banking house, moved part of its records during World War II to Osterley Park, ten miles away. When, after the war, space considerations prevented the return of the material to London, the banking house installed a television camera in Osterley Park, so that record data could be transmitted by microwave to monitors in its offices in London.

Visual Communication. In a sense, all uses of television represent forms of visual communication. In the present section we are restricting our attention to communication uses of a general nature, akin to that of the telephone.

One is the transmission of records, signatures, meter faces, etc., of which we have met a specialized example in bank applications of television. Transmission of visual material by regular television methods over long distances requires the installation or rental of coaxial-cable or microwave links and is accordingly expensive. The cost is greatly reduced if the transmission can take place over regular telephone lines. To take advantage of this fact, the Dage Television Division of Thompson Products has produced a slow-scan system for the transmission of data, which has been demonstrated by the Pennsylvania Bell Telephone Company.[103] In this system the scanning rate is reduced so that a bandwidth of 8000 cycles per second is sufficient for the transmission; a single frame is transmitted in two to four seconds. The picture may be stored on a Skiatron dark-trace tube. In 1956 the telephone company considered offering such a data-transmission service for distances up to 25 miles.

Another application, which played a relatively large role in the early history of television, is the video-telephone.

Demonstrated in 1929 by G. Krawinkel in Germany and shortly thereafter, with higher resolution (72 lines), by H. E. Ives[104] in America, a public video-telephone service was provided on a local and intercity basis by the German Post Office in the years 1936-1940. It was discontinued in 1940 to make its wide-band cables available for message traffic and wired television services.[105]

The above-mentioned videophone service employed a Nipkow-disk flying-spot scanner with a 150-line scanning pattern as transmitter and a cathode-ray tube as receiver. Sporadic demonstrations with higher-resolution scanning patterns and an all-electronic transmission system followed. A recent demonstration of this type took place in San Fran-

[103] See references 116 and Ennes (reference 117).

[104] See Ives (reference 118).

[105] See Goebel (reference 119).

cisco and was arranged by Kay Lab in cooperation with the Pacific Telephone and Telegraph Company.[106] The videophone conversations took place over a distance of one mile and featured Vidicon cameras and split-screen viewing, both participants appearing on the two halves of each kinescope screen. Equipment of similar character—the split-screen operation is optional—has been applied to surveillance of plant entrances. Videophone systems have also been employed on a larger scale for linking the secret White House with other governmental centers in Civil Defense drills.

A significant departure from the usual pattern is realized in a picturephone system built in 1956 by Bell Telephone Laboratories.[107] Here the picture picked up by a Vidicon camera is stored in a storage tube or on a magnetic drum and is transmitted at a greatly reduced rate—namely, with a picture period of two seconds—to a storage unit at the receiver, where it is reproduced on a small cathode-ray tube. The greatly reduced scanning rate permits transmission of the picture over an ordinary telephone line.

Closed-circuit television systems have been used more widely for introducing plant operations to stockholders' meetings and for launching new products at regional sales conventions. Such meetings are commonly held in hotels which are equipped with television projectors or individual receivers. Several organizations, such as Theatre Network Television, Box Office Television, and the Sheraton Hotel chain, have made a specialty of providing industrial concerns with facilities for communicating both visually and orally with groups of distributors, dealers, or sales representatives throughout the country. Numerous industrial leaders, such as Lees Carpets, Dodge, Ford, Chrysler, National Dairy, Frankford Distillers, Pan American World Airways, and International Business Machines have made use of closed-circuit television in this way.[108]

The savings in travel expenses resulting from the replacement of a national meeting or a series of individually addressed sales meetings by local meetings reached by television can be material. Thus, the introduction of a new line of appliances and radio and television sets to 2000 distributors in 27 cities through the medium of television cost the Westinghouse Electric Corporation $75,000, compared with a sum of $450,000 which would have been required to bring the same distributors to a central location. In 1955 the Sun Oil Company indicated that the cost of introducing "Advanced Blue Sunoco" by television to 12,000 Sun dealers was $100,000, as compared with $225,000 spent to introduce a

[106] See reference 120.

[107] See reference 121.

[108] See reference 122 and Halpern (reference 123).

Fig. 4.82. Accommodation of overflow audience at church service by closed-circuit television. (Courtesy of Allen B. DuMont Laboratories, Inc.)

new gasoline in separate dealers' sales meetings across the country fifteen months earlier.[109]

In New York the Seagram Building, a 38-story structure, is equipped specifically for television business sessions.[110] Provision is made for the reception and transmission of closed-circuit color-television programs. Television projectors, public-address systems, and master television outlets serve conventions, sales meetings, and interstaff conferences of the Seagram group of companies and building tenants.

At stockholders' meetings television serves to give the stockholders a view of plant operations, new construction, etc., in the comfort of a conveniently located auditorium. The Foote Mineral Company, the American Telephone and Telegraph Company, and the Rochester Gas and Coke Company have used this technique to advantage.

Similarly, the British Ford Motor Company televised the operation of assembly lines at its factory in Dagenham at a Product Exhibition in Olympia,[111] and the General Electric Company exhibited its new 6442

[109] See reference 124.

[110] See reference 125.

[111] See reference 126.

Fig. 4.83. Television for guest registration (Temple Hotel, Pendleton, Ore.). (Courtesy of Allen B. DuMont Laboratories, Inc.)

lighthouse tube at its Schenectady works to the 1955 annual meeting of the Institute of Radio Engineers in New York.[112] In other instances the objective is simply the accommodation of overflow audiences—one of the earliest applications of closed-circuit television. RCA Vidicon cameras have been used at annual meetings of the American Philosophical Society in Philadelphia for several years. Figure 4.82 shows a DuMont installation at a church service. At the Billy Graham Glasgow All-Scotland Crusade in 1955 an overflow audience of 5000 was accommodated by ten 3 x 4-foot viewing screens; the Marconi image-orthicon field camera provided with a 5 : 1 zoom lens was placed at a distance of 40 feet from the speaker.[113] Thus the number of people enabled to attend the evangelist's services in a six-week period was increased from 400,000 to 600,000. At the Springfield, Ohio, Municipal Hospital closed-circuit television gives patients access to religious services at the hospital chapel.

In the entertainment world, also, closed-circuit television has found many uses. At the Temple Hotel in Pendleton, Ore., two-way television permits a guest to register without leaving his car. When he has made his arrangements, a bellboy brings him a registration sheet and room key and directs him to a parking place in the hotel garage (Fig. 4.83). A

[112]See reference 127.

[113]See Duff (reference 128).

more common use is the transmission to guest rooms of hotel information, such as menus and programs, and of locally originated floor shows. At the Santa Anita Race Track television monitors provide patrons with betting information (Fig. 4.84). More generally, Film Racing Patrol, a firm specializing in the installation of television equipment at race tracks, enables patrons to watch the races from club rooms and other convenient locations.

MILITARY USES

The employment of closed-circuit television by military agencies has been mentioned repeatedly in the preceding sections. In all cases the applications were such, however, that their use by the military was incidental. They might have served equally well in civilian undertakings. The present section considers those which are more peculiarly military.

Weapon Guidance. Of necessity, any account of the use of television for weapon guidance must be decidedly out-of-date. However, a brief description of some of the developments may be of historical interest.

An early suggestion for the use of television in the guidance of a missile launched from a plane was made in a detailed memorandum pre-

Fig. 4.84. Television monitor for announcements to patrons at Santa Anita Race Track. (Courtesy of Kay Lab.)

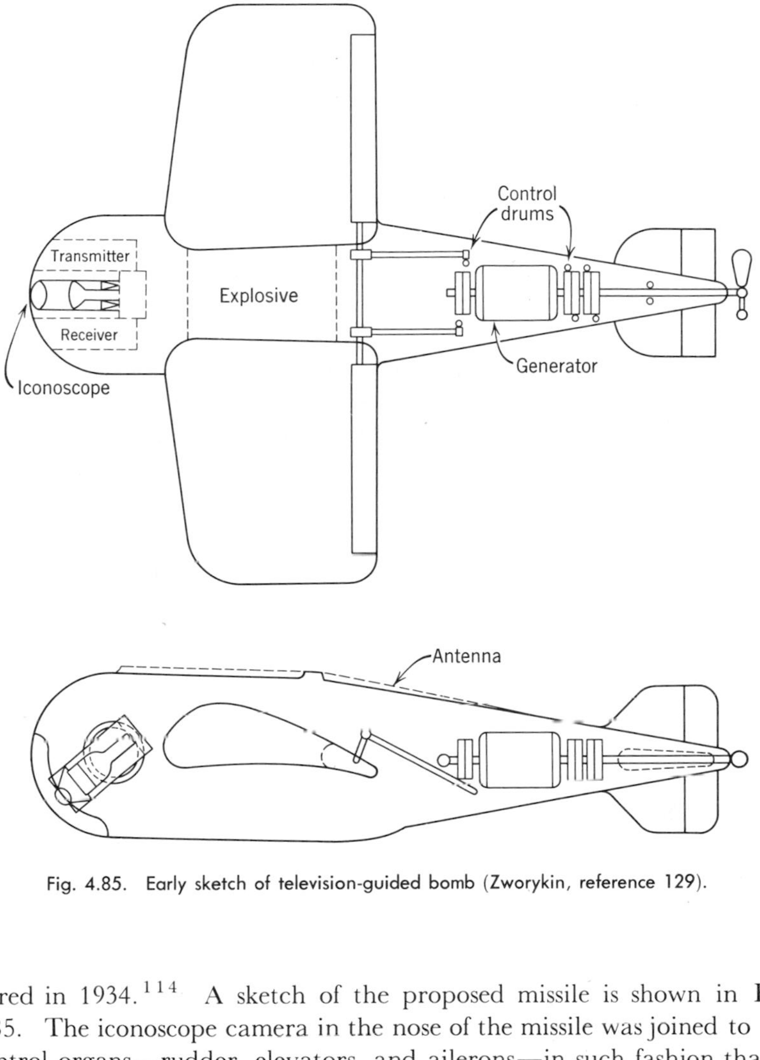

Fig. 4.85. Early sketch of television-guided bomb (Zworykin, reference 129).

pared in 1934.[114] A sketch of the proposed missile is shown in Fig. 4.85. The iconoscope camera in the nose of the missile was joined to the control organs—rudder, elevators, and ailerons—in such fashion that it was always centered on the point at which the missile was aimed. A television picture of the aiming area, surrounded by instrument indications, was transmitted on a radio channel to the mother ship, which in turn controlled the steering mechanism of the missile by means of a second radio channel.

A guided missile which realizes the essential features of the above proposal was produced during World War II by the Douglas Aircraft

[114] See Zworykin (reference 129).

Company.[115] The miniature television equipment constructed for the guidance of the "Roc bird" utilized a miniaturized image-orthicon or "Mimo" camera tube 1½ inches in diameter and 9 inches in length. The entire television transmitter weighed about 50 pounds and operated on a 310-megacyle carrier. The control signals were transmitted from the mother plane on an 84-megacycle carrier.

It was found that useful television signals were received from the transmitter even at a distance of 40 miles. In actual drop tests interference between the direct transmission and ground reflections produced spurious horizontal-bar patterns arising from the Doppler effect. These detracted from the quality of the received pictures. Even so, for a flight altitude 15,000 above ground the target was still readily visible on the plane monitor one second before impact.

Television equipment of less advanced design, following closely the suitcase-type apparatus employed in 1940 for commercial spot pickup, was also employed extensively during World War II in the guidance of glide bombs and radio-controlled drone aircraft employed as missiles.[116]

Reconnaissance. The transmission of visual information from an observation plane to a ground station by television has the obvious advantage over photographic reconnaissance of eliminating or minimizing the time delay between the recording of the information on the plane and its evaluation at operational headquarters. Two types of airborne television developed for reconnaissance during World War II are the Block System[117] and the Ring System.[118] The first of these was lightweight equipment (100 pounds for the entire transmission installation) which employed iconoscope cameras designed primarily for unattended operation in guided missiles and drone aircraft. It operated on 350-line, 40-frame-per-second standards. The Ring system was a high-fidelity system operating on 567 line, 40-field-per-second, interlaced standards and was designed for plane-to-ground television transmission. The then newly developed image orthicon and signal-multiplier orthicon were employed in this system. A typical airborne installation with two cameras weighed 1400 pounds without the power generators and regulators. The reception range of the system, delivering 1400 watts peak power, was found in early tests to be 200 miles. With the transmitting plane 10,000 feet above Philadelphia, the picture received at Patuxent River, Md., 120 miles away, made it possible to distinguish between cars, trucks, and buses in the traffic on the Delaware River Bridge. A 20-inch, *f*/10 objective was employed on the camera.

[115] See Kell and Sziklai (reference 130).

[116] See Marshall and Katz (reference 131).

[117] See Trainer and Poch (reference 132).

[118] See Shelby, Somers, and Moffett (reference 133).

More recently, the U.S. Army Signal Corps developed television systems for ground reconnaissance in which pictures are transmitted from the front lines to the battle commander and his staff.[119] Tests indicated that Vidicon cameras operating on 525-line, 60-field-per-second, interlaced RETMA standards provided adequate detail. The Signal Corps Interim Tactical Television System, tested in "Operation Flashburn" at Fort Bragg, N.C., in April-May 1954 and publicly demonstrated at Fort Meade, Md., in August of the same year accordingly employed three Vidicon chains on the ground and one Block airborne system. The hand-held cameras were connected by 500 feet of cable to the camera controls, which were mounted with microwave transmitters on a jeep or a ¾-ton truck. The signals were received at the Command Unit, installed in a 2½-ton Army shop truck, up to 30 miles behind the front lines, where they were distributed by a 6-channel switching unit.

The demonstration at Fort Meade was broadcast by the National Broadcasting Company over a national hook-up. The views provided by the reconnaissance cameras were supplemented by the color transmissions of an NBC color mobile unit. The exercise, which included a river crossing in amphibious personnel carriers and a successful assault on a fortified beachhead, supplied an excellent illustration of the increased control of the immediate situation given the commander by television.

The employment of jeeps or trucks for the mounting of the camera controls and microwave transmitters is, of course, only a temporary expedient. These vehicles are logically replaced by compact backpack units of the type discussed on pp. 105.[120]

In addition to the general-purpose reconnaissance equipment described above, special-purpose cameras have been developed for transmitting pictures at very low light-levels. Thus an image-orthicon tube with wide-spaced target built by the Radio Corporation of America permits the transmission of clear pictures at illuminations corresponding to those prevailing on a cloudy, moonlit night. The "cat-eye" image-intensifier camera tube developed under Air Force contract by Drs. G. A. Morton and J. E. Ruedy at the David Sarnoff Research Center makes possible the observation of objects under even less favorable conditions of illumination.[121]

Communications. Closed-circuit television also serves the military in various capacities as a simple visual communications aid. Thus the Canadian aircraft carrier H.M.C.S. *Bonaventure* was fitted in 1956 with a closed-circuit Pye television network for the primary purpose of trans-

[119] See Schreiber and Oppenheimer (reference 134).
[120] See reference 135.
[121] See reference 136.

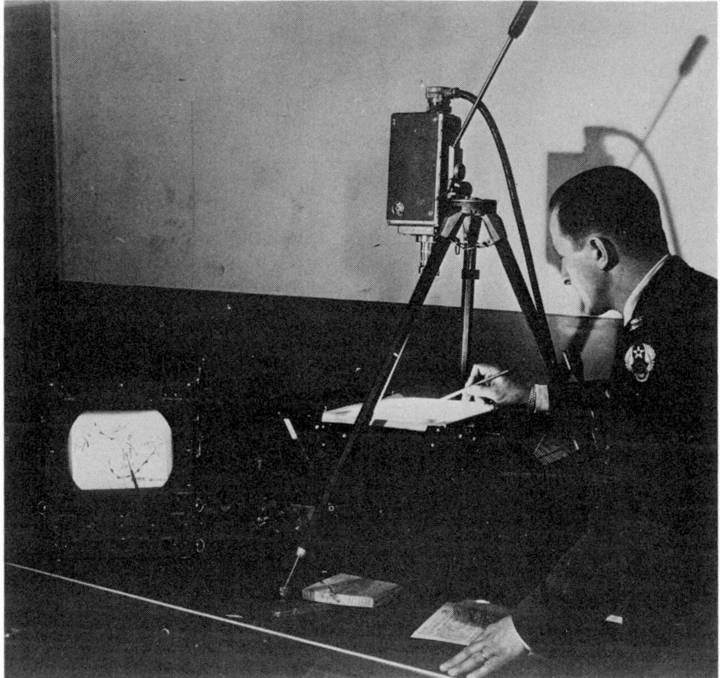

Fig. 4.86. Transmission of weather data by television (Stewart Air Force Base). (Courtesy of RCA.)

mitting operations charts from the operations room to the bridge and other key points,[122] where the tactical situation could be taken in at a glance. On the British cruiser H.M.S. *Cumberland* television serves to transmit performance data from the engine room to the bridge in similar fashion.

In a quite different application Alameda Naval Air Station uses three Kay Lab camera chains to control runway operations half a mile away, the direct view of the runway being blocked by buildings.[123] The employment of a Vidicon camera for the transmission of weather data at Stewart Air Force Base is illustrated in Fig. 4.86.

Television as a Training Aid. More extensive studies of television as a training aid have been made by the Armed Forces than by any other group or agency.[124] The Special Devices Center of the U.S. Navy at Port Washington, L. I., first carried out, in 1949, comparative tests of

[122] See reference 137.

[123] See reference 138.

[124] For a summary, see Carpenter and Greenhill (reference 99).

the effectiveness of regular classroom instruction, television instruction, and instruction by kinescope recordings in basic training and pilot refresher courses. At a somewhat later date, about 3000 U.S. Army reservists were given a series of eight television lessons. Tests before and after the lessons and recall tests given three to six weeks later were employed to measure the retention of material taught by television. In a period from 1951 to 1953 the Signal School at Fort Monmouth, N. J., made a comparative study of the effectiveness of television in teaching technical courses, mainly in radio and radar. Similar studies covering an electronics course were carried out at Keesler Air Force Base in Mississippi with matched groups of Air Force trainees and the same instructors for classroom and television instruction. At Houston University the Quartermaster Training Command compared television teaching with standard methods in a course on food service activities taken by ROTC students. A more limited test of television and conventional techniques of teaching electronics was carried out by the U.S. Naval Academy. Finally, at Camp Gordon, the Human Resources Research Office of George Washington University made a comparison of conventional teaching in a large lecture hall with television teaching of small, proctored groups. Army basic-training subject matter provided the teaching material. The study covered learning and retention achieved with television teaching, the effectiveness of reviews from kinescope recordings, and the relative response of high- and low-aptitude groups.

In all these studies it was found that television techniques gave as good or better results when compared with conventional classroom teaching. This applied both to immediate learning and retention. The last study indicated also that television instruction was even more effective for low-aptitude than for high-aptitude groups.

In brief, the reaction to television teaching in the Armed Forces has been more uniformly positive than in the colleges and universities. A difference of this kind is not too surprising, since the relationship between student and instructor and the mode of selection of students and instructors are quite different in the two instances.

Relatively elaborate closed-circuit installations have been developed to carry out the instruction programs outlined above. Many, like that at Fort Monmouth described on p. 98, are relatively permanent in character. In addition, the U. S. Army Signal Corps has constructed a completely self-contained television system on wheels.[125] This can travel from post to post to suggest to field commanders ways in which television can effectively assist their programs.

[125] See Auld (reference 139).

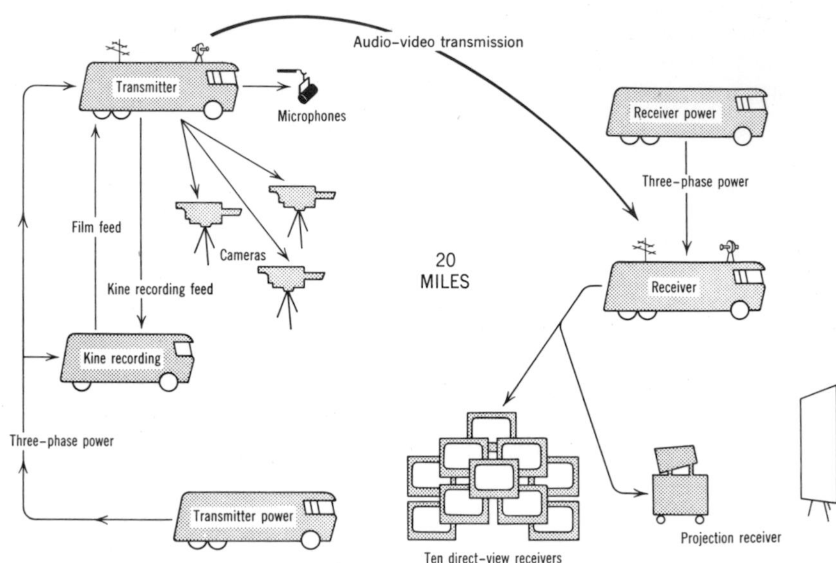

Fig. 4.87. Schematic of Signal Corps mobile television system (Auld, reference 139). (Courtesy of *Journal of Society of Motion Picture and Television Engineers.*)

The Signal Corps mobile television system (Fig. 4.87) consists of five buses. The transmitter bus contains three standard image-orthicon field cameras with power-driven cable reels and a video control console, six microphone inputs with a turntable and tape recorder, a 7125-megacycle video microwave transmitter and frequency-modulation sound transmitter. A video cable connecting it with the kinescope recording bus permits the recording of transmitted programs. In addition, the film recording bus contains a film camera chain so that live programs may be supplemented by film material. Both the transmitter bus and the kinescope recording bus obtain three-phase 208/110-volt power from two 15-kilovolt-ampere motor generators in the transmitter power bus.

The receiver bus is equipped with ten 16-inch receivers and a large-screen projection receiver. The video signal from the microwave receiver is applied to a stabilizing amplifier to clean up the synchronizing pulses. It then modulates, along with the audio signal, a Channel 3 carrier in the so-called "Dumitter," which can supply a standard radio-frequency signal to as many as 125 commercial television receivers by way of 72-ohm coaxial feed. The receiver power bus supplies power from a single 15-kilovolt-ampere motor generator to the receiver bus and provides storage for repair and test equipment. Communication is maintained between the buses by 163-megacycle transceivers.

The first use of this equipment was made in an Army Field Force Commanders' Preventive Training Course held at Aberdeen Proving Ground early in 1952. It involved both studio programs originating in a local auditorium and remote pickup of simulated field operations. An application of somewhat different character consisted in taking the 1952 Convention of the Institute of Motion Picture and Television Engineers on a television tour of the wind-tunnel facilities of the Naval Ordnance Laboratory in White Oaks, Md. This not only avoided clearance difficulties, but resulted in a much more informative demonstration than would have been possible on an actual trip through the tunnels.

Observation of Dangerous Processes. Some examples, such as the dismantling of munitions at ordnance depots, have already been given. Perhaps the most striking use of television in military applications of this character was, however, the observation of the effects of an atomic air blast and underwater blast at Bikini in 1946.[126] Two Block III television transmitting units, developed for airborne use, were mounted on 75-foot steel towers on Bikini Island, three miles from the blast center, overlooking the target fleet and the waves on Bikini beach. In the first test PBY Flying Mariner aircraft relayed the television signals to observers on ships at a distance of twenty miles from the blast. For a period beginning five seconds before the blast and ending eight seconds after the blast the cameras were protected by filters with a neutral density of 2.4. The equipment operated without interruption from the time it was turned on, at 2:00 A.M. before the blast, until fifteen hours later, when it was turned off. The television pictures indicated negligible effect of the airblast on the waves on the beach; for the underwater blast waves five to ten feet in height were observed.

Entertainment Television for Isolated Service Forces. The armed forces have found the use of locally originated television programs of great value in the maintenance of morale at isolated posts.[127] Low-power stations, generally equipped with Vidicon camera units, have been installed for this purpose in Maine, Iceland, the Azores, Tripoli, Greenland, Saudi Arabia, Okinawa, and Johnson Island in the Pacific. The addition of this characteristic feature of present-day American home life helps to dispel the sense of isolation of the personnel.

[126] See Fink and Engleman (reference 140).
[127] See references 141 and 142.

REFERENCES

Industry

1. G. H. Wilson, "Television in Industry," *Elec. Eng.*, Vol. 72, pp. 126–130, 1953.
2. L. M. Exley, "Television in Power Stations for Direct Viewing of Furnace Conditions," *Mech. Eng.*, Vol. 73, pp. 1008–1009, 1951.
3. E. R. Thomas and W. L. Norvell, "Television for Monitoring Stack Emission," *Elec. Eng.*, Vol. 72, pp. 224–227, 1953.
4. "Television Aids Turbine Control," *Electronics*, Vol. 27, p. 200, April, 1954.
5. K. H. Boucher, "Recent Developments in Optical Tooling," *Automotive Ind.*, Vol. 113, pp. 50–52, Aug. 15, 1955.
6. "Inspection: Industrial TV Checks Blade Edge," *Iron Age*, Vol. 176, p. 120, Nov. 3, 1955.
7. "Closed-Circuit TV in Saw Mill," *Electronics*, Vol. 28, p. 214, March 1955.
8. "Industrial TV—Remote Control Setups Tackle a Growing List of Chores in Industry," *Wall Street Journal*, Vol. 146, Aug. 29, 1955.
9. "Industrial TV Monitors Production," *Electronics*, Vol. 26, p. 16, March 1953.
10. F. H. Marshall, "The Electronic Fluoroscope," *Westinghouse Eng.*, Vol. 13, pp. 70–71, March 1953.
11. G. A. Morton and L. E. Flory, "An Infra-Red Image Tube and Its Military Applications," *R C A Rev.*, Vol. 7, pp. 385–413, 1946.
12. M. C. Teves and T. Tol, "Electronic Intensification of Fluoroscopic Images," *Philips Tech. Rev.*, Vol. 14, pp. 33–43, 1952.
13. A. D. Cope and A. Rose, "X-Ray Noise Observation Using a Photoconductive Pickup Tube," *J. Appl. Phys.*, Vol. 25, pp. 240–242, 1954.
14. J. E. Jacobs and H. Berger, "Performance of a Large-Area Photoconductive Pickup Tube," presented at AIEE Winter Meeting, New York, Feb. 3, 1956.
15. "Industrial X-ray Shows in Daylight," *Electronics*, Vol. 29, pp. 182, 184, June 1956.
16. John S. Pruitt, "Scintillation Crystal TV Device X-rays Objects in Motion," *Nucleonics*, Vol. 13, pp. 26–29, August 1955.
17. G. H. Wilson, "Applications of Closed-Circuit TV to Conveyor and Mining Operations," *Mining Eng.*, Vol. 6, pp. 720–723, 1954.
18. "TV Keeps an Eye on Switching," *Ry. Age*, Vol. 136, pp. 42–43, May 3, 1954.
19. "TV 24 Hours a Day in Southern Pacific Yard," *Ry. Age*, Vol. 138, p. 50, Feb. 21, 1955.
20. "Television by Microwave Tested on Rock Island," *Ry. Age*, Vol. 139, p. 52, Sept. 19, 1955.
21. "Television Effective in Supervising Highway Traffic," *Elec. Eng.*, Vol. 74, p. 1028, 1955.
22. "Photographing and Studying Traffic," *J. Soc. Motion Picture Television Engrs.*, Vol. 64, p. 468, 1955.
23. E. Janicki, "Television for Traffic Control," *Public Works*, Vol. 86, pp. 82–83, December 1955.
24. "Hamburg Traffic on TV," *New York Times*, Feb. 4, 1956.
25. "First TV Traffic Study to Focus on New Columbus Circle Plan," *New York Times*, Feb. 27, 1956.
26. "Closed-Circuit Television Tried in Airline Operation," *Elec. Eng.*, Vol. 74, pp. 1027–1028, 1955.

27. P. J. Herbst, I. Wolff, D. H. Ewing, and L. F. Jones, "The TELERAN Proposal," *Electronics*, Vol. 19, pp. 124–227, 1946.
28. D. H. Ewing and R. W. K. Smith, "TELERAN—Air Navigation and Traffic Control by Means of Television and Radar," *R C A Rev.*, Vol. 7, pp. 601–621, 1946.
29. D. H. Ewing, H. J. Schrader, and R. W. K. Smith, "TELERAN—Part II. First Experimental Installation," *R C A Rev.*, Vol. 8, pp. 612–632, 1947.
30. "Fire Wardens Adopt Electronics," *Electronics*, Vol. 27, p. 20, August 1954.
31. "TV Cameras Aid Rangers in Detecting Forest Fires," *Elec. Eng.*, Vol. 74, pp. 745–746, 1955.
32. "Remote Camera Spots Forest Fires," *Electronics*, Vol. 28, p. 178, October 1955.
33. "Closed-Circuit Television Proves Effective in Underwater Research," *Elec. Eng.*, Vol. 74, p. 1024, 1955.
34. "Submarine TV Checks Fish Nets," *Electronics*, Vol. 28, p. 26, March 1955.
35. W. R. Stamp, "Underwater Television," *Scientific American*, Vol. 188, pp. 32–37, June 1953.
36. J. N. Bathurst, "Underwater Television," *Engineering*, Vol. 177, p. 555, 1954, or *Engineer*, Vol. 197, p. 611, 1954.
37. "Underwater Television; Periscopic Camera and Watertight Lamp," *Engineering*, Vol. 177, p. 253, 1954.
38. "Portable TV Camera for Navy Frogmen," *Electronics*, Vol. 28, p. 184, January 1955.
39. G. T. Montgomery, "Underwater Television Camera Hovers or Cruises," *Electronics*, Vol. 28, p. 176, September 1955.
40. A. Abramson, *Electronic Motion Pictures*, University of California Press, Berkeley and Los Angeles, 1955.
41. A. Simon, "The Video-Film Camera," *Am. Cinematog.*, March, 1955.
42. J. L. Caddigan and T. T. Goldsmith, Jr., "An Electronic Film System," *J. Soc. Motion Picture Television Engrs.*, Vol. 65, pp. 7–15, 1956.
43. N. Collins and T. C. Macnamara, "The Electronic Camera in Film Making," *Proc. Inst. Elec. Engrs.* (London), Vol. 99, part III-A, pp. 673–679, 1952.
44. N. L. Halpern, "Developments in Large-Screen Closed-Circuit Television," *J. Soc. Motion Picture Television Engrs.*, Vol. 64, pp. 335–339, 1955.

Physical and Engineering Research

45. "Development of an Electronic Astronomical Telescope," *Electronic Eng.*, Vol. 27, p. 433, 1955.
46. "TV Amplifies Light 40,00 Times," *Electronics*, Vol. 29, p. 16, March 1956.
47. A. A. Rotow, "Image Orthicon for Pickup at Low Light-Levels," *R C A Rev.*, Vol. 17, pp. 425–435, 1956.
48. F. A. Friswold, "Television Monitors Rocket Engine Flame," *Electronics*, Vol. 26, pp. 187–189, October 1953.
49. "Test Observations by Airborne Television; Icing Tests on Proteus Turbopropeller," *Engineering*, Vol. 180, p. 319, 1955.
50. "Controle d'une Centrifugeuse par Television Industrielle," *Electronique*, Nr. 103, p. 50, June 1955.
51. "TV Observes Gamma-Ray Detectors," *Electronics*, Vol. 25, pp. 154–156, June 1952.
52. H. L. Hull, "Remote Control Engineering," *Nucleonics*, Vol. 10, pp. 34–35, November 1952.

53. "Color Television Helps Radioactive Area Work Performance," *Elec. Eng.*, Vol. 75, p. 665, 1956.
54. "TV Camera . .", *Nucleonics*, Vol. 14, p. 110, May 1956.
55. "Oceanographic Television Equipment," *Engineer*, Vol. 195, p. 835, 1953.
56. D. Allanson, "Underwater Observation by Television," *J. Soc. Motion Picture Television Engrs.*, Vol. 65, pp. 311–319, 1956.
57. "Industrial TV Monitors Production," *Electronics*, Vol. 26, p. 16, March 1953.

Medicine and Biology

58. A. K. Parpart, "Televised Microscopy in Biological Research," *Science*, Vol. 113, pp. 483–484, 1951.
59. A. K. Parpart, "The Application of Television to Microscopy," *Trans. Am. Microscop. Soc.*, Vol. 71, pp. 311–313, 1952.
60. L. V. Heilbrunn, *The Dynamics of Living Protoplasm*, Academic Press, New York, 1956.
61. P. O'B. Montgomery, "The Use of U-V Microspectrophotographic and Phase and U-V Television Densitometry Technics in Medical Research," *I.R.E. Convention Record*, Vol. 3, Part 9, pp. 124–130, 1955.
62. M. Luckiesh, *Applications of Germicidal, Erythemal and Infrared Energy*, Van Nostrand, New York, 1946.
63. J. Fisher, "Television Picture Line Selector," *Electronics*, Vol. 25, pp. 140–143, March 1952.
64. E. M. Buyer, "Line Selector Checks Television Wave Forms," *Electronics*, Vol. 26, pp. 153–155, September 1953.
65. G. Z. Williams, "Application of Television Ultraviolet Microscope to the Direct Observation of Cytological Absorption Characteristics," *I.R.E. Convention Record*, Vol. 3, Part 9, pp. 131–137, 1955.
66. C. N. Loeser and C. Berkley, "Electronic Quantitation in Light Absorption and Nuclear Fluorescence in Living Cells," *Science*, Vol. 119, pp. 410–411, 1954.
67. E. T. Griffith, "RCA Demonstrates Color TV for Medical Use," *Broadcast News*, Vol, 85, pp. 39–42, 1955.
68. "Walter Reed Army Medical Center Uses RCA Compatible Color TV System for Medical Education," *Broadcast News*, Vol. 93, pp. 48–59, 1957.
69. M. C. Brown, "Preliminary Report on Biological Applications of Color Television," *Science*, Vol. 123, pp. 589-590, 1956.
70. P. L. Frommer, "An Electronic Blood-Count Meter," *Elec. Eng.*, Vol. 74, pp. 388–391, 1955.
71. F. Roberts, J. Z. Young, and D. Causley, "Flying-Spot Microscope," *Electronics*, Vol. 26, pp. 137–139, July 1953.
72. L. E. Flory and W. S. Pike, "Particle Counting by Television Techniques," *R C A Rev.*, Vol. 14, pp. 546–556, 1953.
73. R. C. Mellors and R. Silver, "A Microfluorometric Scanner for the Differential Detection of Cells: Applications to Exfoliate Cytology," *Science*, Vol. 114, pp. 356–360, 1951.
74. W. E. Tolles, "The Cytoanalyzer—An Example of Physics in Medical Research," *Trans. N. Y. Acad. Sci.*, Vol. 17, pp. 250–256, 1955.
75. W. E. Tolles and R. C. Bostrom, "Automatic Screening of Cytological Smears for Cancer: The Instrumentation," *Ann., N. Y. Acad. Sci.*, Vol. 63, Art. 6, pp. 1211–1218. 1956.

76. W. E. Tolles, R. C. Bostrom, and H. S. Sawyer, "The Application of Automatic High-Speed Measurement Techniques to Cytology," *I.R.E. Convention Record*, Vol. 4, Part 9, pp. 17–23, 1956.
77. S. Goldman, W. E. Vivian, C. K. Chien, and H. N. Bowes, "Electronic Mapping of the Activity of the Heart and Brain," *Science*, Vol. 108, pp. 72 723, 1948.
78. S. Goldman, W. F. Santelman, Jr., W. E. Vivian, and D. Goldman, "Traveling Waves in the Brain," *Science*, Vol. 109, p. 524, 1949.
79. J. C. Lilly, "A 25-Channel Recorder for Mapping the Electric Potentials Gradients of the Cerebral Cortex: Electro-Iconograms," *Elec. Eng.*, Vol. 69, pp. 68–69, 1951.
80. C. Barus, "A Low-Level, High-Speed Switching System for Brain Mapping," *I.R.E. Transactions on Medical Electronics*, Vol. PGME-7, pp. 1–13, December 1956.
81. W. Grey Walter, *The Living Brain*, Norton, New York, 1953.
82. J. J. Wild and J. M. Reid, "Ultrasonic Ranging Speeds Cancer Diagnosis," *Electronics*, Vol. 28, pp. 174–180, March 1955.
83. D. H. Howry, "Techniques Used in Ultrasonic Visualization of Soft Tissue Structures of the Body," *I.R.E. Convention Record*, Vol. 3, Part 9, pp. 75–85, 1955.
84. W. E. Chamberlain, "Fluoroscopes and Fluoroscopy," *Radiology*, Vol. 38, pp. 383–412, 1942.
85. D. H. Steinweg, "X-Ray Movies and Television," *Westinghouse Engr.*, Vol. 15, pp. 152–155, September 1955.
86. H. M. Stauffer, M. J. Oppenheimer, G. H. Stewart, III, and A. W. Blackstone, "Practical Image Amplifier Technics; Fluoroscopy Cinefluorography, Spot-Film Radiography, and Use with Closed-Circuit Television," *Radiology*, Vol. 65, p. 784, 1955.
87. H. M. Stauffer, M. J. Oppenheimer, G. H. Stewart, III, and P. R. Lynch, "Cinefluorography by Image Amplifier Techniques," *J. Appl. Physiol.*, Vol. 8, pp. 343–346, 1955.
88. R. H. Morgan and R. E. Sturm, "Roentgen-Ray Motion Pictures by Means of Screen Intensification," *Am. J. Roentgenol.*, Vol. 70, pp. 136–140, 1953.
89. R. H. Morgan, "Screen Intensification: A Review of Past and Present Research with an Analysis of Future Development," *Am. J. Roentgenol.*, Vol. 75, pp. 69–76, 1956.
90. R. J. Moon, "Amplifying and Intensifying the Fluoroscopic Image by Means of a Scanning X-Ray Tube," *Science*, Vol. 112, pp. 389–394, 1950.
91. R. H. Morgan, R. E. Sturm, L. S. Miller, and D. J. Torrance, "Remote Fluoroscopic Control of Radiation Therapy by Screen Intensification," *Am. J. Roentgenol.*, Vol. 70, pp. 705–708, 1953.
92. B. Cassen, L. Curtis, C. Reed, and R. Libby, "Instrumentation for I^{131} Use in Medical Studies," *Nucleonics*, Vol. 9, pp. 46–50, August 1951.
93. L. Curtis and B. Cassen, "Speeding Up and Improving Contrast in Thyroid Scintigrams," *Nucleonics*, Vol. 10, p. 58, September 1952.
94. T. E. Sopp, S. V. Gyer, and J. S. Lehman, "Economical Scintillation Scanner," *Nucleonics*, Vol. 12, p. 49, December 1954.

Education

95. T. C. Pollock, "Why Experiment with Television," *Educational Screen*, Vol. 35, January 1956.
96. H. Zorbaugh, "Television—Technological Revolution in Education," *J. Soc. Motion Picture Television Engrs.*, Vol. 66, pp. 671–676, 1957.

97. J. R. Brugger, "Television in Washington County Schools, Hagerstown, Md.," *J. Soc. Motion Picture Television Engrs.*, Vol. 66, pp. 680–682, 1957.
98. "High School TV Studio Part of $105,000,000 Building Plan for 1957," *New York Herald Tribune*, June 18, 1956.
99. C. R. Carpenter and L. P. Greenhill, "The Investigation of Closed-Circuit Television for Teaching University Courses," Pennsylvania State University, University Park, Pa., 1955.
100. C. R. Carpenter and L. P. Greenhill, "Closed-Circuit TV is one Answer," *College and University Business*, February 1956.
101. "Physics Experiments to be Televised for Cornell Students," *Elec. Eng.*, Vol. 71, p. 1035, 1952.
102. "TV for an Audience of One or More," *Chem. Eng. News*, Vol. 34, pp. 1058–1062, 1956.
103. A. I. Holleb and F. B. Buch, "Color Television in Medical Education; A Report on Telecolor Clinics," *J. Am. Med. Assoc.*, Vol. 156, pp. 298–302, 1954.
104. P. A. Greenmeyer and P. C. Schmidt, "How SK & F Uses Color Television," *Broadcast News*, Vol. 92, pp. 64–71, December 1956.
105. P. W. Schafer, "Television at the University of Kansas Medical Center," *J. Am. Med. Assoc.*, Vol. 152, pp. 78–82, 1953.
106. "Closed-Circuit Television Aids Psychiatric Training," *Elec. Eng.*, Vol. 75, p. 555, 1956.
107. "Industrial TV Cuts Training Time," *Electronics*, Vol. 27, p. 20, December 1954.

Commerce

108. T. Mackin, "For Private Eyes," *Newark Sunday News*, June 17, 1956.
109. "Electronic Store Dick," *Electronics*, Vol. 27, p. 198, June 1954.
110. "Warehouse Guarded by ITV," *Electronics*, Vol. 29, p. 200, May 1956.
111. "Television Tellers: Provident Institution for Savings, Boston," *Banking*, Vol. 46, p. 102, October 1953.
112. "Bank Accounting Work Cut by Television," *Electronics*, Vol. 26, p. 20, May 1953.
113. "Electronic Bank Cuts Space and Cost," *Electronics*, Vol. 26, p. 15, December 1953.
114. "Television Bank," *Architectural Forum*, Vol. 102, pp. 128–129, February 1956.
115. "Signatures Checked in Drive-In Bank by 'TV Eye'," *Elec. Eng.*, Vol. 74, p. 1035, 1955.
116. "Slow-Scan TV Speeds Business Data," *Electronics*, Vol. 29, p. 10, January 1956.
117. H. E. Ennes, "Slow-Sweep TV for Closed-circuit Use," *Electronics*, Vol. 29, pp. 140–143, November 1956.
118. H. E. Ives, "Two-Way Television," *Bell Lab. Record*, Vol. 8, pp. 399–404, 1930.
119. G. Goebel, "Television in Germany up to the Year 1945," *Archiv für das Post- und Fernmeldewesen*, Vol. 5, pp. 259–392, 1953.
120. "Two Coast Mayors Test Videophone," *New York Times*, Aug. 24, 1955.
121. "Picture-Phone TV Gets a Boost," *Electronics*, Vol. 29, p. 28, September 1956.
122. "Conventions Use Closed-Circuit TV," *Electronics*, Vol. 27, p. 16, September 1954.
123. N. L. Halpern, "Developments in Large-Screen Closed-Circuit Television," *J. Soc. Motion Picture Television Engrs.*, Vol. 64, pp. 335–339, 1955.
124. "Sun Oil Co. Introduces New Gasoline to Dealers on Closed-Circuit TV," *Wall Street Journal*, June 23, 1955.
125. "Closed-Circuit Color TV Put Into New Seagram Building," *New York Herald Tribune*, June 28, 1955.

126. "Televising a Factory," *J. Television Soc.*, Vol. 7, p. 291, 1954.
127. "TV Previews New Tube," *Electronics*, Vol. 28, p. 200, May 1955.
128. R. I. Duff, "An Unusual Television Application," *J. Television Soc.*, Vol. 7, pp. 401–402, 1955.

Military Uses

129. V. K. Zworykin, "Flying Torpedo with an Electric Eye," *R C A Rev.*, Vol. 7, pp. 293–302, 1946.
130. R. D. Kell and G. C. Sziklai, "Miniature Airborne Television Equipment," *R C A Rev.*, Vol. 7, pp. 338–357, 1946.
131. C. J. Marshall and L. Katz, "Television Equipment for Guided Missiles," *Proc. I. R. E.*, Vol. 34, pp. 375–401, 1946.
132. M. A. Trainer and W. J. Poch, "Television Equipment for Aircraft," *R C A Rev.*, Vol. 7, pp. 469–502, 1946.
133. R. E. Shelby, F. J. Somers and L. R. Moffett, "Naval Airborne Television Reconnaissance System," *R C A Rev.*, Vol. 7, pp. 303–337, 1946.
134. E. L. Schreiber and H. C. Oppenheimer, "Combat Television," *J. Soc. Motion Picture Television Engrs.*, Vol. 64, pp. 129–132, 1955.
135. "Reconnaissance TV," *Electronics*, Vol. 29, p. 202, April 1956.
136. "TALOS Guided Missile Air Defense Electronics Products Demonstrated," *Elec. Eng.*, Vol. 75, pp. 657–659, 1956.
137. "Television at Sea," *Brit. Communications and Electronics*, Vol. 2, p. 47, June 1955.
138. "Military Television Gets Off the Ground," *Electronics*, Vol. 29, p. 14, April 1956.
139. J. S. Auld, "Signal Corps Mobile Television System," *J. Soc. Motion Picture Television Engrs.*, Vol. 59, pp. 462–471, 1952.
140. D. G. Fink and C. L. Engleman, "Electronics at Bikini," *Electronics*, Vol. 19, pp. 84–89, November 1946.
141. "Military Telecasting Increases," *Electronics*, Vol. 27, p. 8, December 1954.
142. "Armed Forces TV Comes of Age," *Electronics*, Vol. 28, p. 16, June 1955.

chapter 5

Forecast

In the preceding chapters we have traced the development of closed-circuit television, outlined its areas of service, described its tools, and recounted its achievements. It remains for us to cast a glance into the future.

Clearly, a simple extrapolation from the present status of closed-circuit television will not do. Objectivity forces us to admit that the new medium is still in its infancy. Hence we may properly seek some guidance from the experience of other industries which have attained maturity.

As we do this, we are struck by the fact that the social effects of an innovation are almost invariably underrated. To the men who introduced the automobile it represented simply an improvement in transportation. Yet who will deny today that it has vitally affected the life habits of every one of us, changed the growth pattern of our cities, and modified our landscape. The social implications of radio broadcasting were but dimly perceived when the first broadcasting ventures were launched, and, again, the transition from radio to television broadcasting had far more profound effects on family life and social customs than could have been foreseen.

It would thus be short-sighted to regard closed-circuit television as just an expansion and adaptation of the use of broadcasting equipment. Its potentialities are much greater than that.

In particular, although considerable effort has been expended in the development of terminal equipment for closed-circuit television, relatively little attention has been paid to the connecting link between the camera and receiver. Yet it is clear that the high cost of wide-band video cable is a material obstacle to widespread audio-visual communication. Sooner or later we shall overcome this obstacle by the development of simpler, cheaper wide-band linkages, by the modification of the terminal equipment for narrow-band use, or both.

Let us assume that this technical problem has been solved. The way is then open for the use of the videophone on a wide scale. What are the results which we can anticipate for such a development?

First of all, we can expect a material reduction in personal contacts. Visual and voice communication by wire will replace social calls. Stores as we know them will all but disappear, or rather will be converted to warehouses especially adapted for videophone purchases. Banking, similarly, will be carried out entirely by wire. In brief, many of the activities which fill up people's days will be eliminated, freeing them for others of a less routine nature.

Industrial production and business organization will also be vitally affected by the possibility of instantaneously transferring both sight and hearing to any desired point. In particular, in factory management the task of supervising a large operation in all its phases will be greatly simplified. Immediate access to information from all parts of the plant will facilitate rapid, intelligent decisions.

Even with the closed-circuit television equipment now available, its use in industry for the correlation of activities, supervision, and inspection, which is now sporadic, can be expected to become well-nigh universal. With the introduction of automation in production the primary functions of factory personnel will be the checking of the proper operation of equipment and its maintenance. Television permits the first function to be carried out effectively from central control points at which the time of the skilled supervisory staff is utilized with maximum efficiency. Furthermore, the diagnosis of equipment failures will be accelerated by the use of direct X-ray examination in which television is employed as the medium of observation.

At the same time, we note a trend in industry toward the use of higher pressures, higher temperatures, and other conditions increasingly inimical to human life, which reaches its apex in the practical application of nuclear fusion processes. This is accompanied by the heightened valuation of human life characteristic of an advancing civilization. These two divergent trends will be reconciled by the development of improved means of remote observation and control. The television link, permitting close observation from great distances and across protective barriers of arbitrary thickness, is bound to play a key role in this development. Furthermore, the search for natural resources to supply the raw materials for our industries will tend to penetrate more and more deeply into regions inaccessible to human beings, both at sea and on land. The submarine camera will transmit pictures of the ocean floor and its flora and fauna: it will also telemeter gage readings from arbitrary depths to exploration vessels at the surface. Similarly, a television camera and illuminating unit sent down with the drill in drilling operations will guide the crew by means of visual images of the layers penetrated. In digging operations carried out by machines at great depths difficult and costly ventilation problems will be simplified by replacing as far as possible human observers and operators with television cameras and remote-control devices.

In medicine we can envision the general use of television for remote diagnosis; this would place the ablest diagnosticians at the service of the patient, wherever he may be located. We can also expect the development of miniature pickup devices for internal examination with a minimum of discomfort to the patient. At the same time, television techniques will play an increasing role in the advancement of our understanding of life processes and of the origin of disease and will accelerate and simplify tests for the early diagnosis and prevention of human ailments.

In public-school instruction the most talented teachers of specialized subjects will be made available to all students, thus enabling the classroom teacher to pay increased attention to personal guidance. The closed-circuit system will also permit the localized control and experimentation which are so essential to progress. In the teaching of the sciences and in technical training television will become the preferred medium by giving arbitrarily large groups intimate views of the most detailed processes, even as they happen.

Commercial enterprise, too, will avail itself increasingly of closed-circuit television to project vision at will from the office to the store, the warehouse, or the record room, to communicate visually with associates and subordinates, and to stimulate customer interest with presentations adapted to the needs of the moment. Valuable books and records will be inspected by television to eliminate risk of loss or damage. With the development of narrow-band video terminal equipment, wireless paging systems will add sight to sound, so that visual matter as well as simple messages will reach the addressee, regardless of his location. Pictures will be transmitted directly from the scene of action to the editorial offices of newspapers, there to be selected and recorded.

A market for closed-circuit television equipment which is potentially greater than any of those mentioned so far is, of course, the home, the repository of the vast majority of television receivers currently in use. The technical basis for this application—the miniature Vidicon and the wholly transistorized camera designed for use with the standard home television receiver—has already been created, though further improvements and simplifications will without doubt be added. With them, Everyman will learn to regard television as a tool to increase his leisure, by the simplification of a host of chores, as well as a way to spend it. Television will complete the cycle begun by labor-saving machines and appliances in the home—it will provide the many with the conveniences formerly available to the few through the service of others, whether minding the children, answering the door bell, or supervising the kitchen. In addition, it will supplement the entertainment provided by broadcast television in the same manner in which, today, phonograph and tape recorder supplement the radio receiver.

Finally, we return to our prediction of 1954 that the television camera will be the pioneer observer in interplanetary travel.[1] With the launching of the Earth satellite this moment has come much closer. Even though the first device of this kind does not provide for a television link with the Earth, we can be confident that this possibility will not remain long neglected. Television will inform us of all that is to be seen from a satellite long before we consider entrusting human life to it. Indeed, we can foresee spaceships equipped with sturdily constructed television transmitters sending back visual information to Earth long after their launchers have ceased to be among the living. And if, in the distant future, men should decide to forsake this planet, their flight will not be into the unknown, but subject to known risks and expectations, thanks, in large part, to television.

[1] V. K. Zworykin and G. A. Morton, *Television*, 2nd Edition, Wiley, New York, 1954, p. 1018.

appendix

Comparison of Performance Limits of Vidicon and Flying-Spot Television Microscopes in the Ultraviolet

As a reasonable basis of comparison, we shall assume the following:

1. The sizes of the scanning patterns referred to the specimen are equal, so that a picture of the same area is transmitted.
2. The number of lines, the frame rate, and the transmission bandwidths are equal, so that the resolution in space and time, i.e., the ability to recognize detail and to follow changes in the specimen, is the same. In particular, it may be assumed that the pattern is a 525-line pattern, aspect ratio 4 : 3, with a frame frequency of 30 per second and 2 : 1 interlacing. The video transmission band giving equal horizontal and vertical resolution then has a "nominal cut-off frequency" $f_c = 3.9 \cdot 10^6 \text{ sec}^{-1}$.
3. The "quality" of the reproduced pictures is the same. In quantitative terms this means that the pictures are to have the same signal-to-noise ratio, which will be set equal to 10.
4. The numerical apertures of the four optical systems (objectives and condensers) and the light losses within them are the same. This implies equal optical resolution and quality of the two systems.

Let us assume, furthermore, as a first step that the two systems have ideal performance. This means:

1. The primary photoelectric processes in the camera tube target and in the flying-spot system multiplier phototube have unity quantum efficiency.
2. There is no loss of stored charge in the course of a frame time.

3. Any additional noise introduced by the amplification process is negligible.

4. The persistence of emission of the flying-spot tube phosphor is negligible.

Under these circumstances the signal-to-noise ratio in the picture is determined simply by the number of photons which pass in the course of a frame time through a single picture element. Hence the same *average* illumination of the specimen is required for an ideal flying-spot microscope and ideal storage-tube microscope; in the flying-spot microscope the illumination of any one picture element is concentrated in a sequence of intense, widely spaced pulses; in the storage-tube microscope it remains at a low, uniform level.

The illumination required to give a signal-to-noise ratio of 10 with loss-free optics of numerical aperture 1 in an ideal system is readily computed. It is plotted in Fig. A.1 as a function of the least distance d resolved by the television system; in order that the television system may not introduce a material reduction in resolution in the final picture, d must be chosen smaller than the optical resolving power of the system (e.g., 0.1 micron or 10^{-5} cm). For this value of d the required illumination is seen to be $4.2 \cdot 10^{13}$ photons/(cm^2·sec). In principle a Bacterium coli preparation could be studied for one minute with 2537 A illumination with an ideal television microscope system giving maximum attainable resolution before a fraction 0.63 of the culture had been killed off by the ultraviolet irradiation. Thus high-magnification viewing of living material with short-wave, ultraviolet illumination is feasible in principle.

Conditions are, of course, materially less favorable in practical television microscopes. Listing the several factors in the same sequence as before, the principal deviations from ideal performance are

1. The quantum efficiencies of ultraviolet-sensitive multiplier phototubes, such as the 1P28 or 6903, are at best 0.2 rather than 1;[1] for amorphous-selenium photoconductive targets a primary quantum efficiency of unity is probably approached very closely.[2]

2. Whereas the amplification process in the multiplier phototube is almost noise-free, the output signal of the Vidicon is at a level low enough to permit the succeeding amplifier stages to contribute materially to the noise in the final picture.

[1]The data sheets for the RCA-1P28 indicate approximately constant quantum efficiency of 0.18 between 3400 and 2500 A and reduced quantum efficiency beyond these points. For the RCA-6903, with fused-quartz face plate, the tentative data give a minimum quantum efficiency of 0.11 at 3000 A, increasing to 0.18 at 2000 A and to 0.13 at 3500 A.

[2]See Weimer and Cope (reference 1).

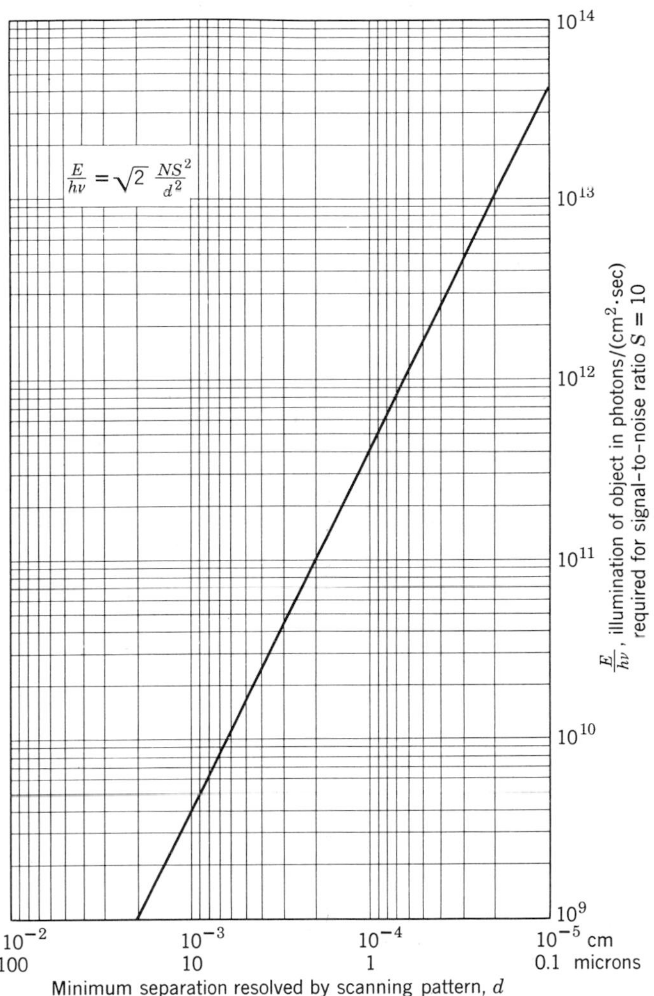

Fig. A. 1. Illumination requirements of an ideal television microscope with frame rate $N = 30\ \mathrm{sec}^{-1}$.

3. The persistence of emission of practical flying-spot tube phosphors is at least comparable to the time required for the beam to sweep across a picture element. Thus the spot is in effect smeared out in the direction of scan. "Aperture correction" or high-frequency peaking networks may be employed to restore high-frequency components in the video signal, attenuated by the spot broadening, to their proper level. Since this process also amplifies the noise, the signal-to-noise ratio in the picture is

reduced in comparison to that obtained without persistence or with a perfectly sharp spot.

A more detailed discussion of the effect of these factors is given below. It is shown there that two to three times as much average illumination of the specimen is required in the Vidicon television microscope as in the flying-spot television microscope.

The circuit for the *Vidicon microscope* is shown schematically in Fig. 4.46*a*. The signal electrode is coupled by a resistance R, shunted by the combined capacity C of the electrode and the input grid of the amplifier, to the thermionic amplifier which raises the signal to a level high enough for the control of the picture tube. Although the vertical resolution in the picture is determined simply by the number of television lines in the picture, provided that the scanning spot is either much smaller than a line width or bears a fixed relation to it, the horizontal resolution is also a function of the range of frequencies transmitted by the amplifying system. It is generally desirable to adjust the transmitted frequency band so as to equate the horizontal and vertical resolution.

Wheeler and Loughren[3] show that if the scanning spot has a cosine-squared distribution and extends to the center of the two adjoining scanning lines ("50 per cent overlap") so that line structure would disappear in a picture reproduced with a similar scanning spot of constant intensity ("flat field"), the "vertical width of confusion" is $\sqrt{2} \times$ vertical line separation. An equal horizontal width of confusion is obtained for a "nominal cut-off frequency"

$$f_c = \frac{1}{2\sqrt{2}} \frac{w}{h} n^2 N = 3.90 \cdot 10^6 \text{ sec}^{-1} \text{ for } n = 525, \ N = 30 \text{ sec}^{-1}$$

Here w is the width of the scanning pattern, h, its height, n, the line number, and N, the frame frequency. The nominal cut-off frequency f_c is defined by the requirement that the integral of the frequency response over frequency from 0 to ∞ is equal to the product of the response at low or intermediate frequencies, which is assumed constant, with the frequency f_c. For many purposes it is permissible to replace the actual frequency response by one which stays constant from 0 to f_c and then drops sharply to zero. We shall do this in the present considerations.

Two factors cause the response of the Vidicon system to decrease with increasing frequency—the Vidicon response itself, as given by Hurford and Marian,[4] and the capacitance which shunts the coupling resistance inserted in the signal lead. The Vidicon response is given, for

[3]See Wheeler and Loughren (reference 2).

[4]See Hurford and Marian (reference 3).

$f_c = 3.9 \cdot 10^6 \text{ sec}^{-1}$ and $f < 6 \cdot 10^6 \text{ sec}^{-1}$, by

$$g(f) = e^{-0.75(f/f_c)^2}$$

It can readily be shown that this response would correspond to a spot intensity (or sensitivity) distribution $e^{-\pi r^2/b^2}$ where b, the effective linear dimension of the spot, is $w/504$. In other words, the spot width is approximately $\frac{1}{500}$ of a line length.

The shunt capacitance C in the amplifier input circuit causes a signal current i_s to produce an input signal

$$V_i = \frac{Ri_s}{\sqrt{1 + 4\pi^2 f^2 C^2 R^2}}$$

with

$$i_s = \mathfrak{N} qe \frac{A_{pe}}{T_{pe}} T = \mathfrak{N} qeA$$

Here q is the quantum efficiency of the photoconductive layer, A_{pe} the picture element area, T_{pe} the time required to scan a picture element, T the frame time ($= 1/N$), A the total scanning area on the photoconductive target, and $\mathfrak{N}$ the number of photons incident on unit area of the target.

The desired response, flat to f_c, will be obtained for a total amplifier response of the form

$$\begin{aligned} G &= (B/R)(1 + 4\pi^2 f^2 C^2 R^2)^{1/2} e^{0.75(f/f_c)^2} & f < f_c \\ &= 0 & f > f_c \end{aligned}$$

With this gain, the signal (within the frequency range of amplification) will be simply

$$V_s = B\mathfrak{N} qeA$$

The noise superposed on the signal arises from four sources:

1. Shot-noise current arising from the photoelectric excitation. For a frequency range df this is[5]

$$d(\overline{i_{ns}^2}) = 2ei_s\, df$$

2. Shot noise in the photoconductor dark current. Since for the amorphous selenium target employed in the ultraviolet-sensitive Vidicon the carrier lifetime can be expected to be greater than the transit time,[6]

[5] See Zworykin and Ramberg (reference 4).

[6] See Weimer and Cope (reference 1).

the noise contribution of the dark current can be written similarly[7]

$$d(\overline{i_{nd}^2}) = 2ei_d\, df$$

3. Thermal noise in the coupling impedance. The corresponding voltage fluctuation is given by $4kT\,df$ times the resistive component of the coupling impedance:

$$d(\overline{V_{nc}^2}) = \frac{4kTR\,df}{1 + 4\pi^2 f^2 C^2 R^2}$$

Here k is Boltzmann's constant and T the absolute temperature.

4. Amplifier noise. This is usually represented by an "equivalent noise resistance," in which the thermal noise, applied to the input of a noise-free amplifier, would produce the noise output generated by the actual amplifier. Thus the noise contribution of the amplifier becomes

$$d(\overline{V_{na}^2}) = 4kTR_t\, df$$

If the contributions to the voltage fluctuation of these four noise sources are added, multiplied by the gain characteristic $G(f)$, and integrated over the frequency spectrum, we obtain for the noise output

$$\begin{aligned}\overline{V_n^2} &= \int_0^{f_c} \left\{4kT\left(\frac{R}{1 + 4\pi^2 f^2 C^2 R^2} + R_t\right) + 2e(i_s + i_d)\,\frac{R^2}{1 + 4\pi^2 f^2 C^2 R^2}\right\} G^2\, df \\ &= B^2 \left\{\left[\frac{4kT}{R^2}(R + R_t) + 2e(i_s + i_d)\right](f_c/\sqrt{1.5})(\sqrt{\pi}/2i)\operatorname{erf}(i\sqrt{1.5}) \right. \\ &\quad \left. + \frac{4kTR_t \cdot 4\pi^2 C^2 f_c^2}{3}\,[f_c e^{1.5} - (f_c/\sqrt{1.5})(\sqrt{\pi}/2i)\operatorname{erf}(i\sqrt{1.5})]\right\}\end{aligned}$$

We may substitute in this expression

$$4kT = 1.6 \cdot 10^{-20}\ \text{joule}$$

$$e = 1.6 \cdot 10^{-19}\ \text{coulomb}$$

$$e^{1.5} = 4.482$$

$$\frac{1}{\sqrt{1.5}}\,\frac{\sqrt{\pi}}{2i}\operatorname{erf}(i\sqrt{1.5}) = 1.836$$

$$q = 1$$

The last equality is justified by the fact that experimental studies of thin amorphous selenium films suggest a primary quantum efficiency very

[7] See Van der Ziel (reference 5).

nearly equal to unity in the blue and near-ultraviolet portion of the spectrum.[8] With the above numerical values,

$$\overline{V_n^2} = B^2 \left\{ \frac{2.94 \cdot 10^{-20}(R + R_t)}{R^2} f_c + 5.88 \cdot 10^{-19}(i_s + i_d)f_c + 5.55 \cdot 10^{-19} R_t C^2 f_c^3 \right\}$$

The noise can be minimized by making the coupling resistance R very large compared to the coupling reactance. Then the first term in the expression for the noise may be neglected. Furthermore, the dark current i_d is negligible in comparison with the signal current i_s under normal conditions of operation. Finally, except for very high signal-to-noise ratios, the signal current itself is small enough to render the second term negligible in comparison with the last term. Hence the optimum signal-to-noise ratio of the Vidicon system may be written

$$S = V_s/\sqrt{\overline{V_n^2}} = \frac{1.34 \cdot 10^9 i_s}{C\sqrt{R_t f_c^3}} = 2.8 \cdot 10^{-20} \mathfrak{N}A/(C\sqrt{R_t})$$

The Vidicon preamplifier normally consists of a cascode stage, in which the gain is so high that the amplifying stages beyond it make no material contribution to the noise. The cascode stage utilizes two tubes, of which the first, the driver, operates with a small voltage gain G_1. Accordingly, the shot noise contributed by the second tube, reflected to the input, is added to the shot noise of the first tube by multiplying the equivalent noise resistance of one tube by the factor $(1 + 1/G_1^2)$. If, to minimize the noise, two WE 417-A tubes are used, with $g_m = 28{,}000 \cdot 10^{-6}$ ohm^{-1} and a noise resistance $2.5/g_m = 89$ ohms, we have, for a gain $G_1 = 2.5$,

$$R_t = 103 \text{ ohms}$$

$$C = 18.5 \cdot 10^{-12} \text{ farad}$$

(allowing 5 $\mu\mu$f for wiring capacity and 4.5 $\mu\mu$f for the Vidicon target capacity)[9]

$$S = 1.5 \cdot 10^{-10} \mathfrak{N}A$$

Thus, for a signal-to-noise ratio of 10,

$$\mathfrak{N}A = 7 \cdot 10^{10} \text{ quanta/second}$$

[8] See Weimer and Cope (reference 1).

[9] With 6BQ7A tubes in the cascode circuit, as used in the commercial RCA-ITV-6 equipment, a similar calculation leads to $R_t = 270$ ohms, $C = 15.2 \cdot 10^{-12}$ farad, and $S = 1.1 \cdot 10^{-10} \mathfrak{N}A$.

In the *flying-spot microscope* the light transmitted by successive picture elements of the specimen is directed onto the photocathode of a multiplier phototube, which acts as an almost noise-free amplifier for the photoemission. Thus the shot effect of the photoemission is the only significant noise source, if noise arising from the graininess of the flying-spot tube phosphor screen is neglected. However, here, too, there is a decrease in signal response with increasing frequency, which must be compensated by giving the amplifier following the phototube an appropriate gain characteristic. The factors which cause this decrease are the persistence of the flying-spot tube phosphor and the finite size of the scanning spot. The decay time of the phosphor will be taken to be

$$\tau = 1.4 \cdot 10^{-7} \text{ sec}$$

This value was deduced from response measurements by R. D. Kell on a typical P16 (cerium-activated calcium-aluminum silicate) phosphor. For infinitely narrow spot the response for a variation in transmission of the specimen given by

$$1 + \cos\,(2\pi x/\lambda)$$

is

$$s = (1/\tau)\int_0^\infty e^{-(t_1/\tau)}\left(1 + \cos\frac{2\pi v(t - t_1)}{\lambda}\right) dt_1$$

where v is the velocity of the scanning spot. With $f = v/\lambda$ this can be written

$$s = 1 + \frac{1}{\sqrt{1 + 4\pi^2 f^2 \tau^2}} \cos\,[2\pi f(t - t_0)],$$

$$\tan\,(2\pi f t_0) = 2\pi f \tau$$

Accordingly, the amplitude response as function of frequency is given by the factor $(1 + 4\pi^2 f^2 \tau^2)^{-1/2}$. To obtain flat overall response, the amplifier must be given a gain characteristic

$$G_0 = B(1 + 4\pi^2 f^2 \tau^2)^{1/2}$$

On the other hand, if the spot is a cosine-squared spot with 50 per cent overlap, the normalized response for the sinusoidal term alone becomes

$$s = \frac{n^2 N w}{h\tau}\int_{-h/n^2Nw}^{h/n^2Nw} dt_2 \cos^2\left(\frac{\pi n^2 N w t_2}{2h}\right)\int_0^\infty dt_1 e^{-(t_1/\tau)}[\cos 2\pi f(t - t_1 - t_2)]$$

$$= -\left(\frac{n^2 N w}{2h}\right)^3 (1 + 4\pi^2 f^2 \tau^2)^{-1/2} \sin\left(\frac{2\pi h f}{n^2 N w}\right)$$

$$\left[\pi f\left(f^2 - \left(\frac{n^2 N w}{2h}\right)^2\right)\right]^{-1} \cos\,[2\pi f(t - t_0)]$$

With $x = f/f_c$ and $f_c = \frac{1}{2\sqrt{2}} \frac{w}{h} n^2 N$ designating the nominal cut-off frequency required to equalize vertical and horizontal resolution, the amplifier gain characteristic needed to give flat overall response now becomes

$$G = B(1 + 4\pi^2 f_c{}^2 \tau^2 x^2)^{1/2} \frac{\pi}{2\sqrt{2}} x(2 - x^2) \operatorname{cosec} \frac{\pi x}{\sqrt{2}}$$

With this gain characteristic the output signal will be given simply by

$$V_s = B\mathfrak{N}qeA$$

assuming 100 per cent efficiency of the condenser system between the specimen and the phototube. $\mathfrak{N}$ is here, again, the number of quanta incident *on the average* in unit time on unit area of the specimen and A the scanned area; q is the quantum efficiency of the multiplier photocathode. The noise output is given by

$$\overline{V_n{}^2} = \frac{2e^2 q}{1 - 1/R} \mathfrak{N}A \int_0^{f_c} G^2\, df$$

where R is the gain per stage (usually of the order of 4) of the multiplier phototube.

For negligible spot width,

$$\int_0^{f_c} G_0{}^2\, df = (1 + 4\pi^2 f_c{}^2 \tau^2/3) f_c = 4.9 f_c$$

for $f_c = 3.9 \cdot 10^6$ sec^{-1} and $\tau = 1.4 \cdot 10^{-7}$ second. On the other hand, for a cosine-squared spot with 50 per cent overlap,

$$\int_0^{f_c} G^2\, df = 7.2 f_c$$

for the same values of the cut-off frequency and the decay time.

Accordingly, the signal-to-noise ratio becomes, for a spot of negligible width,

$$S = \frac{\sqrt{\mathfrak{N}A}}{\sqrt{9.8 \frac{1}{q} \frac{R}{R-1} f_c}} = 6.2 \cdot 10^{-5} \sqrt{\mathfrak{N}A}$$

Here we have set the quantum efficiency $q = 0.2$ and $R = 4$, which are typical values for multiplier phototubes with ultraviolet response. Similarly, for a spot giving a "flat field,"

$$S = 5.1 \cdot 10^{-5} \sqrt{\mathfrak{N}A}$$

Accordingly, for a signal-to-noise ratio of 10,

$$\mathfrak{N}A = 2.6 \cdot 10^{10} \text{ for an infinitely narrow spot}$$

and

$$\mathfrak{N}A = 3.7 \cdot 10^{10} \text{ for the cosine-squared spot}$$

If these figures are compared with the comparable figure for the Vidicon microscope, it is seen that the Vidicon system requires two to three times as much specimen illumination as the flying-spot system to yield the same signal-to-noise ratio 10. If it should prove possible to obtain flying-spot screens with negligible decay time, the sensitivity of the flying-spot system could be increased by a further factor 5.

It will be noted that no mention has been made in either case of the optical spot broadening (Airey figure) resulting from the finite resolving power of the optics in the flying-spot system and the corresponding image diffusion in the Vidicon system. This is justified in a comparative study, since the effects on the signal-to-noise ratio are quite the same in the two instances.

The preceding analysis does not answer the question whether sufficient ultraviolet illumination can be obtained to yield pictures of adequate quality at the desired high magnifications with either microscope.

In the Vidicon microscope the provision of adequate illumination in the desired spectral region presents no particular difficulty. Thus, assume that the source to be employed is a superhigh-pressure mercury arc for projection purposes. According to Uyterhoeven[10] such a source has a peak surface brightness of 91,000 candles per square centimeter. Its radiation is distributed in a substantially continuous spectrum from wavelengths below 2500 A up to the infrared. From data given by Uyterhoeven it may be shown that the radiance in the 2000 to 3000 A range is approximately 390 watts per square centimeter, and in the 3000 to 4000 A range, 680 watts per square centimeter; these figures correspond to $5 \cdot 10^{20}$ and $12 \cdot 10^{20}$ photons/($\text{cm}^2 \cdot$sec) respectively; and $1.6 \cdot 10^{16}$ and $4 \cdot 10^{16}$ photons/sec, respectively, may be concentrated on a standard scanning pattern with a line separation of 0.1 micron. These figures are approximately 10^5 times as large as the radiant flux required to yield a signal-to-noise ratio of 10. Hence with the Vidicon television microscope there is ample latitude for selecting out narrow spectral ranges, if, for example, this is desired to check characteristic absorptions of the specimen.

For the flying-spot microscope the situation is not nearly so favorable. From the point of view of persistence of emission, the only satisfactory ultraviolet phosphors appear to be the cerium-activated calcium-aluminum silicate phosphors with a persistence of the order of 10^{-7} sec, for

[10] See Uyterhoeven (reference 6).

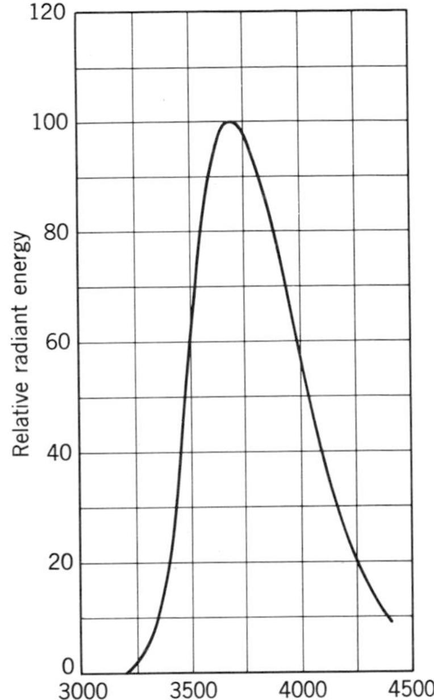

Fig. A.2. Spectral emission of a P16 phosphor.

which the P16 spectral emission characteristic shown in Fig. A.2 is typical. The phosphor employed in the 5WP16 flying-spot tube emits approximately 1 uv photon for 50 ev of electron bombarding energy. Slightly increased emission may be obtained, in general, by shifting the emission peak toward longer wavelengths. Bril, de Gier, and Klasens[11] cite for a similar phosphor peaking at 4000 A an efficiency of 4 per cent (1 photon per 75 electron-volts electron energy). If a flying-spot tube with a 4.8-inch diameter scanning pattern is operated at 25 kilovolts with 100 microamperes of beam current, the screen radiance becomes $1.44 \cdot 10^{-3}$ watts/cm^2 or $2.9 \cdot 10^{15}$ photons/(cm^2·sec). The maximum illumination which can be concentrated on a standard scanning pattern on the specimen, with 0.1 micron line separation, thus becomes $9.6 \cdot 10^{10}$ photons per second. This is only slightly more than is required to yield the desired signal-to-noise ratio $S = 10$, leaving little latitude for filtering out desired spectral ranges. Furthermore, the phosphor in question has practically

[11] See Bril, de Gier, and Klasens (reference 7) and Bril and Klasens (reference 8). Bril, de Gier, and Klasens found at first a dominant component with a decay time $\tau = 10^{-7}$ sec and a much weaker component with $\tau = 2.5 \cdot 10^{-6}$ sec. Later measurements revealed the presence of a component with $\tau = 0.3 \cdot 10^{-7}$ sec, the amplitude of which is not specified.

no emission in the spectral range of greatest interest, i.e., 2500 to 3000 A.

For ultraviolet emission in this region the most favorable phosphor suitable for use in a flying spot tube appears to be zirconium pyrophosphate, with a spectral distribution peaking at 2900 A and retaining 16 per cent of its peak value at 2500 A. Bril and Klasens[12] give its efficiency as 3.5 per cent and its time constant as $2 \cdot 10^{-6}$ second. With these values the signal-to-noise ratio in the flying-spot-microscope picture becomes, for a standard scanning pattern at the specimen with 0.1 micron line separation, $S = 0.9$. This is of course wholly inadequate.

An acceptable signal-to-noise ratio can be attained in the flying-spot microscope with the zirconium pyrophosphate phosphor if the scanning rate is reduced by a factor, for example, of 10. The nominal cut-off frequency f_c of the transmission system may then be reduced by the same factor. However, the formulas given above show that, if this is done, the specimen illumination requirements of the Vidicon microscope become even *less* than those of the flying-spot microscope and that the Vidicon microscope is once more to be preferred.

In brief, at the time of writing, the Vidicon television microscope[13] alone permits the high-magnification viewing of specimens with selected bands in the critical range (2500 to 3000 A) of the ultraviolet spectrum. The possibility of reducing the exposure of the specimen a factor of the order of 2 or 3 through the substitution of the flying-spot microscope depends on the development of phosphors with considerably greater conversion efficiency and/or smaller persistence than are available at present. However, even with a conversion efficiency of 100 per cent the gain in illumination available with the flying-spot microscope is only by a factor of 20 or 30. Thus the flying-spot microscope appears unpromising in applications such as high-magnification color translation microscopy (see p. 135), in which narrow wavelength ranges must be selected from the total illumination.

[12] See Bril and Klasens (reference 9).

[13] Other storage camera tubes, such as image orthicons with special ultraviolet-transmissive face plates, could, in principle, be substituted for the Vidicon. It should also be noted that at the Symposium on Ultraviolet Scanning Microscopy held in Philadelphia in November 1957 an improved flying-spot-tube phosphor was reported which peaked at 2580 A and had a decay time of $7 \cdot 10^{-8}$ second. With it the exposure requirements of the flying-spot-tube system are halved, and high-magnification viewing in the 2500 to 3000-A range at normal scanning rates becomes feasible.

REFERENCES

1. P. K. Weimer and A. D. Cope, "Photoconductivity in Amorphous Selenium," *R C A Rev.*, Vol. 12, pp. 314–334, 1951.
2. H. A. Wheeler and A. V. Loughren, "The Line Structure of Television Images," *Proc. I.R.E.*, Vol. 26, pp. 540–575, 1938.
3. W. L. Hurford and R. J. Marian, "Monochrome Vidicon Film Camera," *R C A Rev.*, Vol. 15, pp. 372–388, 1954.
4. V. K. Zworykin and E. G. Ramberg, *Photoelectricity*, Wiley, New York, 1949.
5. A. Van der Ziel, "Fluctuation Phenomena," in *Advances in Electronics*, Vol. IV (L. Marton, Ed.), Academic Press, New York, 1952.
6. W. Uyterhoeven, *Elektrische Gasentlandungslampen*, Springer, Berlin, 1938.
7. A. Bril, J. de Gier, and H. A. Klasens, "A Cathode-Ray Tube for Flying-Spot Scanning," *Philips Tech. Rev.*, Vol. 15, pp. 233–237, 1953.
8. A. Bril and H. A. Klasens, "The Efficiency of Fluorescences in Cathode-Ray Tubes," *Philips Tech. Rev.*, Vol. 15, pp. 63–72, 1953.
9. A. Bril and H. A. Klasens, "Intrinsic Efficiencies of Phosphors under Cathode-Ray Excitation," *Philips Research Repts.*, Vol. 7, pp. 401–420, 1952.

Author Index

Subject Index